THE YAK

CAI LI

Professor of Animal Science and vice-chairman of Academic Committee, South-west Nationalities College, and lately deputy director Animal Science and Veterinary Medicine Institute (SWNC), Chengdu, Sichuan, PR China

GERALD WIENER

BSc, PhD, DSc, FRSE, CBiol FIBiol

Centre for Tropical Veterinary Medicine, University of Edinburgh, Scotland, UK and Roslin Institute, Edinburgh, and lately deputy director of former AFRC Animal Breeding Research Organisation, UK

Published by the Regional Office for Asia and the Pacific of the Food and Agriculture Organisation of the United Nations, Bangkok, Thailand

This publication is produced jointly by

FAO Regional Office for Asia and the Pacific
and
FAO Regional Project
"Conservation and Use of Animal Genetic Resources in Asia and the Pacific

Cover Picture : *Yak on Qinghai-Tibet Plateau (From "Tibet, The Mother Earth" by kind permission of Xinhua Publishing House, Beijing, China).*

ISBN : 974-89351-0-8

FOREWORD

It is fitting that in this year, the 50th Anniversary of FAO, the Regional Office for Asia and the Pacific acknowledges, by this publication, the unique and special role of the Yak whose natural environment is almost totally within this region.

The Yak is a relatively insignificant species in global terms, yet it is critical to the livelihood security of the herders in a rather difficult environment.

The Yak's ability to survive in harsh conditions and the peoples' ability to derive sustenance from it are classic examples of adaptation by both the animals and the human beings. The need to ensure the maintenance of domestic animal diversity, therefore, cannot be overstated.

The book is not a purely technical publication but tries, through the use of the scientific and other literature available, to provide a comprehensive document describing all aspects of the Yak and its husbandry. It is, however, unique in providing for the first time such a comprehensive document on the Yak in the English language. It will enable a wide audience to learn and appreciate the contribution the Yak makes both to human survival in an inhospitable environment and to biological diversity.

Obaidullah Khan
Assistant Director General, FAO
and Regional Representative for Asia and the Pacific

PREFACE

A preface should perhaps be in the name of both the authors. That convention is broken here in order to provide me, the "foreign" co-author, with an opportunity to pay particular tribute to Professor Cai Li. He has dedicated an entire lifetime, helped by colleagues, students and co-workers, to observing, recording and trying to understand the yak and its characteristics and attributes and its role in the life, culture and economy of the mountainous regions of central Asia. Some of this study has involved personal hardship which most young scientists nowadays would find hard to imagine.

The areas of the world in which yak are kept are in many cases, even now, isolated by distance and difficult terrain. Much of yak husbandry is still steeped in tradition and values which may not be encountered by "animal improvers" elsewhere. It is no mean feat therefore to have gathered the information on which this book is based and it is no discredit to its value that some of the expectations of modern data recording and analysis could not always be observed. Numbers involved in comparisons are often fewer than the observers would have wished, and one of the recurring regrets is that some factors remain confounded - for example between breeds or types of yak and the location where they are found. It is thus not often possible to say whether a particular type of animal is better, or whether it is the conditions under which it lives which is the deciding factor.

The backbone of this book is the work of Professor Cai Li, particularly in his home province of Sichuan. Much of his work has been quoted by direct reference to specific publications, but other information on yak, when not attributed to a specific source also derives from Professor Cai Li's studies. However, it is hoped that readers will also quickly note that this book is based on a large array of information and a mass of data from many different sources and places. It follows that this book differs in breadth and depth from the many popular and a few review articles on the yak, which represent the bulk of the information published in the English language. (In addition there is a growing number of scientific papers on specific topics concerned with yak, also in the English language - and some in French and German). The more general of these articles mostly set out to say how remarkable an animal the yak is, because it has adapted to life in an extraordinarily hostile environment, and then give just a taste of information on body size, reproductive rate, milk yield, and perhaps little else. Usually, this provides no clue to the wide range of variation in performance and habitat of the yak and to the potential of the yak for change. Such conclusions need to be based on a more detailed assessment of the yak and critical evaluation of the results. None-the-less, taken together, these articles and specific studies provide an impressive addition to the literature in the traditional languages for yak publications (mostly Chinese, but also many in Russian), and they have been quoted here whenever appropriate.

It is hoped, therefore, that this book will fill a gap in knowledge and understanding, not only among those concerned with the science of animal production, but also those just interested in the yak and wishing to dig a bit deeper. To accommodate especially the more general reader, an overview has been provided at the beginning of each chapter.

In spite of the claim to breadth and depth for this book, it has to be acknowledged that not every possible piece of information published on the yak has been used. Much of the wealth of articles in scientific journals, reports and proceedings of technical meetings (mainly in the Chinese or Russian language) deals with specific detail under specific circumstances. While it is one of the aims of this book to demonstrate the range of variation found in the management and performance of yak in both practical and experimental situations, and to provide a clue to the underlying factors, it was not thought desirable to make the references exhaustive. To do so would also have required some means of interpreting the causes of the plethora of small differences in performance, or characteristics, of the yak which would emerge. Such interpretation is not possible in the absence of a level and scale of experimentation which has not been undertaken with the yak (or indeed with other types of domestic livestock, if considered over the kind of vast area encompassed by yak territory). The separate chapter on yak husbandry in different countries should go some way towards widening the picture as far as possible.

The publication of this book was requested by the Regional Office for Asia and the Pacific of the Food and Agriculture Organisation of the United Nations to coincide with the 50th anniversary of FAO's foundation. Due to restrictions on time, it has not been possible, in every case, to obtain information for chapter 11, on yak husbandry in different countries, direct from those involved - as was originally hoped. Thus, some of the information for that chapter has had to be compiled from existing, published information.

This preface must end with an apology. The problem of transliterating Chinese, and to a much lesser extent Russian, into the English alphabet may mean that some of the names of authors and the titles of papers and sources given in the list of references may not be totally correct in every detail. Also, it is a matter of regret that some of the references listed will be found difficult to access, even in the form of abstracts, by those wishing to do so. It is hoped that the revolution in communication, in which we find ourselves at the end of the 20th century, will also, in the future, apply to publication across far distant national boundaries for subjects such as the yak.

Gerald Wiener
September, 1995

ACKNOWLEDGEMENTS

Help and encouragement has been received by the authors from many sources and these are most happily acknowledged. Our thanks are listed under headings:

FAO Regional Office for Asia and the Pacific

We are very grateful to Mr Obaidullah Khan (Assistant Director General and Regional Representative for Asia and the Pacific) for his support and kindly writing the Foreword for this book. We are particularly indebted to Mr David Steane (Chief Technical Advisor, Conservation and Use of Animal Genetic Resources) for actively promoting the publication of this book, for making most of the arrangements for this and also for comments on scientific matters. We are also grateful to Dr Masao Sasaki (Regional Animal Production and Health Officer) for his support of the project.

Material for book

The authors are indebted to those who personally contributed material for this book, mostly found in chapter 11. Particular thanks are due to Professors M Tumurjav and M Olonbayar (Mongolia), Dr E V Katzina (Buryatia), Dr R N Pal (India), Dr D D Joshi (Nepal), Dr Lham Tshering (Bhutan), and Messrs A H Cheema and A Ghaffar (Pakistan). Their various and varied contributions have helped greatly to broaden the perspectives of this book. Mr N Lindsay (Curator) and Mr E Flack (Veterinarian) kindly provided information on yak at Whipsnade wild animal park (England).

Scientific help

The authors are most grateful for the time and effort given by Dr J M M Cunningham (Emeritus Professor, Glasgow University) and Dr A J Smith (Centre for Tropical Veterinary Medicine, University of Edinburgh). Each read an entire draft of this book. Their comments and questions, and the discussions held with them by one of us (GW) were most helpful in the development and revision of the manuscript. Professor Crad Roberts (University of Wales) should also be thanked for some initial suggestions on content. Helpful comments on chapter 5 were also given by Dr R Webb (Roslin Institute), on chapter 9 by Dr A G Hunter (Centre for Tropical Veterinary Medicine, University of Edinburgh) and on chapter 4, in relation to haematology, by Dr David Doxey (Veterinary Field Station, University of Edinburgh).

Translation

An initial translation of the Chinese manuscript of the book by Cai Li, "China Yak" (1992) (which provides a backbone to the present book) was made into English by Mr Ma Li and Mr Zi Xiang-dong (both on the staff of the Southwest Nationalities College). Their time and effort are greatly appreciated. Subsequently, almost the entire burden of translation from Chinese into English and vice versa, during the preparation of this book, fell on Mr Zi Xiang-dong. This was a formidable task owing to the copious correspondence between the authors, neither of whom speak each other's language. The work of translation must have greatly interfered with Mr Zi's academic teaching commitments and with his personal life. We cannot thank him enough.

A relatively small but important amount of translation was done by Dr J G Gong (Roslin Institute, Edinburgh) to whom we are also grateful.

Other help

Professor Graham Bulfield (Director, Roslin Institute) is thanked for use (by GW) of the facilities of the Roslin Institute. Its three library staff helped, beyond the call of duty, in tracing and obtaining books and reprints of articles needed for reference but often difficult to locate.

Mrs Frances Anderson undertook the skilled job of preparing camera-ready copy from the material and diskettes supplied by GW.

Grateful acknowledgement is also due to Professor Cai Li's late wife and Dr Wiener's wife for having shown great forbearance of the single-minded and often selfish pursuit of academic interests by their respective husbands. Without that forbearance there might well not have been this book.

Photographs

Front cover photograph from *Tibet, the Mother Earth*, courtesy of Xinhua Publishing House, Beijing. Other photographs by Cai Li except where otherwise acknowledged.

CONTENTS

1 ORIGINS, DOMESTICATION AND DISTRIBUTION OF YAK

OVERVIEW

The domestic yak and its wild ancestor have a long history with fossil remains dating back to the Pleistocene. Over the last 10 thousand years or so, the yak developed in and spread outward from the Qinghai-Tibet plateau, the "roof of the world", which is still the centre of its distribution extending over about 2.5 million sq. km. Yak are usually found at elevations between 2000 and 5000 m (the lower elevations at the more northerly latitudes).

The wild yak was tamed by the ancient Qiang people. Chinese documents from ancient times (8th century BC) testify to a long-established role of the yak in the culture and life of the people. From the south to the north, the distribution of the domestic yak now extends from the southern slopes of the Himalayas to the Altai, and west to east from the Pamir to the Minshan mountains – though some relatively recent introductions have extended the area (e.g. to parts of the Caucasus). Elsewhere, yak are found in zoos, but a very small number are also thought to survive in Canada and Alaska from importations of yak up to the late 1920s.

At the present time the total yak population is thought to number around 14 million – including some crosses with domestic cattle of other species – of which 13 million are in Chinese territories, about 0.5 million in Mongolia and the rest in other countries, notably those bordering the Himalayas and countries within the Russian Federation.

The wild yak population, as distinct from the domestic yak, is now very restricted in distribution and numbers and possibly close to being endangered, even though the animals are "protected". Wild yak are larger in size than the domestic. Because the two types readily inter-breed, there is interest in the use of wild yak to improve the performance of the domestic type.

The yak is integrally associated with the culture, religion and social life of its herders, their families and communities. With outside pressures influencing this life and, at a technical level, yak husbandry itself, the nature of yak-keeping may change.

Introduction

The yak (*Poephagus grunniens* or *Bos grunniens*) is one of the world's most remarkable domestic animals, a herbivore living on the "roof of the world", as the Qinghai-Tibet plateau is often referred to. The plateau itself extends over 2.5 million sq. km (about 1 million sq. miles) described by Miller (1990) as the most extensive high elevation region on earth and the best grazing lands in all of Asia. From that central "core" of the yak's distribution, the animal has also spread to adjacent territories. These areas are, to a large extent, above the tree line and there is virtually no cropping. There is no absolutely frost-free period during any part of the year. Some 14 million yak thus live and provide food, transport, shelter and fuel where few other animals will survive. Though about 30 million sheep and goats (Miller, 1990) – and, of course, the herdsmen's horses – co-exist with the yak over large parts of the plateau, they are not serious competitors to the yak in a lot of yak territory and, as will be shown later, yak and sheep are, to some extent, complementary to each other in their grazing habits. Overall, the territory is marked by severe climate at high elevations and with grazing resources restricted by very short growing seasons, and in some of the alpine regions it is also marked by treacherous terrain. It is quite possible, as has been argued by Chinese historians, that without the existence of the yak, capable of living in such harsh conditions, human civilisation might well not have reached and flourished in these remote areas.

This book attempts to trace the development of this remarkable animal and to describe its characteristics and performance, and its products. There will also be a discussion of some of the investigations which have been undertaken on the yak – work which may lead to improvements in the performance of the yak and to a widening of the opportunities for its distribution and use.

Origins

Unequivocal evidence to link the modern yak to its earliest ancestors is not available. Fossil evidence suggests that yak were extensively distributed in north-eastern Eurasia in the late Tertiary period (2.5 million years ago) and that these are the forerunners of wild yak found as Pleistocene fossils in Northern China, Inner Mongolia (China), Eastern Siberia and northern mid-Asia (Figure 1.1) – and on a line roughly connecting these locations (Dyblor, 1957; Belyar,1980; Flerow, 1980; Olsen 1991).

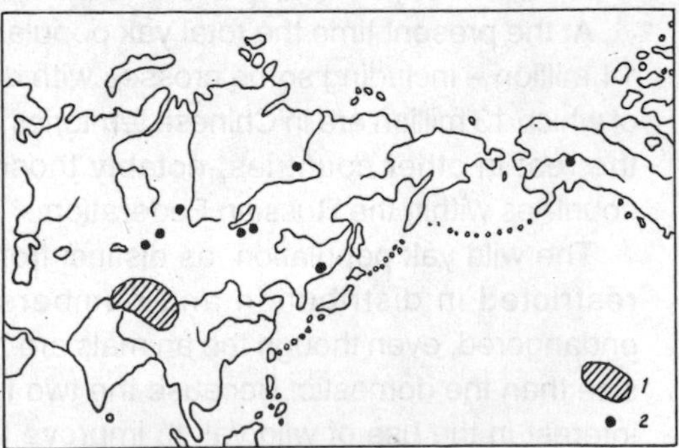

Figure 1.1 Distribution of wild yak
1. Distribution in modern times
2. Location of fossils from Pleistocene

Figure 1.1 also shows the location of the principal area of distribution – adjacent to the Himalayas – for the modern, domestic yak. The Himalayas rose to their present elevation above 4500 metres only in the late Pleistocene epoch. Their rise obstructed the warm and damp air flow from the south and significantly changed the climate of the central area of what is now the Qinghai-Tibet plateau. Forest disappeared from the plateau and was replaced by alpine meadow. Wild yak migrated from north-eastern Eurasia and adapted to life on the plateau and domestication followed.

Domestication and historical distribution

The present domestic yak is descended from wild yak caught and tamed by ancient Qiang people in the Qiangtang and other areas of northern Tibet. This process is thought to have begun in the late Stone Age, about ten thousand years ago, and led to the primary yak industry, beginning in the period of the Longshan Culture of the late New Stone Age (2800–2300 BC) (Qian Yanwen, 1979). The history of China's yak industry is thus at least 4500 years old. Chinese historians regard the ancient Qiang people, around 30 000 years ago, as the first intelligent true humans. They lived and roamed around the present Qinghai-Tibetan plateau, though its average altitude then, at around 3000 metres, was lower than it is now. These people developed probably the earliest animal husbandry culture of excellence in the world – the Qiang Culture. This is a different type of development from that, based on agriculture, of the ancient civilisation of Mesopotamia, widely regarded as the cradle of civilisation. The outstanding achievement of the Qiang culture was the taming of wild beasts for domestic purposes. Sheep and goats had been successfully tamed and this led to taming of yak, horse and other herbivores. Thus developed the original animal husbandry society. Taming of yak in particular led to progress, prosperity and economic development for the people, because of its value as a beast of burden and its products of milk, hair, hides and meat.

Yak expanded outward from that original area of domestication on the plateau. To the east, they migrated from the Bayan Kala mountains into the Songpan grasslands (located in what are now the Aba, Ruoergai and Hongyuan counties of Sichuan province) and into the Danba mountains. To the south, the migration went through passes in the Himalayas on to the

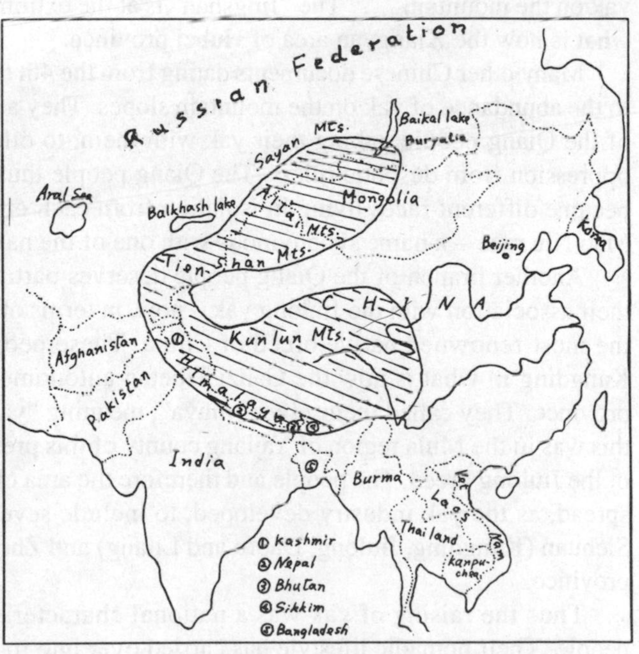

Figure 1.2 Principal area (hatched) of distribution of domestic yak

mountain grasslands of the southern slopes of the range. To the west, yak entered Kashmir through the Ali grassland and to the north the migration took the yak over the Kunlun mountains into northern Pamir, northern and southern Tianshan and Altai. The present-day distribution of the yak developed gradually from these migrations (Figure 1.2).

Nearly all the nationalities which presently keep yak are related to the ancient Qiang peoples, or the nationalities developed directly from the Qiang people, such as Suchas and Tibetans. Menba, Luoba and the Sherpa people of Nepal separated from the original Qiang when they entered the southern slopes of the Himalayan range. The Luoba became the Yi nationality when they migrated to the Yungui plateau from the east. Similarly, nationalities in central Asia and the Tianshan area are known to be related to the Qiang people as are the Mongolian and other southern nationalities.

Many old Chinese documents illustrate these links and the associations with the yak.

For example, the "Guoyu Chuyu" describes events in the late Western Zhou Dynasty (ca. 841 BC): "… The Bapu's rhinoceros and yak cannot be destroyed …" (Bapu was the northern part of the ancient Ba nation located in the present Danba mountain area of Sichuan province). There are descriptions of how yak were raised in large numbers in that area at the time.

A geological document, the "Shanhaijing Zhongshanjing", dating from 400 BC, states: "… In the north-east there is a mountain called Jingshan. Its northern slope abounds with iron and the southern slopes are rich in gold. There are many yak on the mountain. …" The "Jingshan" is at the extremity of the Danba range in what is now the Xiangyan area of Hubei province.

Many other Chinese documents dating from the 4th to the 1st century BC attest to the abundance of yak on the mountain slopes. They also describe the migration of the Qiang people, taking their yak with them, to other areas, often forced by oppression from despotic rulers. The Qiang people thus also branched into what became different races living in isolation from each other. One of these was the Mao Niu race – a name synonymous with one of the names for yak.

Another branch of the Qiang people deserves particular attention because of their association with the Jiulong yak – now, in terms of its performance, perhaps the most renowned native breed of China. These people migrated to southern Kangding in what is now the Ganzi Tibetan autonomous prefecture of Sichuan province. They called themselves "muya", meaning "yak country". The centre of this was in the Mula region of Yajiang county of this prefecture, the original home of the Jiulong breed. The people and therefore the area of distribution of this breed spread, as the yak industry developed, to include several other counties within Sichuan (Kangding, Jiulong, Daofu and Litang) and Zhongdian county of Yunnan province.

Thus the raising of yak was a national characteristic of the ancient Qiang people. Their nomadic lifestyle has carried over into much of yak keeping to this day, with transhumance the normal pattern of management.

Gradually, the distribution of the yak expanded, but it reached some of the areas where yak are now regarded as important only in relatively modern times. Thus, for example, the raising of yak in the Tianshan and Altai mountain areas of the Xinjiang Uygur people is only about 100 years old. Some 100 head of male and female yak were brought from Tibet to the Hejing county in the centre of the Tianshan mountain range and gradually expanded into the Altai and the whole of Tianshan (Yu Daxin and Qian Defang, 1983; Research Co-operative, 1980–87).

Present distribution

Yak are found extensively on China's plateaux in alpine and sub-alpine regions at altitudes from 2000 to 4500 metres with a cold, semi-humid climate. The area, as seen in Figure 1.2, extends from the southern slopes of the Himalayas in the south to the Altai in the north, and from the Pamir in the west to the Minshan mountains in the east. The centre of the yak's distribution is the Qinghai-Tibet plateau, itself interspersed with several mountain ranges. The plateau, extends over about 2.5 million sq. km (noted by Miller, 1990, for those more familiar with the western hemisphere, to be equivalent to the combined areas of the states of Montana, Wyoming, Idaho, Utah, Nevada, Colorado, Arizona and New Mexico in the USA). In 1983 the numbers in Chinese territories were estimated at just below 13 million head of which about 15% were hybrids with (mostly) *Bos taurus* cattle. The majority of the yak were concentrated in 3 provinces or regions. The rest of the world accounts for a further million or so yak. Numbers are shown in Table 1.1.

Most of the yak of Mongolia are found in the Hangay mountains of the western part of the country and in the high altitude area of the Altai, with the remainder in the mountains of mid-north Mongolia. The yak in countries of the Russian Federation are distributed on the narrow mountain area on the borders with China and Mongolia from Pamir in the west to Lake Bakail in the east. Yak were also introduced to the high alpine areas of the northern Caucasus in 1970, and to the Yakutsk valley of Siberia as recently as 1971 (Verdiev and Erin, 1981), to exploit the potential for meat production from otherwise inhospitable alpine grasslands. The yak of Nepal and Bhutan are on the southern slopes of the Himalayas (Joshi, 1982; Zhang Rongchang, 1987) while those of India are distributed in the high altitude northern provinces and in the small territory of Sikkim (Pal, 1993). Other pockets of yak populations are in alpine areas of Afghanistan and Pakistan, adjacent to the Qinghai-Tibet plateau.

In the 1970's and 1980's yak were introduced to cold mountainous areas, but at lower altitude (1500–1800 metres), in northern China in order to increase utilisation of the grasslands in these cold area. The results in Weichang county of Hebei province and in the Linshan region of Beijing suggest a useful role for the yak there (Langjie Zeren *et al.* 1987; Zhong Guanhui *et al.* 1986). Around the same period, yak were introduced to parts of the northern Caucasus and central Yakutia from other parts of the (then) Soviet Union.

Estimates of numbers of yak in different areas are shown in Table 1. Only a few are based on relatively recent data (see also chapter 11 for further information countries outside China). In view of reports of increases in the yak population in some parts of China, the numbers there might well be higher than shown.

Table 1.1 Distribution of yak and numbers (1983 data for numbers in China)

Country, Region Province or county	Distribution at location	Number ('000)
China		
Qinghai	All	4500
Tibet	All	3954
Sichuan	Western plateau and alpine area	3363
Gansu	Southern grasslands and Qiling mountain area	800
Xinjiang	Middle of the Tainshan mountains	250
Yunnan	North-western alpine area	50
Inner Mongolia	Holan mountain area	2
Hebei	Northern mountainous area	0.9
Beijing	Xishan cold mountainous area	0.1
Mongolia		571 (+ 56 yak cross) *(1994)*
Countries of Russian Federation		140 (?)
Nepal		19 (+ 41 yak cross) *(1991)**
Bhutan		30 *(1992)*
India		31 (+14 yak cross) *(1993)*
Afghanistan, Pakistan		2 (?)

*based on Nepal Central Bureau of Statistics 1991 estimates, as quoted by Paudyal (1993) ; Joshi (1982 and reprinted in 1994) estimated there to be only 9 000 yak and 18 000 yak crosses in Nepal.

Distribution outside Asia in modern times

Export of yak to parts of Europe, North America and other parts of Asia began in the mid-19th century. The purpose was mostly for research and for the possible utilisation of cold pasture land. Before that, in 1783, Samuel Turner (see also below), a Briton, had sent two yak bulls from Tibet to England, but one died on the way. The other, when he had recovered from the journey, was mated to British cows. Several calves were born but only one survived to breed itself (with an Indian bull) (Turner, 1800).

In 1854, a total of 12 male and female yak were imported into France, also from Tibet. They appeared to acclimatise successfully but performed differently in different areas due to variation in feeding. They did best in the Cantal province of the central French plateau. Crosses with cattle were made in both ways – producing calves from native cows and calves from yak cows – with calves of the latter being reported as the better. However, the yak disappeared after 1862. None-the-less, local stories continued that animals at high altitude had been produced which were strong, tolerant of rough conditions and with the tail of a horse (Boulnois,1976). The horse-like tail, derived from the yak, led to the legend that the original crosses had been between cattle and horses. Clearly, the yak had left an impression, but no issue.

A number of yak were sent to Canada, first in 1909 and again in 1921 for trials, including crossing with domestic cattle and American bison in an attempt, later discontinued, to produce an animal capable of meat production in the harsh pastoral conditions of northern Canada. A similar project, but using only domestic cattle for the crosses, was conceived and carried out for some years in Alaska, starting with yak born in Canada (White, Phillips and Elting, 1946).

Some yak were present in the late 1980's in the Polar Park of Edmonton, Alberta, Canada. Some further information on these exports of yak to Canada and Alaska will be given in chapter 3, in relation to adaptation. In addition there are yak in a number of zoological and wild animal parks in Europe and elsewhere, including a herd at Whipsnade wild animal park in southern England, to which further reference is also made in chapters 3 and 9.

The name of the yak – a historical note

In the Tibetan language, yak is pronounced as yag. Other languages follow this name closely (yakpho in Nepalese). This is thought to be unusual for a name among the numerous languages of the world.

The ancient Chinese people called the animal Ya Niu. In the Shang dynasty (before 3000 BC) yak was vividly written as [illegible] denoting the yak's characteristic such as large body, outstretched horns, long hair and big tail. Later a word was created which was pronounced as Ya. Later still this, in turn, was mis-pronounced as Mao – and many homophones of that began to appear after the Qin and Han dynasties. These words referred not only to the yak but also to yak hair products (because 氂 Mao means "hair" in Chinese). Some people wrote 毛, pronounced "Mao", as 犛, pronounced Li, and then called the yak Li Niu. The tiny alteration in the script leading to a change of name provides an interesting object lesson for good handwriting! The Chinese letter for Mao first appeared in Lu's Spring and Autumn Annals, a book on Chinese herbal medicine before 220 BC. A distinction between Li and Mao to denote yak was made in the Compendium of Materia Medica published in 1578. Li Niu was said to live in the mountains and denoted the wild yak, while Mao Niu was used to denote the domestic yak.

Present-day names, in spite of a common thread, vary for the yak from country to country and often from locality to locality within a country.

Some observations on the wild yak

Before the wild yak became known as Li, it was called Zhong in the Tibetan language and Zuo by the ancient Chinese in central China.

Li Shizhen in his *Compendium of Materia Medica* of 1578 said: "In the south-western area around yak country, Li Niu (the wild yak) lives in the high mountain. Its appearance, hair colour and tail are the same as those of the domestic yak, but its body is larger." In 1875, N.M. Przewalski, named the wild yak *Bos mutus Prze*, in the belief that the wild yak did not make a sound or "cry". In fact, although the wild yak does not normally cry, it will let out squeaks and cries during oestrus and the breeding season and if it meets other wild beasts, just as does the domestic yak.

Wild yak were numerous in the central and eastern border areas of the Qinghai-Tibetan plateau. Herds of them existed on the cold pastures of western Sichuan province up to the middle of the 20th century. Male wild yak could be seen mingling and mating with herds of female domestic yak. A few individuals with hair colour characters of wild yak can be seen in domestic herds to the present day – the principal visual difference being grey-white hairs found around the mouth of crosses with the wild yak which are absent in the domestic yak.

The excessive hunting of wild yak drove them from the plateau areas into mountainous areas at even higher altitudes, above 4500 meters and right to the tops of the mountains at 6000 metres. By the 1970's wild yak were on the verge of extinction. Some survived in China's Kunlun mountains, but due to protective measures by the Chinese government some wild herds are now reported to have reappeared at elevations between 4000 and 4500 meters.

The wild yak is large in body and strong. Thick, long hair covers the whole body. The colour of the hair is jet brown or jet black – no other colours have been reported. A colour line down the back of the body, behind the withers, is silver grey and there are grey-white hairs around the muzzle. (As referred to earlier, the latter is not found in the domestic yak.) The horns are round and very thick, 15–20 cm in diameter. (Some local herdsmen use these horns as milking vessels which can still be seen in some remote areas of the country.) The horn arch of the wild yak is open (Figure 1.3) and the head shape has a fierce appearance.

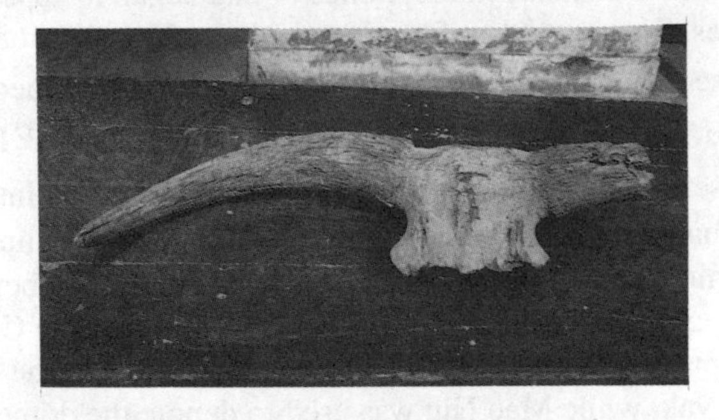

Figure 1.3 Front view of horn arch and part of skull of wild yak found in Heihon river in Ruoergai county of Sichuan Province

Measurements were made on the skull illustrated in Figure 1.3, which is the largest of a number of skulls, presumed ancient remains of wild yak, found in the middle and lower reaches of the Heihe river of Ruoergai county, Sichuan Province. Measurements (cm) are as follows:

Forehead width – highest	34
Forehead width – lowest	28
Distance between base of horns	27
Circumference of base of horns	44
Horn length	99
Largest distance between horns	146
Distance between tips of horns	126

On the basis of these measurements it was estimated that this yak had been 170 cm high at its withers, had a body length of 190 cm, a heart girth of 250 cm and had weighed approximately 950 kg, which is 1.5 times the average for domestic yak in the same area.

Wild yak prefer to live in herds of tens or even hundreds of animals. The wild yak has a very acute sense of smell, is highly alert and timid and tries to escape immediately on sensing or seeing people, or other animals. Wild yak stampede readily, but if angered or cornered they are fiercely tempered and will attack an intruder. Wild yak dislike heat but are highly tolerant of cold and starvation. Wild yak males often wander off individually during the non-breeding season to relatively flat hill areas away from the high mountains. Such males are known to attack people on remote roads.

In times when wild yak were more prevalent, they were known to come down from the mountains to mate with female domestic yak during the breeding season. The first filial generation (F1) was similar in appearance to the wild yak and had a larger body and fiercer temper than the typical domestic yak. The crosses are difficult to manage but the herdsmen like them because of their apparently better growth and development, compared to pure domestic yak. They are also liked because the crossbred males are thought to protect the herd better than their domestic counterparts. Some observations on the body size and performance of such crosses will be given in chapter 6.

Feral yak. There are numbers of domestic yak which have been allowed to run wild, some deliberately set free by pious adherents of the Lamas of Tibet. These feral yak (thought to be fewer in number than the true wild yak) are often wrongly referred to as "wild yak". They are of similar appearance to the domestic yak but have acquired behaviour like that of the true wild yak. They are relatively more easily caught than real wild yak and are known to mix with herds of domestic yak.

Yak in the culture of the people

In the earlier part of this chapter it was noted that the yak has a long, documented history stretching into ancient times, and that as the people branched, migrated and spread, they took their yak with them into wider territory. It is important, however, also to stress how closely tied the yak has been, and is, to the culture, religion and social life of the pastoral peoples of the cold, high mountainous regions of Asia – those peoples, at least, who can trace their history of yak keeping back over the centuries. This point has to be made lest it is otherwise totally forgotten, or ignored, in a book such as this concerned primarily with the attributes of the yak in terms of its adaptation to the environment, its production and its manifold products and uses. It is possible, of course, that the cultural and social importance of the yak may diminish in the life of the herdsmen, in the face of the introduction of market economics, of improved transport and communication. It is also possible that the spread, however slow, of modern concepts of feeding, management and breeding, and the pressures from those proffering such technological advice on yak husbandry, may further diminish the force of traditional values. In some areas, such as Nepal, social change in relation to its yak economy, as documented by, for example, Bishop (1989) has led to a great reduction in yak numbers. It would be a pity if the vast natural resources of the territories now purposefully exploited by the yak were to become less productive or deserted through insensitive management of change.

The yak takes its place alongside other animals, both real and mythical, in the history, legends and mythology of the Tibetan region and neighbouring territories, as illustrated with examples by Cayla (1976). The use of the yak as provider of components for local medicines is but one aspect of the near mystical importance of the yak. Some of the medicines and remedies associated with the yak are described by Meyer (1976).

Religion, ceremony, social customs and attitudes to wealth and its symbols are all intertwined with each other in the life of the people and with the integral role of the yak in all aspects of that life – an intertwining which has its counterparts among nomadic peoples of Africa, but which is rarely applicable to animal husbandry in the western part of the world. It is important therefore to bear these points in mind, lest it be assumed that knowledge of the reproductive and productive attributes of the yak, and of management practices, are all that is required to bring about "improvements" in the economy of yak keeping.

Knowledge of the yak outside its "native" area

The relative isolation of both wild and domesticated yak in the mountainous regions of central Asia, around the Tibet-Qinghai plateau, is illustrated by the dearth of mention of the yak in the 'West' until relatively modern times. If early travellers to the East had attempted to 'export' yak, they might have been frustrated by the poor tolerance of the yak to prolonged exposure to heat at lower altitudes – though, as already referred to, yak do now exist in zoos and animal parks in many parts of the world.

Lydekker (1912) asserted, however, that yak had been known by repute in western Europe from classical Grecian times and given the name of "poiphogoi" (eaters of poa grass – and known to live exclusively on grass). Also, Zeuner (1963) in his 'A History of Domesticated Animals' provides two early references to yak (in one case to only a part of yak). The first of these references dates to the latter part of the first century AD when Martial (a Roman poet of that era) alluded to the use, by the ladies of Rome, of the tail of some kind of ox (*Muscarium bubulus*) as a fly-whisk, or clothes brush. Zeuner deduces that the tail was that of the yak and goes on to point out that this, in turn, suggests that overland trading routes to the East must have been fully open then. (The yak tail fly-whisk has been well-known in India for centuries). Zeuner secondly refers to accounts of the travels of Marco Polo, in the thirteenth century, who appears to have much exaggerated the size of the yak – equating it to the size of the elephant. Boulnois (1976), however, gives a much fuller background to knowledge of the yak provided by travellers from the west from early times, but especially from the 17th century onward.

It is apparent, therefore, that factual information on the yak, as distinct from anecdotes, came to Europe rather late, unlike acquaintance with the yak in China from its documentation in ancient Chinese literature and subsequently. Perhaps the first account by a writer who was also sufficiently impressed by the yak to send it to Europe was Samuel Turner. His book, first published in 1800, 'An account of an embassy to the Court of the Teshoo Lama in Tibet' was re-published in 1971, and describes the characteristics of the yak and its environs vividly and in some detail.

In recent times, apart from much documentation of the yak by Chinese authors and a substantial body of publication in Russian, there are two substantive accounts, in English, on the general performance of the yak in China, arising out of visits by two distinguished animal husbandmen from the USA to various parts of yak country in the 1940s (Phillips and Moyer, 1945; Phillips, Tolstoy and Johnson, 1946). More recently still, relatively brief, general accounts of the yak have appeared, also in English, in FAO publications dealing with the livestock of China and of the USSR, and in a few textbooks. There is a growing number of technical papers on specialist, research topics on the yak and the ecology of its territories which are published in English, French, German and other languages more widely accessible to readers in the west. Many of these are reference sources for this book. These sources are in addition to the considerable output written in the languages traditional for this work. Special mention must be made of the substantial and well-documented study by a team of French scholars ("The yak – its role in the economic and cultural life of its breeders in central Asia") sponsored by the Société d'Ethnozootechnie au Museum National d'Histoire Naturelle (Paris) (1976).

(a) male

(b) female

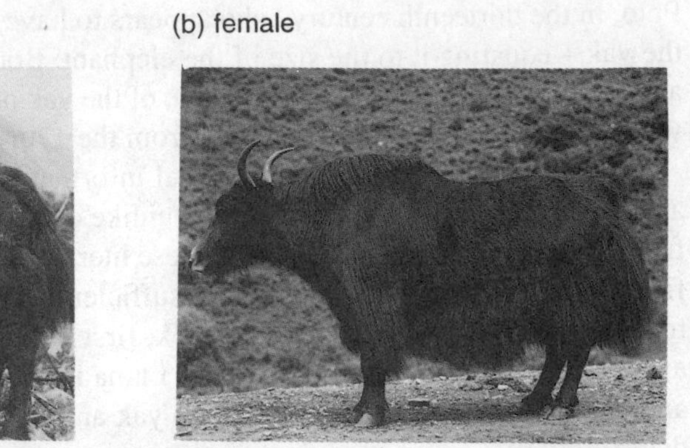

Figure 2.1 Jiulong yak (Henduan Alpine type)

(a) male

(b) female

Figure 2.2 Maiwa yak (Qinghai-Tibet Plateau type)

(a) male

(b) female

Figure 2.3 Tianzhu White yak (Qinghai-Tibet Plateau type)

2 YAK TYPES AND BREEDS

OVERVIEW

Two main types of domestic yak are recognised in China: the Qinghai-Tibet Plateau type ('Plateau' or 'Grassland' type) and the Henduan Alpine type ('Alpine' or 'Valley' type).

Because of the expansive terrain, yak of the Plateau type tend to be aggregated into larger herds than yak of the Alpine type, and herds often mingle. There are, however, at least three generally recognised breeds of the Plateau type – Qinghai Plateau, Maiwa (of Sichuan province) and Tianzhu White (of Gansu province). A number of other breeds, named locally, also exist.

The terrain for the Alpine yak is marked by steep gradients, turbulent rivers and considerable differences in climate between, often agricultural, valley bottom and the tops. The topography leads to more isolation among yak herds of the Alpine type than for the Plateau type. The two main, recognised breeds of the Alpine type are the Alpine yak of Tibet and the Jiulong yak of Sichuan province. Several other breeds are, however, recognised and named in different localities but not necessarily ascribed to a 'type'.

Although there are some differences between the main types in appearance and in aspects of their performance – and similarly among the breeds – it is not yet resolved to what extent such differences are genetic and to what extent they derive from different conditions in the areas in which these yak populations are found.

Outside China, most notably in Mongolia and in countries of the Russian Federation, yak are usually referred to by a name designating the area where they are kept or the area from which they have come. Whether this constitutes different breeds, in the genetic sense, is a matter for debate, and is not generally claimed.

Introduction

The yak was listed by Linnaeus as *Bos grunniens*, the same genus as other domestic cattle. A number of scholars had changed this by the middle of the nineteenth century to *Poephagus grunniens* on closer examination of features distinguishing the yak from *Bos*. There was a return to *Bos grunniens* following Lydecker (1898), and this form continued to be used to the present. However, Olsen (1991) following a re-examination of all the available fossil evidence concludes that only the name *Poephagus grunniens* is appropriate. Increasingly, over recent years, this nomenclature has been adopted.

The yak has the same number of chromosomes (60) as *Bos taurus* and *Bos indicus* and interbreeds with both; the female crosses being fertile and the male crosses sterile. The yak will also interbreed with bison – the female hybrids being fertile, but not the males (Deakin, Muir and Smith, 1935). (These authors also report that the yak-bison hybrid showed stamina and speed to a "remarkable degree").

Types

Domestic yak differ from wild yak in being smaller and, not unexpectedly, they differ in temperament (cf. Chapter 1). It is not clear whether these differences have arisen because of differences in the selection pressures on wild and domestic yak respectively, or to what extent genetic drift and inbreeding may have contributed. However, there are, many attributes in common between wild and domestic yak and, broadly speaking, they share a similar environment and, as already noted, they will interbreed without difficulty, given the opportunity.

In 1982, a number of Chinese experts on the yak agreed to a broad classification of domestic yak into two principal types differing in outward appearance including body conformation and in productive characteristics. The classification took account of the ecological conditions in which the yak were kept and evidence of selection which had taken place. The two types are the Qinghai-Tibet Plateau type and the Henduan Alpine type. As these two main types inhabit, in general, different regions and habitats, the reasons for differences between them cannot be clearly apportioned to heredity or environment.

To resolve the question of the relative contribution of heredity and environment to the apparent differences between the two types of yak would require comparisons of the two types, and of the crosses between them, to be made at the same location and at the same time. Better still, such comparisons should be repeated at a number of different locations typical of the different ecological habitats associated with the two types of yak. It might be expected that outward appearance associated with colour, hair and horn type and to some extent conformation would remain largely distinct, but that aspects such as body size and milk production would converge in a common environment but to an extent that cannot be predicted.

Within each of the two main types of yak a number of breeds have been recognised (Institute of Animal Science [China], 1986). Again, the question of the relative contribution of heredity and environment to breed differences can only be accurately resolved by breeding trials involving different breeds at the same locations.

Qinghai-Tibet Plateau type ("Plateau" or "Grassland" type)
The yak of this type are distributed mainly in the central part of the Qinghai-Tibet plateau including the cold grasslands of Qinghai province and Tibet, the north-western part of Sichuan province, southern Gansu province and the Qilian mountain area. Yak introduced to the grasslands of Xinjiang from Tibet also belong to this type.

The plateaux have many morasses or semi-boggy areas; hill-shaped highlands with gentle slopes and broad valleys present an open kind of topography. The climate is cold with an average annual air temperature below 0°C. An annual precipitation of less than 600 mm makes this a semi-arid area. Alpine and sub-alpine meadows predominate, apart from the marsh and semi-marsh meadows. Grasses (*Gramineae*) and sedges (*Cyperaceae*) predominate in the herbage. Grass stems are short and grass cover variable. The growing season is from 120 to 150 days long. Hay is difficult to make and feed is in short supply in winter and spring.

The ecological environment of the rangeland of the Qinghai-Tibet plateau, the classes of rangeland and its main plant resources are described in some detail (joint Chinese and English text) and beautifully and copiously illustrated by 405 colour photographs in an Atlas of rangeland for that region (Cai Zhaoguang *et al.*, 1986).

Yak of the Plateau type tend to migrate freely compared with the Alpine type because of the open topography of the land. Bulls may move from one area to another and mate with individual cows or even whole herds in neighbouring areas thus leading to some interbreeding between the yak stocks in different areas and blurring of any genetic differences between them. In general, little selection is practised in the yak by the herders. The yak of the Plateau type tend to be among the smaller of the yak breeds. They are, however, of relatively good milking capacity with high butterfat content of the milk. These yak are clearly multi-purpose, being used for milk, meat and draught.

Individual herds of the Plateau type are usually larger than those of the Alpine type.

Black hair, or black with white spots predominate among the animals of the Plateau type. Other colours include brown tinges; piebald yak also occur. these yak, in China at least, are mostly horned, though in some countries, such as Mongolia, polled yak are preferred (see also chapter 3, Table 3.1).

Henduan Alpine type ("Alpine" or "Valley" type)
These are distributed over the alpine region of the Henduan mountain range of the south-eastern part of the Qinghai-Tibet plateau, including the eastern part of Tibet. Other main areas include the southern part of the Yushu Tibetan autonomous prefecture in Qinghai Province, the grasslands in mountains and valleys of south-western Sichuan province and the Dichan Tibetan autonomous prefecture of northern parts of Yunnan province. The terrain of these areas is marked by steep gradients and turbulent rivers. Most of the mountains are over 4000 metres, but valleys fall steeply by between 1000 and 2500 metres. There are large temperature differences between the tops and the valley bottoms where rice can grow and

buffalo are kept. On the mountain meadows above the tree line it is cold and plants do not form seed. There are clear, dry times, mostly in winter, and rainy times mostly in the summer and rainy times of year. The climate is cold but semi-humid.

The topography of the areas for the Alpine type of yak creates sufficient isolation for a number of distinct characteristics and breeds to have developed. Of these, only the Jiulong and the Alpine yak of Tibet are widely recognised by Chinese authorities as distinct breeds with good production characteristics especially for the Jiulong. Other breeds are more by way of local types. Moreover, because of the different topography of the land in which the "Alpine" and the "Plateau" types of yak are found there are more relatively closed populations of yak among the Alpine type which in turn have been subjected to rather more selection by the herders than generally among the Plateau type of yak.

Alpine type of yak are mostly covered by black hair with grey hairs around the muzzle; a few black and white animals are also found, but no other hair colours. The great majority of these yak have horns which are rough and round and curve out widely and evenly. Alpine yak have broader foreheads than the Plateau type and dense hair notably on the top of the shoulder. There is some variation in the conformation and appearance of different breeds of this type.

A number of relatively small local groups – in some cases numbering several thousand head of yak – also exist which have sometimes been described as additional "types" (but see "breeds" below). For example, Cheng Peilieu (1984) lists the "Long-hair-forehead yak" (in Qinghai province) and the "White yak" (of which the Tianzhu White yak of Gansu province is an example) as additional "types" – although these are not recognised as such in the official classification (Institute of Animal Science [China], 1986).

Breeds

Not surprisingly, in view of the relative isolation of different areas from each other, at least in times past, many distinct groups of yak have developed in China. Five of these are listed as breeds (Institute of Animal Science [China], 1986). Classed as yak breeds of the Plateau type were the Qinghai Plateau, the Maiwa of Sichuan province and the Tianzhu White of Gansu province. The Henduan Alpine type includes as yak breeds the Jiulong of Sichuan province and the Alpine of Tibet. Other localised groups of yak have been listed as local breeds in some regional publications. These include the Zhongdian of Yunnan province, the Bazhou of Xinjiang and the Huanhu of Qinhai province. Cheng Peilieu (1984) also refers to a Luqu breed in SW Gansu province as one of the Plateau type.

Some information on the various breeds is shown in Table 2.1a,b and three of the breeds are illustrated in Figures 2.1, 2.2 and 2.3 on page 12.

Breeds in countries apart from China

From the literature it appears that yak in most countries outside China are not specifically classified as "breeds", but referred to as yak of a particular named area in which they are found or from which they have been brought. For example, Sarbagishev, Rabochev and Terebaev (1989) refer in this way to yak in various parts

Table 2.1a Main breeds of yak in China and observations on distribution and characteristics

Location (province or autonomous region)	Breed	Main area	No. ('000)	Topography	Pasture type	Grass type (predominant type)	Altitude (m)	Av. annual temperature (°C)	Rainfall (mm)
Sichuan	Jiulong*	Jiulong county and Sharda region of s. Kendan county in Ganzi T.A.P.**	30	High mountain intersecting valleys	Alpine bush and meadow	mixed sward	>3500	2.0	900
	Maiwa*	N. Hongyuan county and s. Rouergai county in Aba T.A.P.**	200	Hill-shaped plateau	Cold meadow and marsh	Gramineae Cyperaceae	3400–3600	1.1	728
Yunnan	Zhongdian	Zhongdian county in Dinchang Prefecture		Hill-shaped plain among mountains	Alpine bush and meadow	mixed sward and grass	3276	5.4	620
Gansu	Tianzhu White*	Pasture of Xidatan, Yongfentan and Ayuangou in Tianzhu Tibetan county	30	Broad plateau and valley	Sub-alpine meadow	many bush on n. slopes; Gramineae Cyperaceae	[3000]	0.1	300–416
	Gannan	Cold pasture of Gannan T.A.P.** in s. Gansu		Hill-shaped plateau	Alpine and sub-alpine meadow	Gramineae Cyperaceae	3300-4400	0.4	664
Qinghai	Plateau*	Cold area of n. and s. Qinghai	3400	Plateau	Alpine meadow	Gramineae Cyperaceae	3700–4700	from -2 to -5.7	282–774
	Huanhu	Mountainous region around Qinghai lake		Mountain	Sub-alpine meadow, part forest grassland	Grass	2000–3400	from 0.1 to 5.1	269–595
Tibet	Alpine*	Alpine area of e. Tibet; Jarling county	1400	Plateau, mountain	Alpine bush and meadow	mixed sward	>4000	0	694
	Yardong	Mountain area of s. Yardong county		Plateau-mountain	Alpine meadow	Gramineae Cyperaceae	4300	1.7	468
Xijiang	Bazhou	Centre of Tianshan mountains		Mountain	Sub-alpine meadow	Grass	2400	–4.7	285

Table 2.1b Main breeds of yak in China and observations on distribution and characteristics

Location (province or autonomous region)	Breed	Sex	No.	Body measurements (cm)				Body weight*** (kg)	Source
				Height at withers	Body length	Heart girth	Cannon circumf.		
Sichuan	Jiulong*	m	15	138	178	219	23.6	594	Cai Li *et al.*, 1980a
		f	708	117	140	179	18.2	314	
	Maiwa*	m	17	126	157	193	19.8	414	Cheng Xiafei *et al.*, 1981
		f	219	106	131	155	15.6	222	
Yunnan	Zhongdian	m	23	119	127	162	17.6	235	Research Co-op., 1980-87
		f	186	105	117	154	16.1	193	(Duan Zhongxuan *et al.* 1981)
Gansu	Tianzhu	m	17	121	123	164	18.3	264	Research Co-op., 1980-87
	White*	f	88	108	114	154	16.8	190	(Zhang RongChang *et al.*, 1981)
	Gannan	m	10	126	141	189	22.4	354	Research Co-op., 1980-87
		f	159	109	122	157	16.1	210	(Gannan Investigation Group, 1980)
Qinghai	Plateau*	m	21	129	151	194	20.1	398	Research Co-op., 1980-87
		f	208	111	132	157	15.8	228	(Qinghai Investigation Group, 1980)
	Huanhu	m	14	114	144	169	18.3	287	as above
		f	138	103	124	147	15.4	187	
Tibet	Alpine*	m	8	130	154	197	22.4	421	Research Co-op., 1980-87
		f	197	107	133	162	16.1	243	(Tibet Investigation Group, 1982)
	Yardong	m	7	120	137	173	19.0	288	Research Co-op., 1980-87
		f	70	111	125	157	15.2	217	(Tang Zenyu *et al.*, 1975)
Xijiang	Bazhou	m	24	126	140	191	20.6	359	Research Co-op., 1980-87
		f	228	111	124	172	16.8	257	(Yu Beiyuan *et al.*, 1981)

Notes: *listed as native breeds of China; ** T.A.P. = Tibetan Autonomous Prefecture; ***body weight estimated from (heart girth [m]) 2 x (body length [m]) x 70 of the former USSR, and note, for example, that "Yaks bred in Kirgizia are considerably larger than those in Tajikistan" – but they refer to a management difference between the two and do not therefore suggest a genetic distinction. In the same manner, Zagdsuren (1994a) refers to country origin for yak when discussing crossbreeding with cattle of other species, and, still by way of example, Smirnov *et al.* (1990) refer to yak of "Tuva type" when writing about meat production trials in the Northern Caucasus. Verdiev and Erin (1981) have referred to Pamir, Altai and Buryatia types of yak – the area or country names where the yak are. Epstein (1977) writing about domestic livestock in Nepal also does not separate yak into breeds. It thus appears that differences among "local" types are recognised, but whether these types constitute different breeds, in the genetic sense, is a matter for further investigation.

Genetic distance. Recent studies, involving the use of blood-group polymorphisms and other protein polymorphisms, have examined the genetic distance of yak in Buryatia from other Bovidae (Mashurov and Darydov, personal communication, 1995). The methodology is described by Mashurov *et al.* (1993). A specific conclusion is that the yak in Buryatia are not far removed genetically from those in Mongolia and Tadjikistan. But, an unexpectedly low similarity shown by this method to the yak of Kirgizia is attributed by the authors to having insufficient pairs of antigens with which to study that particular relationship. Not surprisingly, the furthest genetic distances were found to be from other genera and species such as zebu, water buffalo and auroch.

This approach, if extended to include all the different types and breeds of yak might answer some of the questions already raised about the genetic differentiation of the various types and breeds of yak. As shown by the authors, the credibility of the results on genetic distance is very dependant on having information on a large number of loci in common in the different breeds studied. Sufficient information is unlikely to be available, as yet, for many of the yak breeds. Machurov and Davydov (pers. com., 1995) express the hope, however, that these studies can contribute not only to understanding of common origins of different breeds, but might be used to develop breeding schemes for generating heterosis – on the assumption that the greater the genetic distance the more heterosis would be generated when making the cross.

3 BREEDING AND CROSSBREEDING OF YAK

OVERVIEW

Pure breeding is the predominant practice with yak. No information has come to hand on rigorous selection programmes consistently applied for the improvement of the performance of yak in China, although some schemes appear to be under consideration both in China and other countries. The dearth of organised selection schemes is not surprising in view of the distribution of yak in a harsh environment in often remote regions and with an absence of written records of performance and pedigrees. Herdsmen in some areas, as for example in respect of the Jiulong yak, have a traditional system of selection for replacement bulls. This pays regard to the performance of the sires and to maternal performance, as well as to many aspects of the physical appearance of the individual. It has to be remembered that the capacity to survive must be one of the chief attributes in the genetic make-up of the yak. This characteristic is likely to be under constant pressure from natural selection.

There is circumstantial evidence that inbreeding is likely to occur in some areas with yak, as a result of traditional pure-breeding methods and, in some countries, because of insufficient interchange of breeding stock across national boundaries. This is likely to be having harmful effects on the performance of yak.

Crossbreeding among the different types and breeds of yak does not appear to be systematic, but, on theoretical grounds, should be advantageous. Crossing of domestic yak with wild yak is, however, receiving widespread attention and favourable results are reported, with indications of heterosis. Crosses of domestic yak with wild yak are also thought to provide a basis for selection.

Crossing of yak with other species of cattle (mainly *Bos taurus* but also *Bos indicus* in some countries) is widely practised. Bulls of local breeds of cattle are used for natural service, but for crossing with relatively high-yielding "exotic" breeds of cattle the use of AI with frozen semen is normal, as the bulls of these breeds have not, in the past, survived for long in the mountainous regions. Crossbreeding with cattle is advocated as a means of increasing milk and meat output from the mountainous regions. Only the first cross is favoured, as later generations of backcrosses have poorer performance (and crossbred males are sterile). However, the F1 females themselves can usefully be mated to males specially chosen for "meat" production. There are both economic and biological limits on the extent to which inter-species hybridisation can be carried out. The biological limit is set by the low reproductive rate of yak. A large proportion of the yak female population is required simply to replace the purebred yak population – even if the size of that population were to remain static and not to increase, as seems to be desired by the herders.

Pure-breeding

Ways of improving yak productivity by selection might be thought to be of great importance to the people who depend on yak for their livelihood. As discussed earlier, the yak is the dominant domestic animal in the alpine regions and the mountain plateaux of western China and adjacent areas to the south and north. The yak also has great importance in Mongolia and several other countries (see chapter 11). It is an integral component of the socio-economic system of peoples in these many remote areas and, often along with sheep, provides the chief support for living to the herdsmen and their families. However, in the past and also in present times, several factors militate against systematic breeding programmes of the type associated with other areas and with other species, both in China and other parts of the world.

The first of these constraints on improvement by genetic selection is that yak are still widely regarded, especially among Tibetan people, as a symbol of wealth. The more yak are owned by a family, or by a village, the richer and stronger it is considered to be. To maintain or increase the number of yak can take precedence over improvements in quality, or even overall productivity. Thus, animals are often kept until they die rather than culled for reasons of poor productivity. This can readily lead to overstocking of pastures and to a potential reduction in the output from the herd as a whole. However, where numbers are the main consideration, these points will be forgotten or intentionally ignored.

A second important reason why genetic selection by herdsmen, or by extension officers acting on their behalf, is hindered, is the absence of the necessary performance and parentage records – although herdsmen will often claim to know the parents of yak, especially bulls. It is doubtful if the accuracy of this knowledge is ever tested.

Thirdly, survival of the yak in a harsh, even hostile, environment is of paramount importance, perhaps of higher priority than any single performance trait (though it is unlikely that this question has been quantified). In terms of selection for survival under these conditions, natural selection is almost certainly more effective than any current procedure devised by man.

None-the-less, in the regions where yak products are in great demand and sought after in the market place, it seems that herdsmen have acquired both the knowledge and skill to improve production traits – even though it may be done unsystematically and perhaps unconsciously. This is a possible explanation for the existence of several localised breeds with apparently above-average performance. In particular, this seems to apply to the Jiulong breed in Sichuan province, for which a system of selection has become traditional. This is described below.

Selection procedure used by herdsmen in the Jiulong area of Sichuan
Selection of yak by the herdsmen in the Jiulong area is relatively systematic. Herdsmen pay more attention to choice of yak bulls for breeding than they do to the cows.

The guiding principle for the herdsmen is to check the ancestors (the parents) first and the bull second. Selection of replacement males starts in the herd of calves from cows which have good conformation and a high milk yield over two parities. The herdsmen require that the sire of the males being chosen as replacement bulls should have copious hair and a large number of progeny. The bulls being selected should themselves have good conformation. In particular, the herdsmen require that the horns of the selected bulls stretch outward from a rough base and that there is a long distance between the horns. The forehead, head, muzzle and mouth have to be broad; the neck thick and the lips thin and long; withers should be high and brisket wide; the back, loin and rump should be wide and flat; the tail hairy; fore-limbs straight and hind-legs curved; the scrotum should be shrunken; acceptable coat colours are black or black with some white specks on the forehead and at the extremities of the body (e.g. legs or tail), but not on the body itself.

It is of interest that selection of bulls in the Jiulong area is made in three stages. The first is a pre-selection at the age of one-year old. There is a second selection from among the first group at the age of two years and a final selection at the age of 3 or 4 years. (The relative importance given to different traits at each stage is not specified). Bulls which are culled are castrated and used for meat or draught purposes. After initial mating with cows, bulls which are found to be defeated in the competition among the bulls for mates and those found to have physical defects or bad conformation are then also culled. The herdsmen aim to have 2 or 3 successors to an excellent, dominant bull that has been working in the cow herd.

These traditional selection methods for Jiulong yak appear to have produced, over a period of many decades, perhaps centuries, an improved breed of yak which is highly regarded. Clearly, the criteria which are applied contain elements which are related to important aspects of production in the yak. However, it is necessary also to make a cautionary comment, lest it be thought that these methods have to be unreservedly commended because they have tradition and herdsmen experience on their side. Geneticists would wish to suggest that there is great scope for improving these procedures, even in the absence of sophisticated indices of breeding value and modern computational procedures. To start with, it needs to be asked how closely related the physical appearance of the yak, so much emphasised by the herdsmen, is to actual performance of the herd – in terms of, say, growth, milk yield or reproductive rate. Usually the relationship is not high. A geneticist would wish to encourage the herdsmen to pay most attention to the characteristics of the yak which provide the greatest economic return. For that reason, it would also be urged that the number of criteria considered for selection be restricted to an essential minimum. Improvement of the important points is diluted, or even lost, when a lot of attention is paid to less important, even trivial, matters – as may be the case now.

Selection objectives for the chief yak breeds in China

In general, among the herdsmen there are no clearly defined breeding objectives and no developed breed structure. Chinese animal scientists decided, however, towards the end of the 1970's, to develop breeding objectives for the principal yak breeds. The intention was to provide technical assistance for a more systematic approach to yak breeding and to aim for earlier maturity, to improve the shape for meat and to develop strains for either milk and meat, or for meat and hair production. The criteria to be adopted therefore stressed body size, growth rate, dressing and meat percentages, milk yield and fat percentage as well as the yield of hair – both coarse and down, but with an emphasis on the latter.

In Jiulong in 1979, in accordance with the above plan, almost 7 000 of the total 21 000 yak in the area were evaluated on physical conformation and body weight. As a result, 4 adult yak bulls were identified which met or approached the pre-determined performance levels – however by the time the bulls were identified they were too old for use. Clearly this was an uncertain start to selective breeding and is more akin to a process of population screening (a search for exceptional individuals) than a process of continuous genetic selection. This particular scheme could not be continued, but consideration is being given to selection of yak at various locations and in different countries where yak are kept. However, the main scientific effort toward genetic improvement of productivity of yak, in these countries, has been directed at crossbreeding with *Bos taurus* and, to a lesser extent, *Bos indicus* cattle, rather than to selection. Some consideration is also being given to introducing, by crossbreeding, genes from wild yak into the domestic yak population as a means of improving productivity (see below). A scheme which uses performance criteria of individual yak and the potential benefits of introducing wild yak was reported by Lei *et al.* (1994).

Sarbagishev *et al.* (1989) refer to an organised breeding programme in Kirgizia based on specifications for yak males and females which were concerned primarily with conformation, growth rate and body size. Pedigrees were included and breeding values constructed. The improvement scheme was spread over a number of stock-breeding farms.

A Yak Frozen Semen Station is in operation at Dangxun in Tibet. It is the only AI centre of the many in China which is specific to yak. Zhang Yun (1994) reported that there were 38 yak bulls, including 28 wild yak, held at the station, though this number had been reduced to 17 in use. At the time of Dr Zhang's report, 50 000 doses of semen had been produced and 2000 yak cows inseminated – as well as a much larger number of yellow cattle to produce hybrids with the yak.

If, in the future, some records of performance could be kept on the purebred yak progeny of these AI yak bulls, as well as on contemporary progeny of other (identified) yak bulls, the way would be opened for a wider identification of genetically superior yak stock. It is also reported (via "Depthnews – Science Service", 1995) that Dr Zhang Yun considers that the distribution of yak semen from this station can play a significant role in counteracting adverse effects of inbreeding, which has been noted in some of the areas of yak where yak are kept.

(Use of semen from this station for the purpose of counteracting inbreeding is also referred to by Dr Pal from India – see chapter 11).

Consideration of inbreeding in yak

Inbreeding has harmful effects on nearly all aspects of the performance of livestock. Inbreeding reduces, for example, reproductive capacity, growth rate, adult size, and milk production and increases mortality, especially among the young. The amount of harm is usually quite closely related to the degree to which inbreeding occurs. It is a matter which should be considered, or at least kept in mind, in relation to yak because the traditional pattern of breeding may encourage inbreeding (cf. chapter 5). In this system, a number of bulls compete for mates and, in due course, these bulls are often replaced in the hierarchy of the herd by their offspring. This makes it inevitable the some inbreeding occurs. Inbreeding can be much reduced if bulls are exchanged across herds and greater distances – but even then the problem may not be avoided, but only postponed, if two villages, for example, were consistently to exchange breeding stock only with each other. Controlled mating, whereby the herdsman decides on the mates for a particular bull, is similar in that it may reduce or postpone inbreeding, but rarely avoid it for long.

What is not known, in the absence of pedigree records, is the extent or degree to which inbreeding occurs. Also, the actual effects in yak are not known since this requires comparison of the performance of groups differing in their degree of inbreeding. This, in turn, requires performance records linked to pedigrees. The probability of harmful consequences of inbreeding in yak is therefore inferred, for the present, from known, corresponding effects in cattle, sheep and other livestock elsewhere.

In some countries, such as Bhutan, Nepal and India (see chapter 11) concern over the effects of inbreeding have been expressed by those on the spot. The yak populations in these countries have become relatively closed. This is a consequence of reduced interchange of breeding stock across national boundaries, relative to former times, and hence an increased likelihood that related animals are mated to each other. The effects of inbreeding must be suspected whenever the general performance of the stock is thought, or known, to have declined relative to an earlier era, and when other systematic changes in husbandry practices, such as, for example overgrazing, cannot account for it. Thus Kozlovskii (1960) stated that yak in the Gorno-Altai region were becoming closely inbred, which, if true, could well account for the earlier view of Denisov (1935) that the yak of that area were inferior, at that time, to those of other regions. Kozlovskii went on to advocate, by way of remedy, the introduction of unrelated yak males and/or of hybridisation with other cattle.

Inbreeding occurs whenever animals which are more closely related to each other than 'average' are mated to each other. For example, if a son or sons of a popular bull are used in a herd as his replacement, they, in turn, are liable to mate with some of their half-sisters or cousins. Even more probably, they will serve less closely related females, but related none-the-less through common ancestors a couple of generations back (grandparents or great-grandparents). Mating of full sibs to each other, or parents to their offspring, which is regarded as close inbreeding, is also not unusual unless steps are taken to avoid it. Pal, Barari and Biswas (1994), writing in relation to yak in India, state that farmers may use a male to serve females consecutively for 2–3 generations.

Inbreeding also occurs as a consequence of selection, a process which is widely and correctly advocated and practised for the genetic improvement of livestock. Selection has the inevitable consequence of bringing about an increase in inbreeding, simply as a consequence of restricting the number of animals which become parents of the next generation. The objective in selection schemes must be to ensure that the beneficial effects of selecting superior stock outweigh the harmful effects of the consequent inbreeding. This consideration is nowadays a routine part of large-scale and long-term breeding plans, such as cattle improvement programmes involving the widespread use of a few bulls through artificial insemination.

The reason for having dealt with this topic at some length is that experience suggests that because the effects of inbreeding are not readily recognised in the short term, they are easily ignored. The circumstantial evidence for inbreeding is strong in at least some yak populations; it is a matter, therefore, which should not be ignored.

Crossbreeding – within the yak species

No systematic crossbreeding appears to be practised among the different breeds or local populations of yak. This is not, perhaps, surprising in view of the relative isolation of different communities and the distances separating them. It is perhaps a little more surprising that it does not seem, so far, to have played more than a minor role in investigations to find out whether hybrid vigour would result from such crossbreeding. To the outsider it seems likely that hybrid vigour would result, although the magnitude cannot be predicted. The likelihood of heterosis from breed-crossing can be argued from the relative isolation, over a long time, of discrete populations of domestic yak in different localities, and from the likelihood that breeding practices within herds have led to inbreeding (although, again, some would dispute this). Crossing under these circumstances could have merits.

Support for this view comes from the attention paid more recently to crossing of domestic yak with wild yak and the claims of improved performance from such crossbreeding. It is not possible in the results presented from such trials to differentiate clearly between the additive genetic effects (e.g. the fact that wild yak are larger than domestic yak) and the occurrence and magnitude of heterosis as a result of the cross, but some results from such crosses will be shown below. Before doing so, it is useful to provide some more information on pure wild yak (see also chapter 1).

Size of pure wild yak

Measurements were made in the 1960's on 5 adult male wild yak by the Agriculture and Animal Husbandry Department of the Tibetan Autonomous Region (Study

Group [Qiangtang], 1978). These animals had been caught in the Qiangtang area of northern Tibet. Measurements are shown in Table 3.1.

Table 3.1 Measurements (cm) on 5 wild yak from Tibet

Head length	61.1	(55–67)
Forehead width	27.3	(26–32)
Circumference of base of horn		(30–40)
Body length	179.3	(171–193)
Height at withers	158.8	(152–163)
Heart girth	240.6	(218–264)
Chest depth	91.1	(90–92)
Chest width	61.6	(53–78)
Canon bone circumference		(22–24)
Estimated body weight (kg)	1000	

Some wild yak calves caught by staff of the Animal Husbandry Institute of the Yushu Tibetan Autonomous Prefecture of Qinghai Province were compared with domestic yak calves under the same conditions of feeding and management (Xu Guiling, 1985a). Table 3.2 shows the weights and weight gains of the two groups. It can be seen from these results that the wild yak calves were 86% heavier than the domestic yak calves at 3 months of age but, relative to their weight, grew more slowly (though not necessarily less in absolute terms) so that by the age of 16 months the wild yak were only 63% heavier than the domestic ones.

Table 3.2 A comparison of the body weights (kg) and weight gains (kg) at various ages of 5 wild yak and 19 domestic yak kept under the same conditions of feeding and management [source: Xu Guiling, 1985]

Age (months):		3	4	5	6	12	16
Domestic yak:	weight	33.6	39.2	48.2	51.5	59.1	67.4
	gain	5.6	9.0	3.3	7.6	8.3	
Wild yak:	weight	62.5	71.9	77.3	81.5	92.5	110.1
	gain		9.4	5.4	4.2	11.0	17.6

Crossbreeding of wild with domestic yak

Some results from the crossing of wild with domestic yak are available. Provided the progeny from such crosses of domestic with wild yak have not been given preferential treatment over the domestic yak alongside them (and that may be a matter for concern), the results suggest that the crosses have an advantage. Lu Hongji *et al.* (1987), for example, has shown that the birth weight of crosses between domestic and wild yak were more than 30% heavier at birth than domestic yak calves. By 6 months old, the advantage in favour of the cross had increased to more than 50%. Calves with only 1/4 wild-yak blood were 16% and 35% heavier at birth and 6 months of age respcctively.

Some comparative measurements were made on adult male F1 and domestic yak (North-West Animal Husbandry Institute, 1965, personal communication) with the results shown in Table 3.3.

Table 3.3 Measurements (in cm) on adult domestic yak and its F1 crosses with wild yak

	F1	Domestic yak
Height at withers	129.5	116.0
Body length	147.3	129.2
Heart girth	189.3	167.7
Canon bone circumference	21.0	19.3

Staff at the Lanzhou Institute of Animal Husbandry and Veterinary Science used some frozen wild yak semen to inseminate female domestic yak on the Datong Yak Farm of Qinghai Province (Lu Hongji *et al.*, 1987). They also produced some backcrosses of the F1 to local domestic yak (to produce 0.25% wild yak) and made some matings of the local domestic yak to males of the Jiulong (domestic) breed of yak. The results are shown in Table 3.4 and suggest that crossing to the wild yak increased body weights and weight gains over the first 6 months of life. These weight gains were greater, relative to the birth weights, in the crosses with wild yak than in crosses with the Jiulong. The local domestic yak showed the lowest relative weight gains to 6 months old. There were no measurements beyond that age.

Table 3.4 Body weights (kg) (± SD) of local domestic yak and crosses with Jiulong yak and wild yak [source: Lu Hongji *et al.*, 1987]

	Type of calf			
	local yak	local x Jiulong (F1)	local x F1 (wild) (25% wild)	local x wild yak (F1)
Birth weight	13.2 ± 2.3 (n=25)	14.0 (n=2)	15.3 ±1.9 (n=76)	17.3 ± 2.3 (n=77)
6-month weight	65.2 ±10.5 (n=64)	73.7 ± 6.9 (n=9)	86.1 ± 4.6 (n=21)	101.3 ± 9.4 (n=33)

Interest in the use of the wild yak to improve production of domestic yak was exemplified by presentation of a number of papers on this topic at the first international congress on yak held at Gansu Agricultural University in 1994. Zhao and Zhang (1994) noted that, historically, herdsmen in the Gannan area of Gansu drove their domestic yak females into regions where wild yak lived, in order to allow natural mating with wild yak bulls. The crossbred progeny would later be selected to improve the domestic yak population. Based on this popular experience, more systematic studies are in progress, using frozen semen from wild yak bulls. Substantial numbers of first-cross and back-cross (25% wild yak) offspring have been born and are reported to become significantly larger than the local domestic yak. The benefits of wild yak blood, as noted in these studies, have also carried over into crossing with the local yellow cattle. When yak bulls which had 50% wild yak blood were mated to yellow cattle, the resulting F1 hybrids were of the order of 20% larger at 6 months old than comparable F1 crosses of yellow cattle with domestic yak.

It is not known, in respect of any of the studies referred to, what is the relative importance of the role of heterosis and of the additive genetic contribution from the wild yak to its cross with the domestic yak.

Results, from another area of Gansu (Lu Zhonglin and Li Kongliang, 1994) suggest that substantial increases in body size, hair production and meat output were achieved in first crosses of wild with domestic yak, relative to the latter. Milk yield was found to have increased by more than 10%. Yan Ping, Lu Zhonglin and Lu H.J. (1994) reported, more specifically, that the fleece weight of adult females was 1.76, 1.65 and 1.47 kg for 1/2 wild, 1/4 wild and domestic yak respectively. These authors also found that, importantly, the proportion of the undercoat was increased substantially with the introduction of wild yak blood – but the strength of the fibres was not affected. The use of wild yak to improve domestic yak performance through a process of crossing and selection was also reported to be under investigation in Qinghai (Lei et al,1994) – but, clearly, only the additive genetic contribution from the wild yak genes will be useful in the actual process of subsequent selection (though the cross will retain some of the advantages from the initial heterosis).

Breed conservation

Taking into account the size of the present domestic yak population as a whole, it would be difficult to argue that conservation measures are a matter of urgency at this point in time. This might change if social or economic pressures were to reduce the extent of yak keeping – as is already evident in some areas, such as Nepal – or if predicted changes in global climate (over decades and centuries) had the effect of restricting the future distribution and size of the yak population.

Preservation of some of the remarkable traits of the yak in terms of its adaptation to a harsh environment and to long periods of severe deprivation should, none-the-less, be regarded as of interest to animal breeders world-wide. There are parts of the world where these characteristics could assist in establishing animal production, and other parts where such resilience, on the part of the animal, could lead to better utilisation of natural resources. At present, however, the gene pool of the domestic yak as a whole is not endangered.

A different situation seems to exist for some of the more localised, and to an extent differentiated, populations or breeds of yak. The total numbers in some of these breeds is not large and crossbreeding with *Bos taurus* and *Bos indicus* cattle further reduces the proportion of the yak population available for its replacement. For example, the Jiulong yak, possibly the best producer among the yak breeds, numbers only 8 000 breeding animals in the centre of the yak-producing area of Jiulong county, and less than twice that number in surrounding areas. The total numbers, however, tell only a small part of the story. The Jiulong breed of yak has been a closed population for hundreds of years, starting from a small herd. Throughout its history, herdsmen are said to have avoided introducing outside blood. Moreover, the system of selection practised by the herdsmen (see above), and the natural competition among bulls for dominance, makes it virtually certain that the effective size of the population is small and that inbreeding occurs (though the extent of this is a matter for debate). Thus, in-so-far as the particular properties of the Jiulong are worth preserving, and are not to be lost through genetic drift, special measures may be required. This was recognised by Chinese experts a number of years ago and led to a decision to set up a random-breeding herd of 100 yak females and 20 males. This is maintained in the Hongba area of Jiulong county and is the responsibility of the Animal Husbandry Station there. Income from the sale of milk and culled animals meets some of the costs. There is also a subsidy from local government to assist this project.

Other yak breeds may be in a similar situation to the Jiulong, with total numbers not large and the size of the "effective" breeding population possibly quite small. The Tianzhu White breed, in an area of Gansu province, could be one such and consideration to its conservation is being given (Wang Yuchang and Wang Yanhong, 1994).

Local breeds may have special merits or characteristics which could be lost in the absence of positive action to maintain such breeds. Investigation of the need for conservation in the yak should therefore receive some attention even if, on present consideration, local rather than general action may be called for. A useful start might be an up-to-date census of the yak population, its various types and breeds and current breeding practices. In combination, such information would help to indicate the (genetically) effective size of the different breeding populations, both in China and elsewhere. A census of numbers alone, as regularly practised in some countries such as Mongolia, though helpful, is not enough for this particular purpose.

Too often in matters of conservation, action has been delayed until damage to the breed, or even extinction of the species, has become imminent. This must not be allowed to happen with the yak.

For the wild yak, it is widely accepted that conservation is a matter of importance and urgency. Accounts from as recently as the 19th century testified to vast herds of wild yak in the Kunlun mountains of Tibet and Qinghai. These are no longer seen. Miller, Harris and Cui-Quan Cai (1994) estimated that wild yak of all ages and both sexes may still have numbered around 15 000 in the early 1990's (more than claimed during personal conversation with others), but this does not give an accurate picture of the threat confronting this wild species. Wild yak are protected by Chinese wildlife protection legislation, but, according to Miller *et al.*, the Departments concerned have inadequate resources for enforcement. The factors which have led to a dramatic decline in numbers of wild yak over the last century still operate, even if to a lesser extent. These factors include excessive hunting, partly for food, the encroachment of the infra-structure of modern society, such as roads, and the increasing competition for grazing land from domestic livestock (Miller *et al.*, 1994).

Inter-species crossing (yak with cattle of other species)

Ancient documents show that yak have been crossed with ordinary cattle (*Bos taurus*) for at least 3000 years. Documents from 11th century China, in the Zhou dynasty, suggest that crossing of yak with cattle by the Quing people gave benefits which would nowadays be called heterosis (or hybrid vigour). The name "Pien Niu", and variants of it, has been used for these crosses from earliest times. However, many other names exist (see below). In some areas, for example northern India, Nepal and Bhutan, crossing of with *Bos indicus* cattle also occurs.

Systematic crossing of yak with other cattle has been recommended and practised for many years – and certainly as long as hybridisation by plant breeders has been in fashion. The crosses find a special niche with herdsmen to provide extra milk and draught animals, usually at somewhat lower altitudes than the typical yak country. Crossing is done primarily of yak females to bulls of local cattle. This is regarded as the normal hybridisation and, in China, the F1 is called "true Pien Niu" (or simply "Pien Niu"). The reciprocal cross of cattle female to yak bull is also practised and regarded as "counter-hybridisation" with the progeny called "false Pien Niu" – and many other local names for this also (see later).

The crosses themselves are always back-crossed to either yak or cattle males. There is no alternative to this as the F1 males are sterile. The herdsmen use, for the most part, the cattle normally available to them in their area – for example the local, so-called "yellow cattle", in China. The crossbred progeny of the F1 generation are then called "local Pien Niu". However, much investigation has gone into the use of "improved" breeds of cattle of dairy, beef, and dual-purpose type. Results of crossing with both local and "improved" cattle breeds will be given in chapter 7. The name which is given to the first cross of yak with "improved" cattle breeds is "improved Pien Niu" – in order to distinguish it from the "local Pien Niu".

In the course of the experiments in the 1920's and 1930's at Buffalo Park, Wainwright, Canada, aimed at developing a meat animal for the cold northern regions there, including Alaska, a small number of crosses were also made successfully between yak (male) and female American bison and half-bison (bison x cattle cross) (Deakin, Muir and Smith, 1935).

Figure 3.1 Pien Niu female (F1 from yak dam and local, yellow cattle sire)

Figure 3.2 "False" Pien Niu female (F1 from local, yellow cattle dam and yak sire)

Nomenclature. In publications from China and some other countries, the backcross generations are often denoted as F2, F3, F4 etc. This nomenclature will not be used here as it could lead to confusion among readers from elsewhere, geneticists in particular, who will be accustomed to this to denote successive generations of crosses mated among themselves. Backcrosses will, therefore, be described here by the letter B, with a number denoting the generation and a letter to show whether the last male used was cattle or yak – when that has been specified. (Thus, B1(C) would denote a backcross animal produced from a mating of a F1 female to a cattle bull, etc.)

Local names for crosses. Names for the first crosses of yak and cattle include, in Tibetan areas, the name "dzo", variants of which extend into Mongolia and other countries, and "chauri", the name used in Nepal. The various types of backcross, both to cattle and to yak, have an especially rich variety of names which differ in different parts of China and elsewhere. Descriptions of these names have been given by, among others, Hu Angang, Cai Li and Du Shaodeng (1960), Zhao Zhengrong (1957), Joshi (1982) and Pal (1993c). However, the uninitiated traveller may also find himself confused by the fact that the local people in China are said to call the hybrids of yak with cattle "improved cattle" – this usage, however, will be avoided here.

Distribution of crosses. In the areas where the Henduan Alpine type of yak predominate crossing of yak females with cattle males is not widely practised, nor is inter-species crossing common in those areas of the pastoral regions at high elevation where cattle cannot adapt. Such crossbreeding is, however, widespread in areas of mixed pastoral and agricultural production at lower altitudes. Table 3.5 shows, by way of example, the relative proportions of pure yak to crosses and yellow cattle in two such areas in Sichuan. In main yak-producing areas, crossbreeding with cattle is normally restricted to only a small proportion of the yak herd (see later).

Table 3.5 Proportions of yak, *Bos taurus* cattle and hybrids in Ganzi county of Sichuan

Type	Pastoral area [%]	Agricultural area [%]
Yak	91.4	16.8
F1	7.8	55.8
Backcross [B1(C)]	0.7	3.7
Cattle	<0.1	21.9
Total No.	*41 541*	*25 560*

The crossbred females are an important source of milk and milk products, for home consumption or for sale, and the males, since they cannot be used for breeding, are used for draught purposes, or are slaughtered for meat.

The reciprocal crossing procedure between yak bulls and yellow cattle females is, in China, carried out mainly in the cattle-producing areas of the cold Minshan mountains, and especially in the Yangchung and Min counties of Gansu province and Pingwu county in Sichuan province. These crosses do not give much milk and are used mainly for draught purposes.

Crossbreeding policy. First crosses of yak and 'ordinary' cattle adapt well to the conditions in which they are used. They have some of the good characteristics of both parental types – resistance to a harsh environment from the yak and extra productivity, milk in particular, from the cattle. Back-crosses to cattle, however, are less well adapted to the environment and their productivity is often little better than that of yak – most probably through loss of heterosis (although there is no strict quantification of this). Backcrosses to cattle are not therefore favoured – one practice being to dispose of the backcross calves immediately after birth, in order to have all the milk from the dam available for use or sale by the herders. The alternative of backcrosses to the yak, however, provide a particular source of animals for meat production. This system is encouraged and practised in China and elsewhere.

Cai Li has shown, from a comparison of two neighbouring and otherwise similar grassland farms in Sichuan, that the output per head of animal, per unit of land and per unit of labour can be seriously reduced if the proportion of backcrosses is allowed to become too high. On one of the farms, Xiangdong Livestock farm, the proportion of backcrosses was not allowed to exceed 5% of the total herd and some selection was practised of those retained. On the other farm, Axi Livestock farm, the backcross progeny of the F1 generation were retained in full. The results of the comparison are shown in Table 3.6.

Table 3.6 Comparison of output of animal products from two neighbouring and similar farms in pastoral areas of Sichuan province (1977–81)

	Xiangdong	Arxi
Total stock	2721	4346
Yak (%)	69.7	31.5
F1 (%)	25.4	21.1
Backcross* (%)	4.7	47.1
Ordinary cattle (%)	0.2	0.3
Output value** of:		
milk	49673	64565
cheese	2405	2931
hide	1753	1789
hair and down	1914	1258
market animals	38760	54825
Total value	*94505*	*125368*
Average output per:		
head of stock	34.7	28.9
head of staff	716	412.4
100 mu grassland	92.8	53.5

* backcrosses are mostly to cattle – very few to yak. ** output value (Yuan) as the mean of 1979–81 calculated according to fixed prices in 1980 as follows: milk 0.33 Yuan/kg; cheese 0.56 Yuan/kg; hide 8.9 Yuan each; hair and down 1.74 Yuan/kg; market cattle 85 Yuan/head.

The use of "improved" breeds. Since around 1939 in China, starting at Datong in Qinghai province, and from 1941 in the area now known as the Ganzi Tibetan autonomous prefecture in Sichuan, some yak were crossed with Dutch Holstein Friesian bulls. Such crossing did not, however, become systematic until the mid-1950's when 200 bulls of various breeds were introduced to the yak-producing areas of China. The breeds included the Holstein Friesian, Shorthorn, Simmental; Latvia, Ala-Tau and Kostrome cattle; the Binzhou, Shanhe, Qinchuan Yingin, and others. More recently, Charolais, Hereford, Limousin and others have been added to those available for crossing with yak. Mating was tried initially by natural mating, but artificial insemination was also used and continues as the predominant practice.

Although the growth and performance of the crosses for both milk and meat production was highly regarded (see chapter 7, for performance results) the bulls of these various breeds (and 75% grade bulls of these breeds with yellow cattle) did not adapt to the local conditions and high altitudes in China. Most of the bulls had died of mountain sickness and for other reasons within two years of introduction and many of them within the first few months. The bulls introduced in the mid and late 1950s left fewer than 1000 F1 and backcross progeny in over 20 years.

Crossing of yak with these "improved" breeds of cattle is now carried out by AI with frozen semen. This procedure inevitably restricts the utilisation of these breeds to the more accessible and well organised yak herds. In practice in many areas, therefore, the *Bos taurus* (and *Bos indicus*) cattle used for crossing with the yak will continue to be the local types of cattle. However, in some countries, such as Mongolia, considerable, organised effort is being put into promoting the use of "exotic" cattle breeds for crossing with yak by AI.

Crossing of yak with "exotic" breeds of cattle has also been practised in other countries for a long time, as, for example some countries of the former USSR. Thus, Denisov (1938) reports on crosses of yak and Schwyz (Swiss Brown) cattle, and more recently Katzina, Davydov and Balnadov (1994) add the Jersey and the Galloway, and a continuing use of the Schwyz (now of American origin, hence probably the American Brown Swiss), to the list of exotic breeds referred to above. Several of the breeds referred to are also used in Mongolia (Zagdsuren, 1994b).

Limits to hybridisation

The relatively low reproductive rate of the yak sets severe limits on the proportion of the female yak population which can be used for crossbreeding with cattle if the numbers of the pure yak population are to be maintained, or possibly increased. In practice, it has been found best to restrict production of hybrids to the F1 generation (whose offspring, in turn, are then slaughtered for meat). The male sterility of the hybrids prevents crossing systems, other than backcrossing to yak or cattle bulls. Reduced productivity, relative to the F1, makes the backcross generations unattractive commercially.

The actual proportion of the female yak population which can be crossed with cattle depends on the reproductive rate, the replacement rate for cows (depending on the rate of death and disposal of the cows) and the loss of female calves before they reach reproductive age. These factors will vary from region to region and from year to year.

If it were assumed that:

- the yak population remained static in numbers,
- an average reproductive rate for the yak cow is around of 0.5 (equivalent to a live calf every second year),
- 10% of cows are eliminated annually and
- 10% of calves are lost before breeding age,

then 50% of the yak cow population could be available for crossbreeding. (These assumptions are equivalent, on average, to a yak cow producing, in her lifetime, two female progeny which themselves survive to breeding age.) Any intention to expand the yak population would reduce the proportion that could be crossed. If an increase of 10% in population numbers were required (and, as indicated earlier, herdsmen like to increase the number of animals they own), then only 10% of the yak cows could be mated to cattle – when the other assumptions remain the same.

Other assumptions would be entirely reasonable. Thus, higher replacement rates for cows and poorer survival of calves would reduce the proportion of yak females available for crossing. For example, if replacement rates for cows and mortality among calves were both as high as 20%, as happens in some situations and some years, no yak cows would be available for crossbreeding if the reproductive rate of the yak did not exceed 50% – even with a static yak population. On the other hand, in some regions and countries, where reproductive rate over a lifetime of the yak may be higher than in the examples given, the proportion of the yak female population available for crossing can be increased.

The precise proportions of the yak population available for crossbreeding thus depends on the circumstances in any particular herd or group of herds. The point has been made often (see also chapter 7) that the production of yak-cattle hybrids can play a useful role in improving the economics of animal production in the mountainous regions and particularly at the lower elevations of the yak territory. But it also needs to be said that such crossing is not a panacea. The pure yak must, perforce, remain the major proportion of the total bovine population in the mountainous regions. The attractions of crossbreeding yak with cattle should not be allowed to detract from the need to consider genetic and husbandry improvements for the yak itself. In fact, improvements in the productivity and reproductive rate of the yak would also increase the opportunities for crossbreeding of yak with cattle, as already apparent in some areas.

4 THE YAK IN RELATION TO ITS ENVIRONMENT

OVERVIEW

Yak have many characteristics and attributes which must be regarded as adaptations to extreme cold; high altitude, with low oxygen content of the air, and high solar radiation; difficult, often treacherous, terrain; cyclical nutrition with short growing seasons for the herbage on which yak graze, and the need for yak to cope with a variety of different kinds of herbage.

In general, temperature is the single most important factor determining the distribution and stocking density of yak. Yak survive and perform adequately if the annual mean temperature is below 5°C and the average in the hottest month is not above 13°C. They can also survive satisfactorily at ambient temperatures down to –40°C. Altitude, as such, is of lesser importance. The further north (of the equator) yak live, the lower, in general, the altitude at which they are found. Yak in animal and zoological parks, found in several parts of the world, may again have re-adapted, over time, to life in these, for them, non-normal situations.

Yak cope with cold by conserving heat, rather than by generating it – which would require food that may not be available. Heat conservation is effected by a compact conformation and a thick fleece of coarse outer hair and an undercoat of fine down. The proportion of down in the coat increases greatly before the onset of winter. Young calves have a fleece composed exclusively of down fibre. Normally, yak accumulate a layer of sub-cutaneous fat prior to winter. This also helps heat conservation and provides an energy reserve. The skin is relatively thick. It contains sweat glands, but, for the most part, these are not functional. This is one reason why yak are intolerant of high ambient temperature.

Adaptation to a low oxygen content of the air arises from yak having a large chest (14–15 pairs of thoracic ribs), large lungs and a large heart relative to their overall body size. The haemoglobin content may not be exceptionally high relative to sea-level cattle, although the content increases with altitude, but the haemoglobin of yak blood has a high affinity for oxygen. Also, anatomically, the yak is designed to be able to breathe rapidly and take in large amounts of air.

The skin is highly pigmented and the predominant hair colour is black. Both of these help to resist the effects of solar radiation. White yak exist, none-the-less, because herdsmen in some localities prefer them.

Yak are adapted to grazing a wide variety of plant species: grass, coarse plants and sedges and some shrubs. Yak can graze long grass using their tongues, as is common for cattle, but they can also graze very short herbage, after the manner of sheep, by using their incisor teeth and lips. When ground is covered with snow and ice, they break through the cover to the wilted grass beneath, using their hooves and helped by the use of their heads. Yak also graze rapidly and for long hours.

To cope with precipitous terrain, yak have developed particularly suitable hooves and a temperament that is suited to potentially dangerous situations such as marshy ground. Yak prefer to group themselves in large herds for protection, particularly against wolves, but they are also nervous of wild animals and man and, if startled, will readily take flight.

Introduction

Features common to the environment in which yak live are extreme cold, mountainous terrain, high altitudes with reduced oxygen in the air, high solar radiation and short growing seasons for herbage and a variable assortment of herbage, sparse in some areas. Plant growing seasons vary from 120 to 180 days, but the periods of relatively vigorous plant growth are even shorter than that. Wilted herbage provides some sustenance for the yak at other times of year, but not in sufficient quantity for their requirements. There is, of course, some variation in these features. Some "compensatory" factors have also to be taken into account. For example, the more northerly the latitude at which the yak are found, and hence, in general, the colder the climate, the lower the altitudes at which the yak will live. These points will be discussed in more detail later in this chapter. Many of the characteristics of the yak can be regarded as adaptations to these conditions, in which cattle of other species have difficulty in surviving.

Distribution in relation to environmental factors

Several studies in China have analysed the distribution of the yak using multiple regression approaches with the stocking density of the yak, in selected areas, as the dependant variable and various factors of the environment as the independent variables. The factors most commonly included in these studies (for example, Wen Zhenzhong and Xie Zhonlun, 1985) are: altitude above sea level, yearly average air temperature, annual precipitation, average relative humidity, average annual sunshine and, in some studies, the type of plant cover.

It has to be noted that these factors are not independent of each other (for example, altitude and air temperature are related, as are annual precipitation and annual sunshine, etc.) and all the factors impinge on the length of the growing season for plants and the type of plant cover likely to be found. With these limitations in mind, it was concluded by the authors of various studies that, in general, air temperature was of major importance for the distribution of the yak and more important than altitude. In analyses where the type of plant cover was also included as a variable (Huang Wenxiu and Wang Sufang, 1980; Dou Yaozong, Yang

Zai and Xue Zhengya,1985) its importance ranked alongside temperature. However, the quantity of available herbage itself must be strongly influenced by the climate of the area. Annual precipitation was generally of less importance to the distribution of the yak and altitude, as such, of lesser importance still.

The effect of air temperature

In the native regions of yak in present times, the stocking density of yak declines as average annual temperature increases. The greatest concentrations of yak are found at average annual air temperatures between –3°C and +3°C. In Qinghai Province the yak are concentrated in areas with annual mean temperatures between –3°C and –4°C, those in Tibet are densest at the range of –3°C to –5°C and in Sichuan province between –1.6°C and +3.4°C.

Li Shihong *et al.* (1981) have reported that above an ambient temperature of 13°C the respiration rate of the yak starts to rise, and at 16°C heart rate and body temperature start to rise. When environmental temperatures reach 20°C yak will stand near water or in shade, if available, without moving, grazing, drinking or ruminating. At the other extreme, yak can feed and move normally on grasslands with air temperatures ranging as low as –30°C to –40°C, or even lower as in the Tibetan Naqu area where the minimum air temperature in the cold season is recorded as –42°C. The lowest temperature that yak can tolerate has not been recorded.

It appears from these studies that air temperature is the single most important environmental factor influencing the distribution of the yak. Yak survive and perform adequately provided the annual mean temperature is below 5°C and the average in the hottest month does not exceed 13°C, though daily maximum temperatures can rise in the summer to much higher levels before falling again at night. (Nonetheless, yak in zoological and wild animal parks elsewhere appear, over time, to have adapted to different sets of conditions.) It is a matter of observation that the further north of the equator that yak live the lower, in general, the altitude of the terrain on which they are found, since average temperature declines with increasing latitude (*cf.* Table 4.1)).

The effect of altitude

Subject to the availability of adequate grazing, the distribution and stocking density of yak increases with altitude, but as already noted, this is also dependent on latitude. Thus at the more southerly latitudes, as, for example, Qinghai province, yak seek out higher altitudes than in more northerly areas such as Mongolia. The few yak introduced to Canada and Alaska in far northern latitudes existed at relatively low altitudes (but see below). It is likely that, as suggested above, the relationship between altitude and latitude is mediated through air temperature.

The highest altitude where yak live normally is at 5500 m in the Tibetan Rongbusi region in the lower ranges of the Himalayas. Yak steers used as pack animals are quite capable of traversing terrain at 7200 metres. Low oxygen content of air and high solar radiation are not therefore barriers to the yak's survival.

TABLE 4.1 External characteristics of yak at different locations varying in altitude

Area	Location* Latitude (N)	Longitude (E)	Altitude (m)	Number observed	Polled %	Black/ brown %	Black with white patches %	Variegated %	White %
Tibet, Pali	27.5	89.0	4 300	529	few	89.0	11.0		
Yunnan, Zhondian	28.0	99.5	3 300	946	0.0	62.4	37.6		
Sichuan, Muli	28.5	101.0	3 500	772	0.0	9.5	90.5		
Sichuan, Jiulong	29.0	101.5	3 800	337	0.0	75.4	24.6		
Sichuan, Liuba	29.5	101.5	3 800	4455	0.5	50.6	49.2	0,1	
Tibet, Pengbuo	30.0	91.5	4 000	96	few	75.0	15.6	9.4	
Tibet, Dangxiong	30.5	91.0	4 400	591	0.0	91.9	8.1		
Tibet, Jali	31.0	93.5	4 500	241	17.0	41.0	50.0	9.0	
Sichuan, Shachong	31.0	101.0	3 200	486	1.6	78.1	21.9		
Sichuan, Ganzi	31.5	100.0	3 800	330	3.0	66.0	31.0	3.0	
Tibet, Naqu	31.5	91.7	4 570	795	9.2	78.4	16.1	5.1	0.4
Sichuan, Se da	32.5	100.5	3 893	245	11.8	75.1	21.6	2.5	0.8
Sichuan, Hongyuan	33.0	103.0	3 500	782	7.4	69.4	22.1	8.1	0.4
Gansu, Gannan	34.0	103.0	3 400	957	57.1	78.2	15.8	6.0	0.1
Qinghai, Tongde	35.0	100.5	3 300	580		81.7	14.1	4.1	
Qinghai, Haiyan	37.0	101.0	3 500	1065	80.0	60.7	25.7	12.7	0.9
Qinghai, Menyuan	37.5	101.5	3 300	1383	43.6	58.2	23.1	7.8	10.9
Qinghai, Gongda	37.5	100.0	3 500	2576	60.6	73.7	16.1	8.1	2.1
Gansu, Shandan	38.5	101.5	3 000	463** 109	46.2	71.6	22.0	5.5	0.9
Xinjiang, Bazhou	40.0	84.0	2 500	280	22.7	57.9	17.5	19.3	5.3

* median latitude and longitude for the area in question; ** 463 observed for horned/polled, 109 for hair colour

The effect of precipitation and relative humidity

Yak live in two distinct zones. One is semi-arid with an annual precipitation of 500–600 mm and a relative humidity of 50–60%. In these areas the potential for evaporation tends to exceed the level of precipitation (e.g. Qinghai and much of Tibet). The other zone has an average annual rainfall of 600–700 mm and a relative humidity of 60%–65% and is described as semi-humid (e.g. eastern Tibet and south-west Sichuan). The two zones differ in the predominant types of vegetation found and, as noted in chapter 2, the two zones are associated with different types of yak.

The effect of sunshine

In general, yak live in areas with more than 2000 hours of annual sunshine. In Qinghai province, the highest densities of yak are in areas with between 2500 and 2700 hours sunshine (Wen Zhengzhong and Xie Zhonglun, 1985) whilst in Sichuan province the greatest density of yak is in the districts with between 2000 and 2200 hours of sunshine per year.

A note on yak in Canada and Alaska

In view of the fact that the yak introduced to these countries represent the most northerly latitudes in the distribution of the yak (other than the progenitors of the modern yak) it may be useful to relate, briefly, the experience with these animals.

Six head of Chinese yak were sent to Canada in 1909, but by the following year only 1 male and 3 females had survived and for the next two years the animals failed to reproduce. This, as noted by White *et al.* (1946), was attributed to the low altitude at which the yak were kept. Reproduction started when the animals were moved to higher altitudes (and probably, therefore, lower temperatures) in the Rocky Mountain Park. In 1919 most of the yak were transferred to Buffalo Park, Wainwright. In 1921, some yak were included in the hybridisation experiments, with domestic cattle and American bison, then in progress at Wainwright, with the aim of producing an animal for meat production for the harsh pastoral conditions of northern Canada. Few of the inter-species crosses survived (Deakin *et al.* 1935) and this series of trials was suspended in 1928.

Similar experience obtained in Alaska (White *et al.* 1946). In 1919, 1923 and 1930, three male and six female Chinese yak, born in Canada, were taken to the Fairbanks Experiment Station in Alaska, at an elevation of approximately 130 m. The yak had great difficulty in breeding, but these difficulties diminished and the general condition of the yak improved when they were moved to an altitude between 400 and 800 m. The intention was to produce animals suitable for the grasslands in the Alaska mountains, southern Yukon territories and plains and tundra of the Alaska-Canada border. Experimental crosses were made with Galloway cows which produced hybrid offspring heavier at slaughter than either the yak or the pure Galloway. However, the crosses did not appear to withstand the extremely low temperatures of winter as well as the pure yak. The trials, were also suspended, in the early 1930s.

Yak in wild animal and zoological parks

Yak are kept in wild animal and zoological parks in many countries of Europe and elsewhere and reports suggest that these animals breed and survive successfully. Many of these locations are relatively close to sea level and thus do not present an atmosphere low in oxygen. Also, summer temperatures at many of these locations will be sustained at higher average levels than for yak in their native territory, even though these temperatures will be less, in turn, than those at low altitudes in the areas adjacent to the yak territory (from which some of the reported problems of yak at lower altitudes emanate). Somehow, therefore, some reconciliation is needed between the evidence of poor adaptation of yak to low altitudes and high ambient temperature based on the experience of yak production in their principal territories, and the apparently adequate re-adaptation of these animals to the conditions of the parks in other parts of the world. Winter *et al.* (1989) also refer to this conundrum. Perhaps it is all a question of the time allowed for such adaptation and how the animals are managed on arrival.

Some information on the herd at Whipsnade wild animal park, on the edge of the Dunstable Downs (elevation approximately 150 m, approximately 52°N) in England, has been kindly provided by the curator, Mr Nick Lindsay (personal communication, 1995) and serves for illustration. The herd was started in 1944, though records of the source are not now readily available. This was followed by small importations from Alberta (Canada), Berlin (Germany) and from Sweden, among others. Currently, the herd numbers about 17 animals with a second herd of 12 established at another park with animals originating from the Whipsnade herd.

According to Mr Lindsay, the yak cows do not calve annually, but each has, on average, approximately 2 calves in every three years. The animals grow normally and survive extremely well. Small numbers of yak have been sent to other countries (e.g. a recent export of 4 to Turkey). There is no obvious seasonality to the breeding and over the years 1990–94 calves (all pure yak) have been born in March, April, May, July, August, September and November. It appears that some of the yak at Whipsnade may breed as early as their second year of life. Since the start in 1944 there have been more than 80 yak in the Whipsnade herd (with the offshoot herd in addition) and the vast majority of them have been born at the park.

In summer, the animals are said to seek shade under trees and shed much of their fleece, but show no obvious discomfort. The only recurrent health problems were found to be associated with copper deficiency. Following diagnosis of the condition some years ago, it is now is fully controlled by regular supplementation and occasional copper injection (E. Flack, personal communication, 1995). This matter will be referred to more fully in chapter 9 as there is a possibility that yak may be prone to this deficiency for genetic reasons because other cattle are not equally affected on the same diet. Other data from the herd are also presented later in this chapter.

Adaptive characteristics

The ability of the yak to live in conditions in which other bovines will not survive, or, at least, not thrive, suggests that the yak has developed specially adapted characteristics. These will now be considered.

Resistance to cold

Conformation

The yak's body is compact with short neck, short limbs, no dewlap, small ears and a short tail. (The limb length index, defined as {[height at withers – chest depth]/ height at withers} x 100, is small, at 40–42%, relative to other cattle in the region). The scrotum of the male is small, compact and hairy, and the udder of the female small and also hairy. The skin has few wrinkles and the surface area of the yak is relatively small per unit bodyweight (0.016 m2/kg [Li Shihong *et al.* 1984]). The yak has only few functional sweat glands (see below). All these factors result in dissipation of body heat being minimised.

Though not strictly relevant in the context of heat dissipation, it should be noted as part of the appearance of the yak that they can be either horned or polled. The distribution of these two forms appears to depend on the regional preferences of the herdsmen. Thus, yak in Mongolia, for example, are predominantly polled (not dehorned) whilst those of Tibet or Nepal are nearly all horned. The distribution of the horn types is shown in Table 4.1.

Coat of the yak

Heat conservation is enhanced by a thick fleece on the whole body, composed of an outer coat of long hair and an undercoat, made up of a dense layer of fine down fibres in the colder season. As already noted, hair colours vary from black and brown through variegation to white. Since white absorbs less heat, the existence of this colour must be attributed to herders' preference rather than to adaptive usefulness. It is significant, however, that white yak are more prevalent at more northerly latitudes. In such areas, solar radiation is not as intense as in the more southerly latitudes, or at the higher elevations where black is the predominant colour (see Table 4.1)

Details of fleece production and physical and structural properties of the fibres will be given in chapter 6. The purpose here is to discuss the coat as a feature of the adaptation of the yak to its environment.

In general, the coat of the yak seems well suited to insulating the animal from cold, protecting it from heat and repelling moisture. All these factors are important to survival in the prevailing climate. As noted by Yousef (1985), a thick winter coat is a general adaptation of animals living in extreme cold, e.g. arctic mammals. Thus conservation of heat takes precedence over extra generation of heat. To generate extra heat would ultimately require additional feed which is in short supply over winter. It is of interest in the present context to observe that one of the most successful of all the yak breeds, the Jiulong yak of Sichuan province, has a fibre strain which produces, on average, between 3 and 5 times as much fleece as other types of yak. This strain also inhabits one of the coldest, dampest and most fogbound areas of all yak territory. It is probable that it is the dense, heavy coat which has helped the Jiulong yak to survive in these conditions.

Insulation from the fleece. The coat consists of 3 types of fibre: coarse, long fibres with a diameter in excess of 52 μ, down fibre with a diameter below 25 μ and mid-type hairs with diameters between these two values. The down fibre is a particular attribute of the winter coat of the yak to provide the additional insulation then required. Coats with a mixture of fibre types have been shown to maintain a stable air temperature within the coat. Ouyang Xi *et al.* (1985) measured temperatures at the skin surface and at the middle and top of the staples of various parts of the yak body, viz. ear, forehead, sides of neck, shoulder and rump, the back, belly, tail and legs. Measurements were made on 10 animals on 3 successive days in the cold season in February (mean ambient temperature –18°C) and on 9 animals on 3 days in the warm season at the end of May (mean ambient temperature 22°C – but somewhat windier at that time than in February). Figure 4.1 shows the results.

The results (Figure 4.1) show that the gradient in temperature between the skin surface and the top of the staple is far greater in winter than in summer for parts of the body trunk like shoulder, rump and belly, but that the seasonal difference in the temperature gradient from skin surface to top of staple is much less at extremities of the body, such as the ears, where vasoconstriction occurs during cold.

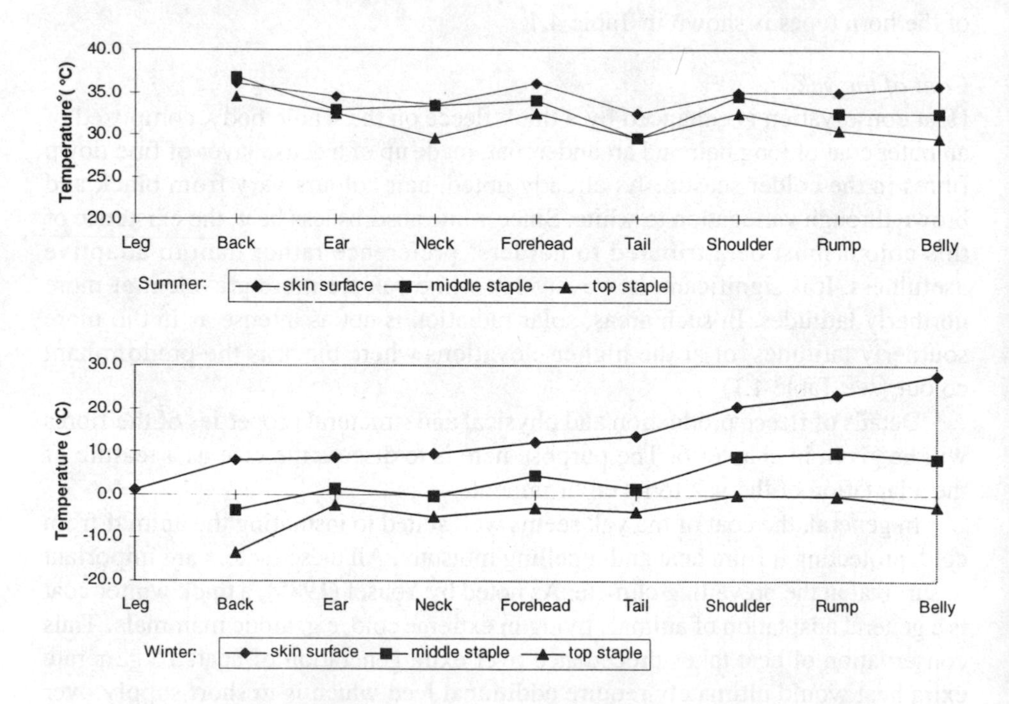

Figure 4.1 Temperature (°C) at the skin surface, the middle of the staple and the top of the staple on various parts of the body of mature female yak in the warm season and in the cold season with ambient temperature of –18°C [source: Ouyang Xi *et al.*, 1985]

For this reason, temperature varies at the skin surface, during the cold season, between the different parts of the body, as shown in Figure 4.1. The results also show clearly the insulation from cold provided by the fleece (though these features are not unique to the yak; the effect of a fleece on heat regulation, and consequently on the energy metabolism of the animal, have been demonstrated for a long time, for example in relation to the sheep – e.g. Blaxter, Graham and Wainman, 1959).

No case of frost bite has been recorded in the yak even at the extremities of its body.

The function of the yak coat in helping yak to survive in very cold and wet conditions is enhanced by the low water absorption of the coat (Xue Jiying and Yu Zhengfeng, 1981).

The *arectores pilorum* muscles are highly developed in the dermis of the yak (Ouyang Xi and Wang Qianfei, 1984) and their contraction makes fibres stand up and effectively increase the depth of the coat and reduce heat loss under stress from cold.

Seasonal changes. Hair growth and the composition of the coat changes with season. As air temperatures falls with the approach of winter, down fibres grow densely among the coarser hairs, especially on shoulder, back and rump. Ouyang Xi *et al.* (1983) found, in a herd recorded both in summer and in winter, that the proportion of down fibre increased by between 17.5% and 30.0% in winter, through the activation of down follicles which had lain dormant. The proportion of coarse hairs, therefore, correspondingly decreased. As air temperature rises with the onset of the warm season, down fibres begin to shed from the fleece (see chapter 6).

As a consequence of the abundant grazing in summer and early autumn, yak are able, normally, to lay down a layer of sub-cutaneous fat which then helps to insulate them from cold and also provides an energy reserve to be used to withstand their nutritional deprivation over winter and spring.

Breed and location differences. The amount of down fibre on the yak's back may vary with breed. From different studies it appears that down fibre was more than twice as dense in Tianzhu White yak in Gansu province as in Luqu yak of Southern Gansu, with the Maiwa yak of Sichuan province somewhat intermediate (Zhang Rongchang, 1977; Lu Zhongling *et al.* 1982; Wang Jia *et al.*, 1984). However, breed type is here confounded with the area in which the different breeds are kept. To establish that it is breed and not location which is responsible for the differences would need the different breeds to be compared at the same location.

Fibre density has been shown to decline when yak are moved to areas with warmer summers and longer frost-free periods. Thus, yak introduced in the 1970's to the Jingbei plateau of northern Weichang county of Hebei province had an average density of fibres of 3167 per cm^2 at that time, but subsequently this declined to 1870 fibres per cm^2. The changes occurred through a decrease in the density of down fibre in particular, but the coarse hairs decreased in length. These changes allowed better heat dissipation at the warmer times of year. The changes can be assumed to have occurred in response to the changed environment acting directly on the animal rather than due to selection among the yak.

Age effects. In calves under the age of 6 months, the coat consists almost entirely of down fibre, thereafter the proportion (by weight) declines to 62% by 1 year and 52% by 2, 44% at 3, and 43% at 4 and 5 years old (Research Co-op. 1980–87 [Zhang Yingsong *et al.*, 1982]). There was a corresponding increase in the deposition of subcutaneous fat as the animals grew older.

Skin thickness and sweat glands

Skin thickness is greater on the back of the yak than on other parts of the body – and this is associated with the fact that the back is the part of the animal most exposed to wind, rain and snow. Li Shihong *et al.* (1984) measured skin thickness on the shoulder blade, the back and the knee of 70 live female yak and found the average thickness at the three positions to be 5.6 ± 0.36, 7.5 ± 0.83 and 5.6 ± 0.40 mm respectively. Ouyang Xi *et al.* (1984), using histological sections, measured thickness of epidermis and dermis combined. The back again had the thickest skin (average 5.13 mm) and densely-haired parts had a thickness as little as 2.36 mm. Averaged over the different parts of the body, the skin thickness was 3.37 ± 1.38 mm, but the epidermis itself was very thin, 0.044 ± 0.019 mm.

Sweat glands are distributed in the skin over the whole body and are of the apocrine type. Density per cm^2 was found to be greatest on the forehead (891 cm^2) and least on the rump (138 cm^2), with an overall average of 399 ± 251 cm^2 (Li Shihong *et al.*, 1984; Ouyang Xi and Wang Qianfei, 1984). However, the function of the sweat glands is poorly developed. Tests made by these authors, using different methods, agree in detecting sweat secretions only on the muzzle and not on other parts of the body. The absence of sweating in the yak assists cold tolerance, but helps to make the yak intolerant to heat.

Energy metabolism

Hu Linghao (1994) studied the energy metabolism of growing yak at three different ages (1, 2, and 3 years old) and compared it with that of yellow cattle, both kept at three different altitudes (2261, 3250 and 4271 m). The author reports that the fasting heat production of the yak remained fairly constant irrespective of altitude, whereas that of the yellow cattle rose markedly. This could well point to an adaptive response of the yak to life at high altitude and to the nutritional deprivation which yak experience in winter.

At the lowest of the three elevations in the trials conducted by Hu Linghao, the absolute fasting heat production of the yak was higher than that of the yellow cattle, but not so at the higher altitudes. Also, in another experiment by the same author, the yak generated a little more heat in the course of walking than did the somewhat larger yellow cattle. The author attributes the difference in heat production to the difference in body size, as smaller animals are expected to generate more heat. Clearly, these and similar experiments are important for understanding the factors which lead to adaptation and may in due course provide a means for devising improved grazing and management strategies.

Adaptation to low atmospheric oxygen and high solar radiation

At the elevations of 3500 m above sea level, where most yak live, the oxygen content of the air is some 35% lower than at sea level. On even higher grazings, at an altitude of 5000 m, the oxygen content is halved. Also, in most of the areas there is more than 2000 hours of sunshine and levels of solar radiation are between 130 and 165 Kcal/cm^2 (540–690 kJ/cm^2) annually, depending on elevation. The yak has adapted to these conditions: it is considered to take in larger volumes of air than most other cattle, to retain a higher proportion of the oxygen breathed in, and to be protected against harmful effects of solar radiation by the colour of its coat and skin.

Vertebrae, thorax, heart and lungs

Vertebrae. Yak have 14 thoracic vertebrae and 14 pairs of ribs – 1 more than other cattle – although several authors report 15 ribs i.e. 2 more than in other cattle. This gives the yak a larger chest capacity. Lumbar vertebrae, number 5, 1 less than for other cattle. The number of coccygeal vertebrae is variable in the range from 12 to 16 (other cattle have 16). Sacral vertebrae number 5 and cervical 7, the same as for other cattle. Total numbers of vertebrae are thus fewer than for other species of cattle.

Thorax and organs. Yak ribs are narrow and long with a relatively large distance between ribs and a good development of muscle between. Relative to local cattle it is considerred to have a large thorax (heart girth index = 150 i.e. [heart girth x 100/height at withers]) allowing the development of large lungs and large heart. These, in turn, assist the intake and circulation of adequate amounts of oxygen in conditions where it is in low supply. Lung weights of the Chinese yak range, for different breeds, from 1.1% to 1.5% of body weight, and the heart weighs between 0.5% and 0.75% of body weight. Specifically, Li Shihong *et al.* (1984) measured 5 female yak with an average body weight of 248 kg. and found the lung weight to be, on average, 1.12% of body weight. Zhang Rongchang (1985) quotes corresponding values from 14 yak steers with heart at 0.78% and lung at 1.21 % of body weight. These proportions are higher than for other cattle in the region.

Denisov (1958) found that the alveolar area occupied 59% of the cross-sectional area of the lungs of yak compared with 40% for Jargas cattle in adjacent areas. This is evidence that the yak lung also has a relatively large surface area from which to absorb air in order to compensate for the lower oxygen content of the air.

The trachea of the yak is also particularly large to allow a high rate of intake of air. Zhang Rongchang *et al.* (1994) state that trachea length in Tianzhu White yak is shorter than in other cattle but that the diameter is appreciably greater. Li Shihong *et al.* (1984), for example, give 43 cm for length of trachea and 5.5 cm for the diameter, measured in 5 females. Apart from variation in trachea dimensions among individual animals, the size of the trachea will also vary with the general body size of the yak, as affected by breed and location. The annular cartilage of the trachea was found to be narrow, and adjacent cartilages of the trachea to be about 4 cm apart. This allows the yak to breathe rapidly and to quickly increase air intake into the lungs when conditions demand it.

Circulation and oxygen intake and absorption

Heart and pulmonary pressure. A study of 5 yak at high altitude (Ladakh, India, 4500m) and 6 yak at low altitude (Whipsnade Park, England, 150m) by Anand *et al.* (1986) found that the pulmonary arterial pressure was not significantly different in the two groups, but the pulmonary arterial resistance was slightly higher in the yak at high altitude than in those at virtually sea-level (0.58 vs. 0.34 mm Hg l^{-1} min). A higher resistance would be expected if vasoconstriction has occurred in the pulmonary arterial system.

Vasoconstriction commonly occurs in order to reduce blood supply to under-ventilated areas of the lung and maintain homeostasis in other respects (Anand *et al.* 1986). For example, in an animal with a pneumonic lung, even at low altitude, the vasoconstriction reflex will shut off oxygen to the damaged area and make more available to the functional areas of the lung. However, at high altitude, as Anand *et al.* (1986) argue, such vasoconstriction would not be a good long-term response to permanently hypoxic conditions. Because at such high altitudes the whole lung becomes a low oxygenated area, the vasoconstriction reflex would be very damaging, as it would then affect the whole lung. However, as shown by these authors from comparisons of yak with cattle, it seems the yak has adapted to prevent this vasoconstriction happening to all but a very small extent.

Thus, when comparing yak with Himalayan (hill) cattle and crosses of these with yak, all at the high altitude, Anand *et al.* (1986) found that whilst arterial pulmonary pressure in the cattle was somewhat higher than in the yak, the pulmonary arterial resistance in cattle was more than three-fold greater. In these respects the first crosses of yak with these cattle were intermediate in their pulmonary haemodynamics, but considerably closer to the yak. Backcrosses to cattle (3/4 cattle, 1/4 yak), however, had a bi-modal distribution – with some animals closer to cattle and others closer to yak, especially in respect of the resistance trait. Anand *et al.* (1986) concluded from this study that there was an inherited basis to pulmonary arterial resistance and that the yak had gone a long way towards eliminating the vasoconstrictor response to high-altitude-low-oxygen living.

Anand *et al.* (1986) provide a cautionary comment to their conclusions, by saying that they cannot be certain to what extent the differences in resistance between the hill cattle and the yak are an expression of the differences in the size of the animals (the cattle were much smaller). However, if the results are confirmed, a genetically attenuated vasoconstrictor response to low-oxygen conditions is clearly an adaptation of importance.

In an effort to explore the subject further, Anand *et al.* (1988) did a further study in which sheep and goats were also included. Their later results supported the earlier thesis, in relation to the reduced vasoconstriction response in the yak, and also added data (albeit from only one yak), suggesting that the yak has a relatively larger right ventricle of the heart than found in crosses of yak with cattle. Moreover, the yak, unlike cattle, had a smaller medial thickness of the small pulmonary arteries (further suggesting a reduced capacity for vasoconstriction).

Belkin *et al.* (1985) reported, on the basis of a study of 40 hearts from mature yak, that there was a higher degree of capillarisation of the right ventricle of the heart compared with the left. This suggests a further adaptive response of the yak to high altitude, conditions which require the right ventricle to cope with increased loading.

Respiration. Cai Li *et al.* (1975) took observations on 48 adult female yak at pasture at an altitude of 3450 m. in July and August. Respiration rate was between 20 and 30 per minute when the air temperature was below 13°C, but above that temperature the respiration rate rose rapidly. Respiration rate was significantly higher in the evening than in the morning, but was not significantly correlated with humidity, wind speed or the prevailing weather. As would be expected, respiration rate was also found to be higher during periods of activity than during inactivity.

Zhao Bingyao (1982) examined seasonal differences in respiration rate. He used 5 adult female yak at an altitude of 3400 m on cold grassland. Over a period of a year, the animals were observed each day between 06 and 08 hr and again between 18 and 20 hr. Respiration rate was found to be highest in August and pulse rate highest in June. Both rates declined gradually after the warm season ended and were at their lowest in March. Body temperature, also measured, was virtually unaffected by season and averaged 37.6°C in the morning and 38.5° C in the evening. All of this shows that yak alter their respiration rate not only in response to a changing need for oxygen, but also to regulate body temperature. The yak, with its thick skin, absence of sweating and a heavy coat has few means at its disposal for heat dissipation, other than respiration rate. The lowest pulse rate in March corresponds to the time of year when yak are in their poorest condition and often at a point of exhaustion and when they have a low metabolic rate, following the shortage of feed over winter, leading to near starvation.

Blood cells and haemoglobin. The capacity to take in sufficient air, by virtue of anatomical features, respiration rate and physiological response, is clearly an important aspect of the yak's adaptation to life at high altitudes. However, it is also important that absorption and retention of oxygen from the air should be adequate for the need. This also may be specially adapted in the yak. In this respect, the evidence from red blood cells and haemoglobin content is not totally conclusive. Data from 18 different sources are presented in Table 4.2. These results suggest that, relative to adult cattle (*Bos taurus*) at or around sea level, the yak in these various studies do not have exceptionally high numbers of erythrocytes per unit volume of blood. The values range from 5.4 to 10.3, with an average of 7.0 (10^{12}/l) for the 14 mean values shown. This compares with a mean of 7.0, and a range of 5.0–9.0, given as normal values for other cattle in a review article by Doxey (1977).

The average of the 18 Hb values (g/dl) in Table 4.2 is 12.1 (range 8.3 to 18.4). These values are slightly higher than the average of 11.0 (8.0 – 14.0) given as the normal values by Doxey – and the mean values of only two of the groups of yak fall outside the range for the cattle examined. It will be noted, from Table 4.2, that the haemoglobin concentration in blood increased, in general, with an increase in

Table 4.2 Red cell counts, haemoglobin (Hb) concentration, packed cell volume (PCV), and estimated mean corpuscular volume (MCV) in adult yak from various sources

Area	Altitude (m)	No.	Red cell count [10^{12}/l] mean	[SD]	Hb content [g/dl] mean	[SD]	PCV [l/l] mean	[SD]	MCV [fl]		Source
Whipsnade Park, UK	150	7	6.4	0.9	13.7	1.7	0.38	0.04	59.3	(m)	Hawkey *et al*., 1983
Whipsnade Park, UK	150	18	5.4	0.7	10.9	0.9	0.31	0.04	57.4	(s)	Hawkey *et al*., 1983
Xinjiang, Bazhou	2500	5	7.3	8.3							Res. Co-op, 1980-87 (Sai Beiyan, 1981)
Gansu, Tianzhu	3000	35	6.6	0.9	8.6	1.2	0.33	0.03	50.4		Zhang Dasou *et al*., 1985
Tibet, Linzhi	3000	??			11.3						Zhang Rongchang *et al*., 1994 [quote]
Yunnan, Zhondian	3300	11	6.6		10.0						Res. Co-op, 1980-87 (Zhang Shuiqn, 1981)
India, Sikkim	3300	10	6.1	0.4	13.2	0.2	0.39	0.05	58.0		Sahu *et al*., 1981
Qinghai, Gonda	3400	57	6.9		10.3						Res. Co-op, 1980-87 (Li Jinxuan, 1985)
Sichuan, Ruoergai	3450	56	10.3	1.1	12.9	0.9				dry	Cai Li *et al*., 1975
Sichuan, Ruoergai	3450	52	7.5	0.9	12.7	0.7				lact	Cai Li *et al*., 1975
Sichuan, Hongyuan	3500	5	7.6	10.7							Res. Co-op., 1980-87 (Liu Qibui, 1963)
???, Yakuti	????	26	5.8	0.1?	11.5	0.34	0.38	0.014	65.0		Zhang Rongchang *et al*., 1994
Bhutan, (east)	4000	13			13.5	1.3	0.39	0.04		(s)	Winter *et al*., 1989
Qinghai, Darri	4200	38	6.9		10.8						Xu Rongchan & Wu Zhiqiang, 1984
Tibet, Naqu	4366	??			15.4						Zhang Rongchang *et al*., 1994 [quote]
Tibet, Dangxiong	4400	30	7.4		11.6						Res. Co-op., 1980-87 (Tang Zenyu, 1982)
Tibet, Longzhi	4500	??			18.4						Zhang Rongchang *et al*., 1994 [quote]
Tibet, Yagao	4700	10	7.6		13.6						Survey grp. Chin. Acad., 1981 (Huang Weixui)

Notes on restraint of yak: (s) = sedated with xylazine; (m) manually restrained; others: form of restraint not specified, manual restraint assumed; dry = dry adult females; lact = lactating adult females.

altitude, particularly if only the data from yak at high altitude are considered. It is in fact of some interest that the yak at Whipsnade park, little above sea level, were so similar to the values for yak from China, Bhutan and India. Taking account of the altitude effect, it seems, however, that yak are not exceptional relative to cattle. (There is no particular explanation for the fact that two of the values quoted by Zhang Rongchang *et al.*, 1994, for yak in Tibet at altitudes of 4366 and 4500 m, are markedly higher than the other values from that area). Only a few authors provide data on packed cell volume (PCV) and these are, on average higher than the normal mean given in the article by Doxey, already referred to. None are outside the range he quotes. A useful parameter, which can be derived from a combination of PCV and red cell count, is the mean corpuscular volume (MCV) which provides an indication of red cell size. The average of the seven estimates available is 59.8 and puts this at the top of the range quoted by Doxey for cattle. This, then, may indicate that yak have larger red cells with a greater surface area and a higher capacity for the retention of oxygen. (Larrick and Burck, 1986, in a general article on yak in Tibet, give a contradictory view by suggesting that yak have very small red cells in relation to sea-level bovines, but vastly more cells per unit volume of blood; unfortunately no actual data or references are provided to verify this claim).

An intriguing paper by Lalthantluanga, Wiesner and Bravnitzer (1985) shows that, in yak, two types of –a and two types of –b chains are found in the haemoglobin, and that there has been a substitution of valine at position 135 of the b^{II}–chain, in place of the more usual alanine. This was considered by the authors to be the reason for the intrinsically higher oxygen affinity of yak haemoglobin compared to that of lowland cattle, which is quoted by them and other authors as an established finding in the yak.

It seems, therefore, that factors concerned with air intake, combined with a high oxygen affinity of yak haemoglobin, provide the basis for the yak's adaptation to life at high altitudes.

Before leaving consideration of Table 4.2, attention should be drawn to the difference between yak manually restrained and those sedated with xylazine, in their blood values at Whipsnade park. The act of struggling by the animals in the course of manual restraint was shown by Hawkey *et al.* (1983) to release reserves of red cells from the spleen and hence raise the values of several of the blood parameters above those of sedated animals. This point was noted by Winter *et al.* (1989), who also sedated their animals. It has to be assumed, in the absence of information to the contrary, that all the other estimates presented in Table 4.2 are based on manually restrained animals. The values from the majority of the sources are likely, therefore, to be higher than they would have been from sedated animals. It seems possible that the degree of struggling by the animal, in the course of restraint, may also affect the results, though there are no data presented on that point.

Seasonal variation in Hb content. There is some seasonal variation in the Hb content of blood of the yak. It is relatively low in May (10.5 g %) and higher in October, after the end of the summer grazing season (14.6 g %), based on some observations of female yak in Menyuan county of Qinghai Province (Research Co-op. 1980–87). Similar observations were made on yak in parts of Siberia by Belyyar (1980) who recorded an Hb content of 10.2 g % in the spring of the year and 12.8 g % in the autumn. He also noted that the diameter of the erythrocytes in these yak was 4.83 μ, which was larger than for contemporary Yakut cattle (4.38 μ) in the same area.

Other blood cells and constituents. Most of the papers quoted in Table 4.2 also provide values for white cell content of the blood. They average 10.2 (10^6/l) (8.6–12.5) suggesting that the animals were in normal health at the time of bleeding.

Cai Li *et al.* (1975) also provide some evidence on age differences and the difference between lactating and dry adult females. Age effects were not significant with the numbers involved (groups of 17 to 58 for female yak). However, lactating yak had lower red cell counts than dry cows (as shown in Table 3.2 for data from Ruoergai). As expected, the lactating females also had significantly lower blood glucose levels (61.5 vs. 66.5 mg% for the dry females). Blood calcium and phosphorus concentrations (mg%) for the different groups of females in this study ranged from 8.7 for dry adult cows to 9.5 for calves (for Ca) and from 5.5 for the dry cows to 7.4 for the calves (for P). The blood pH was 7.0, on average, in these data.

Colour of coat and skin

The predominantly dark coat colours of the yak (see chapter 2) help to protect it against the effects of solar radiation, which is particularly intense at the southern latitudes. The lighter colours and white yak are found further north and at lower altitudes where solar radiation is less intense. However, were it not for selection and colour preferences by man, it is unlikely that the lighter shades, and white yak in particular, would exist. These light shades are not generally found among wild yak where these would be expected to be at a disadvantage in terms of natural selection. Hair colours of yak, in different areas at different elevations, are shown in Table 4.1.

The cells of the epidermis of the yak contain many pigmented granules, especially in the cells of the *stratum basale*. These pigmented granules can help to prevent injury from ultra-violet light in the deeper layers of the skin. Yak with white faces generally have eyes surrounded by black hair. The black eye sockets of Maiwa yak of Sichuan province are accepted as a breed characteristic. Also, the hair on the forehead of yak is well developed and can cover the eyes. No specific research appears to have been done on the possible protection against solar radiation afforded by this forehead hair to the eyes and face, but it is reasonable to assume that the hair has such a function.

Adaptive characteristics related to grazing conditions

The cold pastures on which yak graze have predominantly short grass in some areas, rough grazing conditions with sedges and shrubby plants in others. Yak have developed organs for food intake and a grazing behaviour peculiarly suited to this environment.

Grazing procedure and grazing behaviour

Mouth. Yak have a broad mouth, small muzzle and thin flexible lips. The front (incisor) teeth are hard and broad and have a broad and flat grinding surface. The tip of the tongue is also broad and blunt and the filamentous papillae on the surface of the tongue are highly developed and cutinized. The surface of the tongue feels rough and "thorny".

Grazing hab it. Yak can graze long grass, using their tongue as do other cattle, but they can also graze in the manner of sheep, using incisor teeth and lips to graze short grass and creeping stems and roots of grass. Yak will also take tender branches of shrubs in alpine bush meadow. Under most normal conditions yak have learnt to avoid poisonous or thorny plants with the result that recorded instances of poisoning are very rare. However, there are reports of extensive pyrrolizidine alkaloid poisoning in Merak Sakten, a part of Bhutan (Winter *et al.*, 1992). This was thought to be due principally to grazing of *Senecio raphanifolius* (although other plants may also have been involved) (Winter *et al.*, 1994). This plant, as pointed out by the authors, was almost certainly eaten by the yak because of overstocking of the pastures concerned, leading to overgrazing. Otherwise, with a more plentiful supply of feed, the yak would have avoided these plants.

Yak will also readily graze the rough stems and leaves of sedges in low-lying marshy areas. Zhou Shourong (1984) has recorded more than 60 different species of grasses in the diet of yak on alpine, sub-alpine marsh and semi-marsh meadow.

When the ground is covered with snow, as, typically, it is for long periods, yak will paw through quite thick snow layers, and they will use both head and face to help them in this task to gain access to the wilted vegetation underneath.

Yak will reduce grass with a height of 15 cm to between 2.6 and 5.2 cm (Ren Jizhou and Jing Juhe,1956). In the spring, yak will graze green shoots no more than 2–3 cm above the ground – though it would be surprising if they could not graze more closely than that if necessary (as sheep in Scotland, for example, are known to do). In addition the yak take stems and leaves from the residual wilted grass still available in the spring.

The grazing time of yak is affected by season, weather, type and quality of grazing and the structure of the herd in terms of age and sex. This has been studied by many workers (e.g. Ren Jizhou and Jin Juhe, 1956; Cai Li, Hu Angang, and Du Shaodeng, 1960; Zhang Rongchang *et al.*, 1982; Qi Guangyong, 1984; Lei Huanzhang *et al.*, 1985; and Zhang Hongwu, Zhao Yibin and Lei Huangzhang, 1985).

The general conclusions are that the intake time varies between 34% and 80% of the total time available for grazing. However, in herds of mixed age, where females have young calves at foot, the grazing rhythm is disturbed as the calves suckle and themselves learn to graze. Under such conditions, the intake time may be curtailed.

The speed with which the yak moves over the pasture varies with season and pasture conditions, but is usually faster at the start of the day than later on, and it is also more rapid in the cold season than in warm weather. With the approach of snow or hail storms, yak can be seen to run over the pasture, in bursts of speed up to 57 m per minute – up to 4 times the normal speed at the start of the day.

There is relatively little variation in the bite rate – around 0.8 to 1.1 mouthfuls per second. However, intake varies with season, sward height, and other factors, from around 28 to 38 kg herbage over a period of 10 hours in the summer, to only 13 kg or less, in the same period, when grazing wilted grass, in the cold season. The energy and protein intakes are adequate to meet maintenance, work and production, but in the later parts of the winter and the early spring they fall below the requirements and yak then lose weight and condition.

Rumination. Under normal conditions, when grass is abundant in summer, yak have four periods of rumination each day. The first of these is generally 2 hours after the start of morning grazing. A second period is around noon, when the ambient temperature is high and yak stop grazing. A third period of rumination occurs about 2 hours before the animals are driven from the pasture back to the campsite. A fourth period is in the evening. Rumination periods generally last between 0.8 and 1.9 hours.

If yak are allowed to graze at night, as well as during the day, the periods of rumination are different. In yak used for work, the periods of rumination fit in with the timing and intensity of the work being performed. Occasionally yak will ruminate at night, but usually they lie in a state of light sleep.

Contractions of the rumen reticulum was studied in 48 yak over a 3-day period (in Ruoergai county, Sichuan) and showed contractions at the rate of 8.7 ± 1.6 (mean and SD) per 5 minutes immediately before grazing, and almost the same (9.0 ± 1.2) after grazing. Similar results were obtained at other locations. In other types of cattle, the frequency of contractions when the animal is resting or ruminating may be only half the rate during feeding (Phillipson, 1970). It is possible therefore that the results on yak suggest a different behaviour, which could reflect an adaptation to the grazing conditions.

Sure-footedness

Yak can walk freely in precipitous places at high altitudes which cannot be reached by horse or sheep (very few domestic goats are found in these areas) and they can cope well with marshy ground. As vividly described by Phillips *et al.* (1946), yak, if in danger of sinking in a marsh, will spread out their legs and use the underside of their bodies to prevent themselves from sinking. They will plod on with a swimming kind of motion rather than panic and thrash around as a horse might. Yak can swim across rapids and are at ease trekking through snow. They can even be used to make tracks through the snow to clear paths for people – a sort of "biological" snow plough.

To help in meeting the challenges of difficult terrain and inclement climate, yak have strong limbs and small hooves of compact texture, with a narrow and sharp hoof tip, hard hoof edges and a close hoof fork. There is an area of soft cutis on the sole. As noted by Zhang Rongchang (1985) the characteristics of the yak hoof make deep imprints in the ground, which allow the yak to control its momentum when going downhill – an important component of its aptitude to move freely in difficult, precipitous terrain.

Adaptation of reproduction

Zhang Rongchang *et al.* (1994) argue that two aspects of yak reproductive characteristics (see chapter 5) are also adaptive responses to the environment. The first of these is that the breeding season of the yak is delayed the higher the altitudes. This allows calves to be born in somewhat warmer weather, or closer to the onset of such weather, and during, rather than before, the start of significant grass growth in the following warm season. From that point of view, a delay in the ability to breed must be regarded as a sensible adaptive response. Nonetheless one must question whether nature, in this case, has not chosen a second-best strategy, because yak that are mated late in the season have less chance of being re-mated that year, should conception have failed, than females mated earlier in the season. Also, calves that are born late in the year have insufficient time to get into good body condition to improve their chances of surviving the rigours of their first winter.

The second adaptive response claimed by these authors is the short gestation length of yak females (258 days on average – see chapter 5) relative to other species of cattle. Short gestation, with consequently smaller calves, leads to a less stressful and quicker parturition, and this must be a matter of some importance in the yak environment, especially in the face of danger from wolves. However, it should be a matter of debate, whether the consequent, relatively low birth weight of the calf may not be a disadvantage to the calf itself.

A further aspect of reproduction in the yak, which might be regarded as an adaptation to its environment, is the fact that many yak females show only one oestrus in a breeding season and, if not then pregnant, the next occurrence of oestrus will be delayed to the following year (see chapter 5). It is thought, though hard evidence is not presented, that priority is given by the yak late in the breeding season, not to conception, but to the deposition of internal fat reserves. These assist the animal to survive the ensuing harsh winter and spring with its shortage of feed to the point of starvation. (In some countries, however, as discussed in chapter 5, yak regularly come into oestrus several times in one season).

Aspects of general behaviour

Behaviourally, the yak is active and easily excited, and can have a ferocious temper. Its conditioned reflexes make it respond rapidly to danger and external forces. In the grazing situation yak will often jump and run, pursuing each other with tail in the air. Yak can gallop like a horse – a fact which is enjoyed be herdsmen who organise annual races. Yak can also roll over on pastures after the manner of horses and unlike other bovines.

Yak have the ability to be readily trained to aid their feeding and management. This ability helps the herdsmen in the feeding and management of the yak, especially as most yak are kept all the year round on grazing and not housed, and not usually fenced in or tethered, except for milking. In some pastoral/agricultural areas of Mongolia, housing is sometimes practised (see chapter 11). The yak are trained by the herdsmen to return to the camp-site, when required, by the call of their names or by special cries or singing. Yak are also readily tamed and trained for use as pack animals or for riding. Once trained, yak retain their acquired behaviour.

Yak are easily frightened and vigilant to attack by wild animals, wolves in particular. The yak will form a defensive position and fight off aggressors. It is often reported, from the grasslands of western Sichuan province, that male yak have killed wolves with their horns.

Yak are very gregarious. In herds of 100 or more it is highly unusual to lose an animal from attack by wild animals, as the yak protect each other. When grazing, they are never far apart from each other. If yak are suddenly attacked whilst resting and not on guard, they get very frightened and will flee from the herd and may get killed by wild predators. Also when startled on a hillside from above, by either human disturbance or by cries from wild beasts, they can panic and slip or roll down a hill and die in the fall. Dong Baosen (1985) reported that 312 yak had died through rolling downhill in 4 separate instances in Gen county of Xinjiang – three of these due to incorrect driving of the yak by the people involved.

In ones or twos, however, yak are difficult to drive or manage, although some yak steers trained as pack animals will work individually, as will yak trained for ploughing. Yak will even find their own way back to the camp-site without a herder – if it is not too far away. Groups of 10 or more yak steers, trained as pack animals, however, can be easily managed as a group.

5 REPRODUCTION OF YAK

OVERVIEW

In general, the reproductive rate of the yak is low under normal grazing and rearing conditions. Female calves born early in the year may show oestrus for the first time when 16–18 months old, but those born later in the season will not show oestrus until they are more than 2 years old. Yak are seasonal breeders with mating and conception restricted to the warm part of the year. In a few areas, under favourable conditions some of the yak may be mated for the first time after they have reached the age of 2 years or, very exceptionally, even a year earlier. Normally, however, and in most places, yak are not mated for the first time until they are 3 years old, and often not until 4 years. Thereafter, yak females are most likely to calve once every 2 years or twice in 3 years – producing, on average, perhaps 4–5 calves in a lifetime. Many yak cows will have only one annual oestrus, irrespective of whether they calved in that year or not. The next oestrus will often not occur until the following year. Under better conditions, in some areas and some countries, yak cows do, however, show oestrus up to 3 or 4 times in a season, if they are not already pregnant. Statistics for Honyuan County of Sichuan province, over the period 1976–1980, showed that from nearly half a million female yak of breeding age (themselves representing 39.1% of the yak population in the county) 43.8% produced calves, which also survived, in any one year. Some "improved" breeds such as Jiulong may do better, and so will yak in areas where improved husbandry is practised. Clearly, the seasonal and general environmental conditions affect the reproductive rate quite markedly. In exceptionally harsh years, mortality rates of cows and calves can be very high.

Behavioural changes in the yak cow, as a result of oestrus, are not usually as clear as in other domestic cattle. The duration of oestrus is usually less than a day, although some reports give longer averages and the range for individual animals is much greater. The average length of the oestrus cycle is approximately 20 days. Gestation length is around 258 days, on average, shorter than in other cattle. It is longer when male calves are carried by the dam than it is with female calves. Also, the gestation length is by as much as 20 days longer, on average, when the yak female carries an F1 hybrid calf (having been mated to a bull of another species of cattle). Abortions and other causes of premature termination of pregnancy are between 5 and 10% when yak are bred pure, but higher in inter-species hybridisation, when the calves born are much heavier.

Physiological parameters in oestrus and gestation are similar to those in other types of domestic cattle. Hormonal treatment can be used to induce oestrus and can increase reproductive rate, though the evidence on conception rate following such induction is somewhat conflicting. Conception rates are nearly always much better following natural mating than after artificial insemination

There is sufficient evidence to suggest that the reproductive rate of yak can be increased by a variety of improvements in management and by techniques to increase oestrus frequency and conception rate. Successful detection of first oestrus and good timing of mating can be useful aids particularly when mating is artificially controlled or assisted. Whether the economic rewards from such improvements are a sufficient incentive to incur the costs involved is a separate question.

Male yak start to show mounting behaviour around the age of 6 months, but sperm have not been found in the ejaculates of yak males before the age of 2 years. Bulls usually start to mate at 3 or 4 years old, but then have to establish their position in the mating hierarchy of the herd. Bulls reach the peak of their mating ability around the age of 6–7 years. Bulls fight with each other for possession of females and the dominant bulls have the most mates.

Left to their own devices, yak cows will not allow a bull of other cattle species to approach them, and such a bull has no chance of mating when in competition with a yak bull. In the same way, yak bulls prefer females of their own species. Wild yak bulls, however, will readily mate with domestic yak. All matings of yak cows with *Bos taurus* or *Bos indicus* bulls have to be assisted by people, either by keeping yak bulls away from the females or, more often, through restraint of the cow followed by use of a bull or artificial insemination.

Introduction

The survival and spread of the yak species over the centuries testify to an adequate level of reproduction for this purpose – in the face of an adverse environment. In the context of livestock improvement, however, it is important to consider the limits set by reproductive rate. Reproductive rate affects the opportunities for selection of improved purebred stock and also the opportunities for crossbreeding systems, which depend on "surplus" numbers of purebred yak available to sustain crossbreeding. Reproductive rate also affects the economics of yak production. The purpose of this chapter is, therefore, to document the reproductive performance of the yak under various sets of circumstances. Consideration will also be given to components of the reproductive process, in order to indicate which of these are the most limiting, or most amenable to change in the yak.

The information is derived from investigations on experimental stations or in herds to which the investigators have been given access. Because farms or herds involved in investigations are, in that sense, exceptional, it cannot be known with certainty whether the results obtained are fully representative of those applicable to ordinary herds in remote areas. This problem in not unique to yak, but needs to be considered in assessing the results. In situations where the taking of observations and records is not usual, the act of doing so might be thought to have led to some improvement in performance.

Some results are also provided on anatomical features and physiological parameters of the yak in relation to reproduction. Male reproduction will be considered in a separate section from the reproduction of females.

Reproduction in the female

Female organs

The structure of the reproductive organs of the yak differ in some respects from those of dairy cattle of *Bos taurus* type. In order to facilitate and improve techniques for artificial insemination, Cai Li dissected the reproductive tracts of 38 female yak over the years 1976–1986. It was found that:

- The cervix has 3 transverse circles (a very small number of yak have 4)
- Each circle consists of many small, tight folds (19 on the outer circle, 13–15 on the middle circle and 9–10 on the inner circle)
- The cervix is less than 30 cm from the vulva
- The cervix is 5.0 ± 0.9 cm long and 3.2 ± 0.7 cm in diameter
- The *corpus uteri* is relatively short, with a length of 2.1 ± 0.8 cm
- A long and distinct septum (approx. 6 cm long) extends downward from the bifurcation of the uterine horns towards the *corpus uteri* (and is part of the wall separating the horns).

Because of the short *corpus* and the long septum it is easy to deposit semen in optimal positions such as the *corpus uteri*, uterine horn or its tip, especially as the cervix is relatively free within the pelvic cavity and can be readily held. However, deep insemination of female yak, using a rectovaginal technique, is more difficult in the yak than in ordinary dairy cows.

The histological structure of the reproductive organs of the yak is similar to that in dairy cattle (Qiu Zhongquan and Zhu Qiming, 1981).

Oestrus of the female yak

Puberty

First oestrus occurs, generally, in the second or third warm season (summer and autumn) following birth, i.e. at ages between 13 and 30 months. Puberty occurs earlier in yak of the Alpine type than in yak of Plateau type – but since the two types are not normally in the same areas, this finding is, of course, partially confounded with factors of the environment. Magasch (1991a) made a detailed study of 104 female yak in Mongolia. The distribution of first oestrus in these animals is shown in Figure 5.1. As noted already, oestrus occurred only in the warm season.

The results of Magasch (1991a) show that little more than 10% of the yak females came into oestrus for the first time in the second summer of their life and most females did not show oestrus for the first time until their third summer, when they were more than 2 years old. Magasch points out that the 12 females which

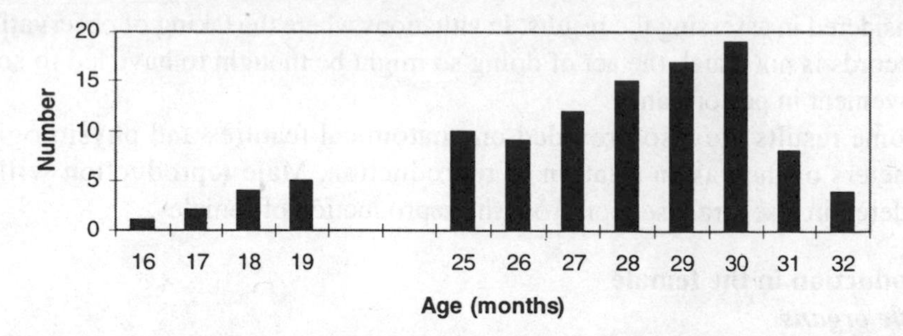

Figure 5.1 Frequency distribution of first oestrus in 104 female yak in Mongolia, by age (months) [source: Magasch, 1991a]

showed first oestrus when they were 16–19 months old had all been born in March or April of the previous year – and had managed to make more growth before the onset of winter than those born later in the season. Those not born until May or June had first oestrus delayed for a further year, when they were 25 months old, or older. Magasch concluded from his study that the onset of first oestrus was determined more by body development at the beginning of the breeding season than by age as such. Very similar results, based on observations on yak in (what was at the time) the Tuva autonomous republic, were reported by Katzina and Maturova (1989).

In China, the majority of yak are mated for the first time at the age of 3 years – in the 4th warm season following birth, but under favourable conditions some yak may be mated a year earlier. Such conditions prevailed among 197 primaparous Jiulong yak in Sichuan province studied by Cai Li et al (1980b) : 32.5% of them calved at 3, 59.9% at 4, 6.1% at 5, and the remaining 1.5% (3 yak) at 6 years old. At these ages, as will be shown in the next chapter (Table 6.4), these yak had reached between approximately 75% and 100% of their mature weight. In this context, Katzina and Maturova (1989) noted that in the Tuva autonomous republic (an area at more northern latitudes, but an elevation of only 1500–2500 m) yak females reached fertile oestrus at approximately 90% of mature body weight compared with 60% for *Bos taurus* cattle in that region. First mating at the age of 2 years, though it also occurs in China, is more common among yak in some other countries (see chapter 11).

Breeding season

Yak are seasonal breeders. The onset and the end of the period in the year when female yak come into oestrus is affected by climatic factors, grass growth and both latitude and altitude. When temperature and humidity starts to rise, the ground begins to thaw and grass starts to grow. The yak females then improve in body condition and gain weight – following their long period of deprivation and weight loss over the winter – and they come into season. On the north-western grassland of Sichuan this time occurs around June (Hu Angang *et al.*, 1960). At the higher elevation of Laqu County in Tibet the breeding season may not start until July. Similar observations are reported from Kirgizia where it was recorded that the annual onset of the breeding season started on 25 May at an elevation of 1 400 m. and became progressively later until at the altitude of 2 700 m oestrus started on or after June 22 (Denisov, 1958) – though it would be surprising if these precise dates applied to every year.

The breeding season reaches its peak in July and August when temperature is at its highest and grass growth at its best. Thereafter, yak oestrus decreases in frequency and stops around November. Two sets of data on the onset of oestrus by month of year are summarised in Table 5.1 – one set derived from Datong cattle farm in Qinghai Province the other from the Chovosol district of Mongolia.

Table 5.1 Oestrus in yak females according to month of year

[month] Location	Percentage in oestrus from June to November [6]	[7]	[8]	[9]	[10]	[11]	Number	Source
Qinghai	3.5	21.7	28.7	18.3	15.6	12.2	115	Zhang Rongchang, 1979
Mongolia	5.5	12.1	41.2	14.3	6.7		342	Magasch, 1990

The form of distribution shown in Table 5.1 is fairly typical of the general situation. Accordingly, if mating and conception does not occur, some yak may not return to oestrus in that season. Yak showing only a single oestrus in a season are not uncommon.

The vast majority of all mating takes place naturally between bull and cow at pasture (several bulls competing for the privilege – see later). For matings to other species of cattle, the yak cows are normally restrained (also in some areas for mating to yak bulls). For matings to "improved" breeds of cattle, artificial insemination is now always used (as the bulls of these breeds do not adapt to the climate and altitude).

Signs of oestrus

Changes in the appearance of the reproductive organs are more obvious than behavioural changes, although these occur (LuoSang Jiangcuo and Chen Yu, 1987).

The vulva becomes swollen and the vagina reddens. Mucus is discharged from the vulva in a majority of females in oestrus, but a substantial minority show no such discharge. Vagina and cervix dilate, the female tends to raise her tail and urinates frequently. As in other cattle, yak females on heat search out and ride other females and like to be approached by male yak – but these signs are less pronounced than in *Bos taurus* cattle. When a specific mating is required by the herder and mass mating is not practised, heat detection usually requires the use of a marker bull. It is thought that the use of a marker bull, on yak females in heat, will increase pregnancy rate following either natural mating or artificial insemination. Katzina and Maturova (1989) also make the point that signs of heat in yak are less obvious than in other cattle and detection by herdsmen is unreliable.

Daily milk yield shows a dip during oestrus (Cai Li *et al.*, 1960) although this could not, on its own, be used to accurately indicate the presence of oestrus. However, Yu, Huang and Chen (1993) have reported that the pre-ovulatory peak of oestradiol 17β and the progesterone profiles in both blood and milk are similar in yak to those observed in dairy cattle. Magasch (1991a) has made similar findings.

Time of day of oestrus. Most yak start their oestrus in the early morning or in the evening and only rarely at other times of day. Among 633 female yak on Xiandong livestock farm, Cai Li observed that two-thirds of the animals started to show heat before 09.00 hr when they had started grazing, and most of the remaining third started after 19.00 hr when grazing had ended for the day. Similar observations were reported by Lei Huanzhang *et al.* (1964). Magasch (1991a), however, with records on 73 yak in Mongolia, found that only 38% came on heat between 02 and 08 hr, and 34% between 16 and 22 hr. This still left a substantial remainder to show oestrus outside those hours – mostly between 22 and 02 hr.

Length of oestrus cycle

Table 5.2 shows various estimates of the length of the oestrous cycle.

Table 5.2 Length of the oestrous cycle (days) (different sources of observations)

Number of observations	Mean	[SD]	Source
1184	20.5	5.4	Liu Wulin and Liu Shengyu, 1982
308	20.1	8.2	as above
53	22.5	5.4	Zhang Rongchang *et al.*, 1979
12	18.3	6.1	Anim. Vet. Inst. Tibet 1978
35	20.4	1.6	Yu *et al.*, 1993
90	19.1	(10–28)*	Katzina and Maturova, 1989
54	20.0	4.0	Purevzav and Beshlebnov, 1967
74	19.8	(10–27)*	Magasch, 1991a

* range

There is some variation in the length of the oestrous cycle from year to year. For example, the 1184 observations shown in Table 5.2 were collected over a period of 5 years with the annual mean length of the oestrous cycles varying from 19.2 to 21.6 days.

A feature of all the studies summarised in Table 5.2, except that of Yu *et al.* (1993), is the large amount of variation among individuals – the coefficient of variation among these studies ranged from 16 to 41 percent. The reason for this is that oestrus in the yak is greatly affected by the environment. When the weather is unfavourable, the onset of oestrus is delayed, while in favourable circumstances the onset of oestrus in female yak is advanced. The interval between heat periods can vary up to three-fold.

Duration of oestrus

The duration of the oestrous period is not easily determined in the yak because the symptoms of oestrus are not always clear. Estimates from north-western Sichuan suggest 12–16 hours, whilst a report from yak in Shandan, Gansu Province suggests 1.6 ± 0.8 days. In a very small proportion of yak oestrus may last 4–5 days, but 1–2 days is not unusual. Thus, a study with 41 well-fed and closely monitored yak females showed that 26 of them had an oestrus lasting 24 hours or less and 3 yak an oestrus of up to 72 hours. More than 80% of these animals ovulated within 24 hours after the end of oestrus (Yu *et al.*, 1993). There is a tendency for the proportion of yak with heat periods of 1–2 days to increase later in the breeding season (August/September) when air temperature begins to decline. Katzina and Maturova (1989) report an unusually long average duration of 3.7 days (range 1–6 days) for yak in the Tuva region, but, in this context, it is of interest to note that the majority of their yak were reported to conceive in September. By contrast, Purevzav and Beshlebnov (1967) record substantially shorter heat periods. Among 54 Mongolian yak, 26 were recorded on heat for between only 0.5 and 6.5 hours, a further 17 between 6.5 and 12.5 hours, 7 between 12.5 and18.5 hours and only 4 yak with longer oestrus duration. To account for some of the differences between the different studies, it is difficult not to conclude that the observational criteria of what constitutes the length of oestrus must vary among the studies.

Post-partum anoestrus

The average duration of post-partum anoestrus at Xiandong farm in Sichuan Province was found to be 125 days. That figure, however, was subject to much variation. At this farm, females which had calved did not usually show oestrus again in their year of calving. The exceptions were cows which had calved early in the season – before June – and which acquired good body condition and good fat deposits over the summer. Post-partum anoestrous periods were found to be much shorter (70.5 [SD 18.5] days) for yak in good condition than for those in poorer body condition (122.3 [SD 11.8] days) (Liu Wulin and Liu Shengyu, 1982). The anoestrous period following calving has been reported to be related to month of calving: 131, 124, 90 and 75 days for females calving in March, April, May and June respectively. (As reported earlier, for yak that calve later, only a few return on heat in the same year.)

Magasch (1990) provides results on the interval between calving and first postpartum oestrus for yak females in Mongolia. These show clearly a relationship with month of calving – the earlier the calving the longer the interval. However, in these results there was a considerable amount of variation around the average intervals. The results of Magasch are shown in Table 5.3.

In the same study, Magasch (1990) reported that, as might be expected, the service period following calving (on average only 8 days longer than the oestrus interval) showed a very similar seasonal pattern to that seen in Table 5.3, for the interval between calving and first post-partum oestrus.

Magasch (1990) was also able to show, for Mongolian yak, that the interval between calving and the first postpartum oestrus was longest in cows that had calved only once (around 120 days) and that it then declined to its lowest interval in females between 5th and 7th calving (around 85 days) and increased again thereafter for older cows.

Table 5.3 Interval between calving and first postpartum oestrus in yak – according to month of calving [source: Magasch 1990]

Month of calving	Number animals	Interval (days) mean	range	SD
March	38	120.5	69–188	25.3
April	87	96.1	59–172	36.3
May	69	75.4	40–145	29.1
June	21	53.6	30–106	21.6
Overall	*215*	*90.2*	*30–188*	*34.9*

Proportion of cows in oestrus

The proportion of yak females which come into oestrus in any one season depends on the previous calving history of the females as well as on their individual body condition. Yak females of reproductive age can be divided into 3 categories: those which have calved in the current year and are lactating and nursing a calf ("full-lactating yak"); those that calved in the previous year, are not pregnant, but may or may not be still nursing their last calf ("Yama" or "half-lactating yak"), and those which have previously had a calf, but not for at least 2 years and are not lactating ("Ganba"). At Xiandong livestock farm (from June to mid-September) "Yama" had the highest proportion of females in oestrus during that period (112/161), "Ganba" came next (217/408) and "full-lactating cows" the lowest proportion 90/629). Similar observations were made by Zhang Rongchang (1979) at Datong Cattle farm in Qinghai (84.3% of Yama, and 36.6% of cows nursing a calf of the current year). Relative to the full-lactating cows with a calf at foot, the Yama and Ganba classes have had a better opportunity to recover from the drain on their body resources, consequent on calving and lactation, and more than 95% of them show oestrus (Yong Conglie *et al.*, 1982).

In ordinary production herds in the mountainous regions of China, a general average figure is that 50–70% of yak cows of suitable age show oestrus in any one year, and that such yak females are mated and calve twice in 3 years or once every second year.

However, in different production conditions there are reports of yak females capable of showing oestrus up to 3–4 times in the same season, as in the report of Katzina and Maturova (1989) for yak in the Tuva republic, and Magasch (1990) for yak in Mongolia, both referred to earlier.

Use of hormones to induce oestrus. Various studies have shown that oestrus can be induced in yak and that reproductive rate can be increased by that means. For example, at Xiandong livestock farm, Cai Li gave an intra-muscular injection of an analogue of LRH early in August – approximately one month after calving had ended – to induce oestrus in yak cows that had calved and were nursing a calf. Table 5.4 summarises the results from the three-year investigation.

Table 5.4 Reproductive rate of yak cows with induced oestrus and normally occurring oestrus (control) [source: Cai Li]

Group	Year	No.	Calved next year (%)	Calved and surviving (%)
Induced	1976	120	30.0	30.0
	1977	120	90.0	84.2
	1978	110	73.6	73.6
Control	1976	722	42.8	40.0
	1977	871	45.2	44.9
	1978	914	53.4	53.3

The results from Table 5.4 show that the induction of oestrus by hormonal treatment, followed by mating, was not very successful in terms of calves born in the first year of the trial (1976), but the proportion of cows in which oestrus had been induced which then calved, and the number of calves which survived to the end of the year, had improved markedly in 1977 and 1978. (Calf survival was not, apparently, reduced by the increase in calving rate). Results of Magasch (1991a), with yak in Mongolia, agree in showing, albeit on much smaller numbers of animals, that oestrus rate in yak females can be increased by hormonal induction, compared with untreated controls. But, in his trial, there was a generally reduced conception rate following artificial induction of oestrus (similar to the result in year 1 of Table 5.4). Thus, following a single hormonal treatment, conception rate recorded by Magasch was of the order of 56% compared to 75% in controls and following 2 hormonal treatments the conception rates in the treated and control groups were 78% and 86% respectively. In another report, Magasch (1991b) noted also that the success of oestrus induction increased from June to August, approximately doubling over that period (the actual oestrus rates depending on the method of induction). This is analogous to the increase in oestrus rate which occurs naturally over that period, as was noted earlier.

Other workers, at varying locations in China, have used a variety of different hormonal treatments to induce oestrus in the yak. These trials have shown, for the most part, that the onset and timing of oestrus can be controlled in the yak, as in ordinary cattle species (e.g. Shao Binquan and Zhao Yanben, 1984; Yang Tingyou, 1984; Liu Zhiyao and Shuai Weiwen, 1985; Shao Binquan *et al.*, 1986). The use of triple hormone injections was usually the most effective in these experimental situations. In one set of trials, Chinese traditional medicine ["Injecting Herba Epimedii compound"] (Ma Tianfu, 1983) produced an increase in the number of animals on oestrus compared with the control group (44% vs. 18%).

Gestation and parturition

Pregnancy rates

Conception following mating at first oestrus of the season is generally high. Among 68 female yak on heat, Cai Li found, by rectal palpation, that 53 had well-developed follicles and 15 had not, due to diseased reproductive organs. In a trial (Liu

Zhengqui, 1981) with 265 yak which had calved previously, 72.4% had become pregnant following first oestrus of the season, a further 23.4% following the second, and 3.4% and 0.8% following the third and fourth cycles respectively. In an investigation with 342 yak in Mongolia, Magasch (1990) found that 70.5% were pregnant after a first service, 19.3% conceived to a second and 4.6% to a third service, giving an overall pregnancy rate of 94.4%. It appears that, in the part of Mongolia involved, yak which do not become pregnant at a first service are able to return to oestrus up to three times in the same season, as already referred to. Conception to first service improved as the breeding season advanced, and was best in September.

In one particularly well-maintained group of yak, on grassland in Gansu province, where the yak had also been given some supplementary feed in late winter and early spring, a conception rate of 94.3% was achieved (Yu *et al.*, 1993). A pregnancy rate of 74.9% following insemination with frozen semen at first oestrus of the season has also been recorded by Cai Li in trials involving 621 yak.

Many studies, apart from the trials quoted above, have shown that, once mating has occurred, whether naturally or by artificial insemination, pregnancy rates in yak females above 70% are not uncommon, provided matings have been to yak males (Table 5.5 and also: Northwestern China Institute, 1965; Anim. Vet. Inst. Tibet, 1978; Du Fusheng, 1987a; LuoSang Jiangcuo and Chen Yu, 1987). There is, however, a marked difference between pregnancy rates resulting from pure breeding of yak and those from inter-species crossbreeding. When the yak female is inseminated with semen (or mated by a bull) of other species of cattle, antagonisms appear to arise and the pregnancy rate falls. As apparent from Table 5.5, the proportion of calves born and surviving was more than halved when yak cows were mated to *Bos taurus* bulls. The situation was even worse, and dramatically so, when AI was used with semen from such bulls. A combination of circumstances (in this particular situation, poor detection or occurrence of oestrus, poor conception rate and high loss of foetuses from the few pregnant cows) led to only 3 calves surviving from the 217 such cows initially available for service. It is possible that advances in methods and AI technology (Zhang Rongchang, 1979; Yong Conglie *et al.*, 1982; Li Shihong, 1985), developed since the time when the trial recorded in Table 5.5 was conducted, would have led to an improvement on that situation.

Effect of age and physiological state. The three types of female described earlier – Yak cow nursing a calf born in the current year, Yama and Ganba – differ in pregnancy rate (see Table 5.6 and also: Yong Conglie *et al.*, 1982; Cai Li *et al.*, 1984a). But age of female also has an effect, with 5–6 year-old females being the best, on average, although not by a large margin. By the age of 9–10 years the conception rate starts to fall away. Some results are shown in Table 5.6. However, a separate word of explanation is required in respect of the youngest age group – the yak females aged 3–4 years old (this includes the summer following their 4th birthday when, strictly, the females may be 4.5 years old). Some of these animals will have calved previously at 2 or 3 years of age – namely, that relatively small

Table 5.5 Effect on success of mating, conception and calving in yak cows of different types of mating [Xiangdong farm, Sichuan, 1976 and 1977]

Mating of yak female*	No. females of breeding age available	Mated [%]	Conceived of those mated [%]	Foetuses lost of those pregnant [%]	Calving of those pregnant [%]	Cows with surviving calves of those pregnant [%]
Yak male – natural service	323	51.1	87.3	11.1	88.9	36.8
Bos taurus male – natural service	59	52.5	54.8	41.2	58.8	16.9
Bos taurus male – AI	217	22.1	25.0	66.7	33.3	1.4
Yak male – natural service after failure of AI**	205	47.3	93.8	3.3	96.7	39.5

* natural mating to yak bulls: July-October
AI with *Bos taurus* semen: July-August
re-mating, to yak bulls, of cows which failed to conceive to AI: September-October
** note months of re-mating (see above)
*** calves surviving to 6 months of age

proportion of yak females which had achieved this because of particularly good bodily condition and favourable circumstances earlier in their life. If then they had not become pregnant again after their first calving, they, also, can be categorised as Yama and Ganba even at the age of 3–4 years.

Table 5.6 Conception rate (%) of 3 types of yak female according to age (years)

Type of female	3–4 years no.	3–4 years %	5–6 years no.	5–6 years %	7–8 years no.	7–8 years %	> 9 years no.	> 9 years %
Yak cow with calf*	11	9.1	27	11.1	39	7.7	15	13.3
Yama**	52	30.8	135	39.3	117	45.3	82	40.2
Ganba***	53	22.6	436	22.2	537	18.8	308	14.6

* Yak cow nursing calf born in current year
** Yama = cow calved in previous year – with or without calf
*** Ganba = cow that has calved, but not for at least 2 years

The gravid uterus

Cai Li dissected the reproductive organs of 38 female yak at Xiandong farm (Sichuan), 17 of which had been pregnant for between 1 and 4 months. Eleven of these 17 had the foetus implanted in the left uterine horn and 6 in the right. The size of the ovary and the oviduct on the side of the gravid horn was substantially greater. However, the maternal caruncles and cotyledons were about equally developed in both uterine horns. Up to 1.5 months after conception the gravid and empty horns had the same diameter and up to that time the foetal placenta can invade both horns equally. Thereafter, the septum dividing the horns becomes indistinct and disappears as the foetus grows. The gravid horn sinks below the pelvic brim after pregnancy of 2 months. In early pregnancy, diagnosis of pregnancy by rectal palpation depended mainly on size and shape of the 2 ovaries and on changes in the shape of the septum referred to.

As in other cattle species, the progesterone level in milk fat increases during gestation and can therefore also be used in pregnancy diagnosis (see Figure 5.2) and between about days 18 and 24 after mating has a high degree of accuracy (Xue Liqun, 1983; Magasch, 1991b).

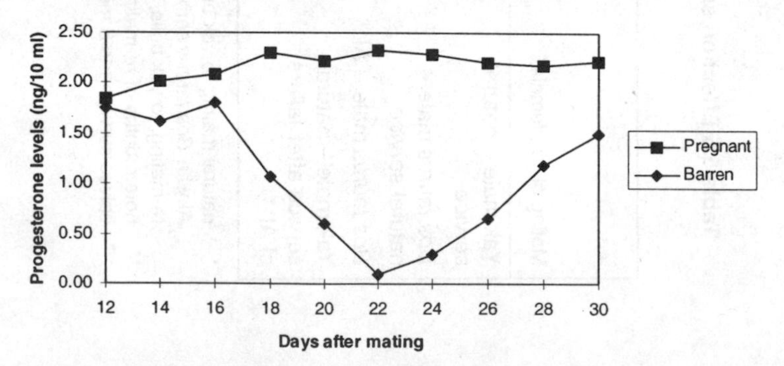

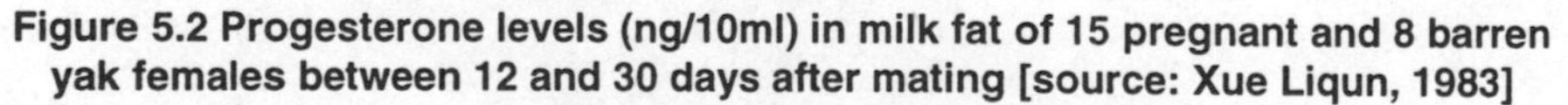
Figure 5.2 Progesterone levels (ng/10ml) in milk fat of 15 pregnant and 8 barren yak females between 12 and 30 days after mating [source: Xue Liqun, 1983]

Gestation length

The gestation length of yak females is shorter than that of *Bos taurus* cattle, particularly when a pure yak calf is carried. Yak females bred pure have, on average, a shorter gestation length than when carrying an inter-species crossbred calf (Pien Niu) (see below). For yak with purebred calves, Denisov (1938) reported an average gestation length of 258 days; Lei Huanzhang *et al.* (1964) recorded a gestation length in 36 yak of 260 (253–278) days for those carrying male calves and 250 (226–283) days for those with female calves. Dubrovin (1992) recorded an average gestation length of 258 days for 800 yak cows in the Caucasus; Katzina and Maturova (1989) a gestation length of 259 days (228 to 280 days) for yak in the Tuva region; and Yu *et al.* (1993) an average of 254 days [SD 2.7 days, range 248–258 days] for yak in Gansu province. Joshi *et al.* (1994) gave an average of 258 days for the gestation length of yak in Nepal.

The average gestation length of yak cows with Pien Niu calves (yak x cattle hybrids) was found by Cai Li to be around 270 days (273.2 with a SD of 12.7 days for 371 cows with male F1 calves and 268.6 with a SD of 10.2 days for cows with female F1 calves). The breed of bull used in Cai Li's study appeared to affect gestation length, as also noted by Zagdsuren (1994b) for yak in Mongolia. Denisov (1938) noted an average gestation length of 276.2 days for yak females mated to Schwyz cattle.

The wide range of gestation lengths quoted by some authors seems surprising, as do some of the differences among studies. The wide ranges, when not otherwise stated, will include the differences in gestation length attributable to sex of calf, and any differences which may be associated with age of dam (though none such are reported). It is also possible that there are differences attributable to type or breed of yak, which would here be usually confounded with location (although, again, there are no specific reports of breed differences in gestation length for the yak, though these are documented for other types of cattle). In order to explain the protracted gestation lengths, one must perhaps also wonder whether both females with yak calves and those bearing inter-species crossbred calves are included together in the ranges, although this is not apparent from the reports. These considerations would still leave unexplained the very short gestation lengths reported at the lower end of the range. The problem with the ranges quoted is that they provide no clue to whether the extreme values are isolated cases, and might, for example, include pre-mature parturition.

Parturition

Almost all births take place during the day and only very few at night, when the yak cows are normally at the herders' camp site.

When the time for parturition approaches, the female yak looks for a sheltered spot, such as a depression in the ground or a ditch, at a distance from the herd. Typical behaviour of the yak during labour includes lying on her side and standing up again for delivery when a pure yak calf is carried. When a hybrid calf is carried, the female will deliver the calf whilst lying on her side – presumably on account of the larger size of the calf and the longer time needed for the delivery.

Dystocia is a rare occurrence in yak females with pure-bred calves. Herdsmen offer no assistance. The umbilical chord is broken by the act of mechanical stretching, as the cow gets up or the calf falls down after delivery. Inflammation of the chord or calf diseases are rare. Yak cows with hybrid calves, however, require help for delivery and dystocia occurs to some extent – for example, there were 28 cases among 861 such calvings (3.3%) over a period of 10 years in one study in Sichuan.

Twins are rare – in general about 0.5% of all births, but in exceptional herds higher rates have been recorded.

Behaviour. The dam generally licks the new-born calf for about 10 minutes, after which the calf attempts to stand up and suck. Again, differences in behaviour have been observed between dams delivering purebred yak and Pien Niu calves. Some results are presented in Table 5.7. They show that time intervals are markedly longer when a Pien Niu calf is involved than when pure yak calves are born.

Table 5.7 Intervals between successive events at parturition according to type of calf [source: Qi Guangyong, 1984]

Nature of events	Interval (range – min. & sec.) between events pure yak calf	crossbred calf
Appearance of calf to end of parturition	3' to 16'	45' to 107' (with help)
Calf out to calf being licked	0' 2" to 0' 5"	0' 3" to 0' 7"
Calf out to calf starting to stand up	14' 2" to 21' 30"	60' 0" to 99' 14"
Calf out to first sucking	15' to 22'	74' to 103'
Duration of first sucking	3' 0" to 5' 30"	5'32" to 11' 21"

The placenta is ejected within half an hour up to 6 hours after parturition.

In the period shortly after birth, the dam is intensely protective of her calf and will attack any person coming close. She may not, however do so directly. For example, the dam may retreat, as though afraid of the person, and then attack from the side or from behind. This is a time for humans to take care!

Bonding of dam and calf depends mainly on smelling and licking. Longer times of parturition and dystocia militate against such bonding and thus place Pien Niu calves at a disadvantage to pure yak calves – at least on average. Yak cows can distinguish their calves by smell from among quite large groups of calves.

Calving season

The calving season is obviously connected with the time in the previous year when oestrus and mating occurred and is therefore prone to the same environmental and physiological constraints. Table 5.8 shows the distribution of calving from March to August at various locations.

On the basis of the distribution of month in which yak cows in Mongolia were mated, as reported by Magasch (1990), it can be estimated that a small proportion

Table 5.8 Distribution of calving in different months of the year at different locations

Location [source]	no.	March [%]	April [%]	May [%]	June [%]	July [%]	August [%]
Qinghai – Datong [1]	155	12.3	39.3	24.5	15.5	8.4*	
Qinghai – Datong [2]	137	4.4	39.4	33.6	18.2	2.9	1.5
Gansu – Zhangxian [3]	98	20.4	24.5	27.6	21.4	6.1	
Sichuan – Ganzi [4]	34		17.6	35.3	41.2	5.9	
Yunnan – Zhongdian [5]	34		8.8	26.5	38.2	23.5	2.9

* including August
Sources: (1) Lei Huangzhang et al, 1964; 2) Liu Zhengqui, 1981; (3) Xiong Zaiyue, 1982; (4) Hu Angang et al., 1960; (5) Jiang Ruisheng and Bai Yinhua, 1985.

of the yak cows calved in March, probably around 25% in April, many more than that in May, the peak month, and a declining number in June and July.

Denisov (1958) reported from Kirgizia that the calving season for a herd of 597 yak extended from February to December but with only 5 calves born in February, and 116, 253 (42.4%) and 113 respectively over the next 3 months and tailing off rapidly thereafter.

When crossbreeding yak to produce Pien Niu, it is common to attempt the hybridisation – either by natural mating or AI – in the first half of the breeding season and to follow this by the use of yak bulls, to catch cows that have not conceived and have returned on heat. Thus it is not uncommon for the crossbred calves to be born earlier in the season than the purebred.

Calf survival – pre- and post-natal

Abortions and other causes of premature termination of pregnancies account for perhaps 5–10% of all pregnancies, as was shown in Table 5.5 with observations from Sichuan. Similar incidences were reported from observations on 971 yak females in Laqu, Tibet with an abortion rate of 5.7%. At Datong farm, Qinghai, 85.9% of 2357 pregnant yak cows calved normally (Northwestern China Institute, 1965).

As already indicated, the normal calving rate is lower when inter-species hybridisation is carried out. Among 1348 such yak cows (carrying crossbred calves) in north-western Sichuan, 20% lost their calves during pregnancy and, in another study with 158 young pregnant yak females, 14 lost their crossbred calves before normal parturition (Yong Conglie *et al.*, 1982).

Calf survival is generally high when the calves are allowed to suckle and the dams are not milked, but can fall greatly when the cows are also milked as shown in Table 5.9.

Since the two rearing methods were conducted in different years (Table 5.9), it is possible that a year effect may have affected the results. The apparent difference between the groups in the proportion of calves born is difficult to explain unless it is a "random" year effect, or unless it is a carry-over effect from the

Table 5.9 Survival of calves according to rearing method [source: Wu Derun and Ma Juru, 1985]

Rearing method	No. cows	Calves born [%]	Calves born which survived*** [%]	Reproductive rate*** [%]
Dam milked*	1366	66.0	57.9	38.2
Dam not milked**	2542	81.1	93.7	76.0

Year of records: * 1975–76; ** 1977–79. *** with calf to 6 months old.

previous year which might have arisen if the cows milked in the current year were also those milked in the preceding year, and those not milked were also not milked in the year before (information on this point is not given). It would be surprising, however, if a year effect negated the large rearing effect on calf survival after birth, as similar results to those shown in Table 5.9 have also been obtained in other sets of observations (Agric. Livestk. Bureau Ganzhi, 1984; Northwestern China Inst, 1965).

A 90% survival rate is typical among purebred calves, e.g. 1328/1470 among Jiulong yak in Sichuan (Agric. Livestk Bureau Ganzhi, 1984), 1818/2025 for purebred calves at Datong farm, Qinghai (Northwestern China Inst., 1965). In contrast to the greater problems before and during parturition experienced with Pien Niu calves, the crossbred calves once delivered have a slightly better survival rate, after birth, than pure yak calves. Results at the same locations showed survival for Pien Niu calves to be about 2% better.

Detailed observations (Ouyang Xi *et al.*, 1984) on 20 yak calves on a farm at an elevation of 3500–4100 m. showed that neonatal survival was also related to the maintenance of body temperature in the calf. The fall in temperature in the first hour after birth (average fall 0.38°C) was significantly correlated (r 0.69) with birth weight (the greater the weight, the less the temperature loss) but much less strongly correlated with ambient temperature. Thus, the body condition of the dam during pregnancy affected calf survival through its effect on birth weight. The body temperature of the calves returned to normal, on average, after 3 hours.

Supplementary feeding of yak cows during pregnancy has also been shown to have a small effect on the number of calves born, probably through reduced embryonic loss, and a somewhat greater effect on calf survival. This result is derived from an experiment conducted at Longri farm in the Aba autonomous Prefecture of Sichuan (part of project undertaken by the South-west Nationalities College with support from UNDP and FAO). Results from this trial will also be referred to Chapter 6, in relation to growth and milk yield; the design will therefore be described here in outline.

Three groups of females, equivalent to each other in all respects, which had previously had normal opportunities to mate, were allocated to three treatments. One group was given hay from mid-December to the end of April. The amount eaten by the cows in mid-winter varied around 4 kg per animal per day, but fell to less than 1 kg, on average, in April. This treatment was repeated over two years.

A second form of supplementation was practised in the first of the two years, by allowing a group of cows access to grass paddocks which had been closed off in the autumn. The yak in this group were allowed into these paddocks, with standing wilted grass, for 45 days from the beginning of April – the latter part of pregnancy for most of the animals. The third group of yak cows received no supplementary feeding and were subjected to the management normal for the area. This group acted as a control. The results, in respect of the number of calves born and calf survival, are shown in Table 5.10.

Table 5.10 Percentage of Maiwa yak cows calving and calf survival from three groups of cows (a) fed hay from mid December to end of April, (b) allowed access to conserved grass paddocks from 1 April for 45 days, and (c) unsupplemented, control [source: Wen Yongli *et al.*, 1993]

Year	Treatment group*	No. cows	Calving %	Calf survival (%)	Calves surviving per 100 cows mated
1989/90	hay	75	58.7	93.2	54.7
	paddock grass	75	56.0	90.5	50.7
	control	148	55.4	85.4	47.3
1990/91	hay	59	64.4	92.1	59.3
	control	150	60.0	85.6	51.3

* for details see text

It is tempting to suggest, in relation to the results in Table 5.10, that provision of hay may have stopped before the final stage of pregnancy when foetal growth is at its fastest. However, as indicated above, the cows began to reduce their hay intake already in the latter part of the feeding period, as the first green shoots of grass started to appear on the pastures. The overall effect of feed supplementation cannot be judged, however, by only the small increase, about 8%, in the proportion of surviving calves per 100 cows mated. Other effects, shown in chapter 6, need to be considered. Unfortunately there is no information as yet on possible carry-over effects on the subsequent conception rate of the supplemented and control groups of cows.

Length of reproductive life

Exceptional yak females may live to an age of about 24 years, but 15–16 years is the normal upper limit for reproductive activity. The peak reproductive ability is considered to be between the 5th and the 9th year of life. In one study (Ding and Chen, 1994), 82% of females of reproductive age were 10 years old or less (see also chapter 11).

Reproduction in the male

Male organs

The anatomical and histological structure of the genitalia of the yak bull are virtually the same as those of other bovine species, apart from the small, hairy scrotum – an adaptation to the cold environment (Xu Kanzhu *et al.*, 1964).

Puberty and mating

Yak males start to show mounting behaviour around the age of 6 months – towards the end of the first warm season in their year of birth. In the following year, this behaviour continues and intensifies to include searching for yak females and mounting. No sperm, however, were found in epididymal fluid of yak bulls before the age of 2 years in a study by Wang Xiaoxin (personal communication, based on a 1964 Research report of a former North-west Animal Husbandry Institute). Puberty thus occurs in the third warm season following birth, when the male is over 2 years old. In practice, bulls start to mate from the age of 3 or, more usually, 4 years onward, reaching their peak ability at around 6–7 years old – after establishing their position in the mating hierarchy after 4 years in the same herd. After the age of 8 years yak bulls start to lose to younger bulls in the competition for females (see below).

A sexually productive life expectancy of not more than 10 years for a yak bull was reinforced by results from an AI stud of 38 yak bulls in Tibet (elevation 4300m) where ejaculate volume and the concentration and motility of sperm in the semen rose steadily from the age of 3 to the age of 9 years and then declined (Zhang Yun, 1994).

A study by Magasch (1990) provides interesting additional evidence from Mongolia on the age changes in the mating activity of yak bulls in relation to their age. This is summarised in Table 5.11.

Table 5.11 Mating activity and success of yak bull in Mongolia according to age of bull [source: Magasch, 1990]

Age of bulls (years)	Number of cows mated	Number of mounts per cow	Percentage of cows pregnant
7	61	1.5	72.1
6	43	1.8	83.7
5	27	2.1	92.6
3	11	2.3	90.9
Total/average	*141*	*1.8*	*80.9*

The results of Magasch (1990) with Mongolian yak, shown in Table 5.11, indicate that the older the bull (within the age range shown) the more females the yak bull was able to serve – consistent with the courtship behaviour and dominance hierarchy of bulls as discussed below. But, interestingly, the results also show that the younger bulls, with fewer females at their disposal, mount their mates more often. Thus, the 3–year-old bulls served their mates half as often again as the 7–year-old bulls. It is also interesting that fertilisation seemed to be more dependant on the number of services than on the age of the bull, in line with the results of Magasch, quoted earlier from the same study, which showed that overall pregnancy rate of females increased with the number of services.

Behaviour

Bulls stay with the herd only during the breeding season. They spend winter and spring alone. Bulls can pick up the scent of females on heat at a distance of several kilometres – even ten km have been reported.

Courtship behaviour. When among a herd of females, bulls will fight with each other to obtain possession. Only the strongest attain the dominant position in the herd and such bulls have the most mates. Other strong bulls will, however, also get an opportunity to mate cows, though in smaller number. Old, feeble bulls retain no mating position in the hierarchy of the herd. They then no longer try to mate and they leave the herd. Young bulls do not usually win a place in the competition for mates until they are 4 years old and then only after some experience of fighting in the previous year. (Yak bulls in Mongolia, as judged from the results in Table 5.10, are apparently more precocious and reach that stage a year sooner). Such competition among bulls, to the extent that it introduces an additional element of natural selection, must provide the yak with some advantages in surviving in an unfriendly environment. By also ensuring that old bulls are replaced, generally before their daughters in the herd have reached breeding age, this competition for dominance may also have a role in reducing the chance for inbreeding to occur. The extent to which inbreeding is avoided, however, must be uncertain, as there is nothing, other than human intervention, to prevent bulls from mating their siblings, or from bulls being succeeded in the herd by their sons.

Mating behaviour. Yak bulls get sexually very excited. Those that have won a mating position in the herd will mate several times a day. The bulls are so intent on mating that when in the process of doing so they will not attack other bulls, unless strongly provoked. It would be interesting to have information on the extent to which dominant bulls, which mate frequently, lose body condition as a result of their sexual activity over the mating season. This is known to occur in some wild animal populations (e.g. deer) and, when it happens, it gives less dominant males the chance to mate.

Artificial insemination

Training. Yak bulls can readily be trained to provide semen for artificial insemination and once trained they will retain this capacity into the next breeding season. The bulls can be taught, in as little as 7 days, to mount dummy cows and supply semen into an artificial vagina (Du Fucheng, 1987 a, b; Li Kongliang *et al.*, 1986). More detail is given in chapter 8.

Semen quantity and quality. Volume and quality are generally considered good. In one trial with over 14 collections (Du Fu-sheng, 1987b), the average volume was 2.4 ± 0.9 ml with average sperm density of 2680 ± 590 million/ml, motility of 0.82 + 0.05 and a malformation rate of 8.3% (6.3–10.4%). The yak semen retains good fertility after diluting 3-fold for use fresh, or after pelleting and frozen storage.

The densities referred to above are, however, more than twice those reported by Zhang Yun (1994) from a station in Tibet (at an elevation of 4300 m.) producing frozen semen from yak bulls (the density values shown are also higher than those usually quoted for bulls of the "improved" cattle breeds (for a review see Setchell,

1993) although the volume of ejaculate in such bulls is usually greater than in the yak). The sperm concentrations (per ml) reported by Zhang Yun were in the range 7.4–12.1 (thousand million) depending on month of year and age of bull. Ejaculate volume in these bulls varied with month and age, from 1.2 ml (in March) to almost 3.0 ml (in August) and from 2.0 ml in 3-year-old bulls to 3.3 ml in 9-year-old bulls. Semen quality was also at its best from the 9-year-old bulls, and in August in that part of Tibet.

Relations with other cattle species

Left to their own devices, yak cows do not allow bulls of other cattle species to approach them, and yak bulls show no inclination to mate cows of other cattle species. The reluctance to mate across the species has been reported from a number of different regions, as, for example, by Bonnemaire and Teissier (1976) in their studies from Nepal.

When forced to graze in herds of mixed species, the antipathy of the yak to members of the opposite sex from the other species of cattle declines, though it may not disappear altogether. When bulls of both species are present at the same time in a herd, a yak cow on heat will only allow a yak bull to mate with her. Bulls of the other species do not win in any competition with yak bulls for yak females. In situations where a yak cow has been mated by a bull of another species and is then served again by a yak bull in the same oestrous period, the calf is almost always pure yak and not a hybrid – suggesting a preferential fertility for the yak sperm. Thus, to obtain hybrid calves, the yak cows must be kept with the bulls of the other species, and access to yak bulls has to be prevented. One way of doing this is, as referred to earlier, to restrain the yak cow in a mating crate and then allow her to be served by the bull of choice, or by artificial insemination.

As was noted in chapter 3, wild yak bulls readily mate with domestic yak females and produce wild x domestic crosses. In that case there is no preferential fertilisation from domestic yak bulls, when they are present in the same herd alongside the wild yak bulls.

6 PRODUCTION CHARACTERISTICS OF YAK

OVERVIEW

Growth. Rapid growth of the yak calf in the first few months of its life is a prerequisite for survival over the first winter and for a good start to continuing growth in the following year. Thus animals which are born early in the warm season have a better chance than those born late. Calves which have exclusive access to the milk of their dams have the best opportunity for growth, especially if they are allowed to graze at night alongside their dams – but such night grazing is not common practice. Calves with dams that are milked once daily grow appreciably better than those with dams milked twice daily. This is on account of the larger amount of milk available to them and the longer period of time they have for grazing. Males become heavier than females, but they grow relatively more slowly in the early years of life, but continue to grow for longer. Typically, in China, males are brought into the adult herd at 6 years old and females at 4 years; but in some other countries this occurs a year earlier. Breeds of yak appear to differ in size and growth rate, but this observation is usually confounded with differences in location. There is much seasonal variation in body weight.

Heavy losses in weight over winter and spring are recovered during the following warm season, when young animals recover what they have lost and make all their additional growth. This pattern is repeated each year. Approximately 25% of the weight at the end of the warm season is normally lost over the succeeding winter and spring – except in the first year of life when that loss is only about 12%. Linear body dimensions of the animals reach their final size at an earlier age than does body weight – although there are differences among the dimensions in this respect. All the linear body dimensions show less seasonal variation in size than does body weight.

Milk production. Milk yield in yak is low and seasonal. The amount produced is only what would be needed for the good development of the calf. However, as milk is an important product for the herdsmen, milking is done at the expense of the calf – though once-a-day milking has relatively little adverse effect on calf growth compared with twice-a-day milking. Although there are differences in milk yield among breeds kept at different locations, there are no specialised milking strains of yak. Milk yield is low, but the solids content, and fat in particular, is high (6.5% is not uncommon).

The single most important factor influencing yield is the supply and quality of grass in the warm season of the year. Daily yield mostly reaches its peak in August. Supplementary feeding, though effective in maintaining yield out of season, is not practical or economic under most present conditions.

Yak do not dry off when milking ceases at the end of the warm season, and the calf, when present, continues to take some milk. Lactation can continue into a second year without pregnancy recurring and reach between one-half and two-thirds of the yield in the year of calving. The yak does not readily let down its milk without stimulation from the calf, and milking is, in any case, hard to do because of strong muscles in small teats.

Meat production. Yak meat is obtained mostly from animals which are surplus to other requirements. In particular, surplus males are castrated – usually at a fairly mature age – and slaughtered as steers. Meat quantity is determined largely by body weight which is subject to seasonal cycles and depends also on breed and the location where the animals are kept. Animals are normally slaughtered in September or October when they are in the best and fattest condition.

Dressing percentages range, most commonly, from around 45% to 58% and the ratio of lean to bone from as little as 3:1 to as high as 6:1, depending on the source and condition of the animal. The fat content of the carcass and the fat content within the meat are generally low.

Fibre production. Hair is an important by-product of the yak. Quantity produced varies with the age and size of the animal, with breed and sex, and with the method of harvesting. There are two distinct types of fibre – down fibre and coarse hair – differing in diameter, length, degree of medullation and other properties; there is also an intermediate "mid-type" hair. The proportions of the different types of hair vary on different parts of the yak body. The proportion of down fibre is high in calves and declines as the animal gets older. Down fibre grows as additional protection for the yak over winter and has to be harvested prior to being shed in the early summer. The down fibre is much valued in textiles.

Draught performance. Yak steers are used widely for carrying packs, for riding and, in some areas for cultivating land. Yak have a high endurance for work and can carry heavy loads in relation to their own body weight. They are particularly valued for their ability as pack animals to cope with dangerous terrain and marshy ground at high elevations.

Introduction

The yak is a multi-purpose animal, providing its owners with milk, meat, hair, hide, work as a draught animal and faeces – important as fuel in the absence of trees, but also as manure and for building. As noted from earlier chapters, the harsh but varied environment greatly affects the performance of the animals and the output of the various products. There are, however, also differences among types and breeds of yak, though these differences are usually also associated with differences among the locations where these types and breeds are found.

This chapter will look, in turn, at each of the main performance characteristics of yak. Discussion of management of the yak and of the harvesting and utilisation of the products will be left to later chapters.

Growth

As would be expected, growth and development of the yak is highly influenced by the seasons, which, along with the location, largely determine pasture growth and hence the feed supply. Age, sex, and type or breed of yak are among the other main causes of variation..

Body weight

Birth weight

In general, birth weight is low, ranging from 10 to 16 kg and accounting for about 5% to 7% of adult female weight. The relatively low birth weight is a consequence of a relatively short gestation length (see chapter 5) and the fact that in mid and late pregnancy the yak, typically, has to exist on ground which is frozen and covered with ice and snow and, normally, without the benefit of supplementary feeding. For these nutritional reasons, the physical condition of the female yak is at its lowest in late pregnancy thus leading to nutrient deficiency for the foetus at the time that the foetus is at its most demanding. The consequence is a relatively poor foetal development. Table 6.1 provides some results from different sources and breeds – showing the Jiulong yak of Sichuan Province with the highest absolute birth weights and the "Pengbo" yak in Tibet with the lowest. Although breed differences in birth weight may exist, it is not possible to differentiate between the effects of breed and those of location. Female calves are, on average, about 1kg lighter at birth than the males.

Supplementary feeding of dam over winter. An experiment conducted at Longri farm examined the effect of two methods of supplementary feeding of the dams during pregnancy. (This experiment, conducted by the Southwest Nationalities College with support from UNDP/FAO was already referred to and described in chapter 5 in the section on calf survival). Table 6.2 shows the effects of supplementary feeding of dams in winter or early spring on birth weight and subsequent daily gain of the calves.

Weng Yongli *et al.* (1993) report that the effects of supplementary feeding of the dams had a statistically significant effect on both birth weight and weight gain after birth ($P<0.05$), though small in absolute terms. The improved weight gain is likely to be attributable to both the advantage of higher birth weight and the slightly better milk yield of the supplemented dams (see Tables 6.6 and 6.12). Any advantage in terms of body weight must also be viewed in conjunction with the small but positive effect of the winter feed supplementation on the number of calves born and reared (see Table 5.10).

Parity and age of cow. Both parity and age of yak dam have effects on the birth weight of their calves, as shown in Table 6.3 and as also widely reported in studies on ordinary cattle elsewhere. Data are again taken from the Longri experiment involving trials of the effects of supplementary feeding during pregnancy. (Because

Table 6.1 Birth weights of male and female yak of different breeds at different locations in China

Location	Breed*	Male no.	Male weight (kg.)	Female no.	Female weight (kg.)	Source (first author *et al.*)
Sichuan	Jiulong	27	15.9	24	15.5	Cai Li *et al.*, 1980a
Sichuan	Maiwa	77	13.4	71	11.9	Chen Xiafei *et al.*, 1981
Sichuan	Maiwa	76	14.9**	80	12.7**	Chen Zhihua *et al.*, 1993
Yunnan	Zhongdian	11	14.5	14	12.8	Res. Co-op, 1980–87 (Duan Zhongxuan)
Gansu	Tianzhu White	25	12.7	24	10.9	Res. Co-op, 1980–87 (Zhang Rongchan)
Gansu	Maqu	45	14.6	46	13.5	Zhao Bingyao *et al.*, 1984
Qinghai	Plateau	11	13.4	11	13.1	Lei Huanzhang, 1983
Qinghai	Datong	52	13.2	59	11.8	NW China Inst., 1965
Tibet	Alpine	45	13.7	32	12.8	Res. Co-op, 1980–87 (Qi Zhengzhong)
Tibet	Pengbo	(63)***	(10.5)***			Res. Co-op, 1980–87 (Dou Yaozhong)
Xinjiang	Bazhou	8	15.8	17	14.3	Agric. Exploit. Acad., 1984

* Jiulong, Maiwa, Tianzhu White and Alpine are listed Chinese yak breeds.
** Least squares means to allow for disequilibrium in the data set. The published values have been adjusted here to remove the effect of supplementary feeding in winter of some of the dams of calves ("Longri" expt.)
*** Number and average of male and female yak calves combined.

Table 6.2 Birth weights (kg) and weight gain (g per day) to 90 days of age of Maiwa yak calves from three groups of dams (a) fed hay from mid-December to end of April, (b) allowed access to conserved grass paddocks from 1 April for 45 days, and (c) unsupplemented, control. Least squares means and standard deviations (kg) [source: Weng Yongli *et al.* 1993]

Year	Treatment group	Number calves	Birth wt. (kg) mean	Birth wt. (kg) SD	Number calves	Daily wt. gain (g) mean	Daily wt. gain (g) SD
1989/90	hay	36	16.2	2.2	32	300	83
	paddock grass	41	16.0	2.2	36	298	54
	control	81	14.5	2.5	66	279	51
1990/91	hay	35	18.1	2.4	30	316	88
	control	98	15.6	3.7	98	295	57

supplementary feeding of the dams has affected calf weights in this experiment, the overall mean birthweight of all the calves is also somewhat higher than it would be without the inclusion of the fed groups [the least squares mean for each treatment group were shown in Table 6.2]. Therefore, effects of parity and age of dam, shown in Table 6.3, are presented as deviations from the overall fitted mean of the data).

Table 6.3. Effects of parity and of age of yak cow on the birth weight (kg) of her calf – shown as deviations from the least squares fitted mean [source: Chen Zhihua *et al.*, 1994]

Parity of dam	Number of cows	Deviation of birth weight	Age of cow (yrs)	Number of cows	Deviation of birth weight
1	37	–0.02	4	33	–0.52
2	27	–0.34	5	9	–0.24
3	26	–0.26	6	3	–0.23
4	28	–0.90	7	20	0.62
5	20	0.81	8	21	0.25
6	18	0.71	9	32	0.54
			10	38	–0.42

It is apparent from the results of Chen Zhihua, Wen Yongli and Cai Li (1994), shown in Table 6.3, that calves born in early parities are lighter in weight than those born later. However, unlike in most results from "improved" cattle breeds, calves born to first parity dams were not at great disadvantage. Similarly, the effects of age (as distinct from parity) show that young yak cows had calves slightly lighter in weight than those from older cows – though the oldest age group started to show an expected decline in the birth weight of its calves. However, the variation is not large (though statistically significant) and there are some estimates which disrupt a steady trend (e.g. the estimate of a relatively large negative effect of fourth parity). It is not clear, however, how accurately an analysis such as this can estimate the effects of parity and of age of dam when both factors are included at the same time, since the two are partially confounded. Some aberrant values are not surprising.

Effects on birth weight and growth

Month of calving. Most calves are born from April to July, with May the peak month. Birth weight varies to a some extent with month of calving (Table 6.4), as shown by an experiment at Longri farm in Sichuan, also referred to above. (As in respect of Table 6.3, and for the same reason, the results in Table 6.4 are presented as deviations from the overall least squares mean).

Apart from the unexpectedly low birth weight of calves born in the second half of June, there is a steady increase in birth weight from the middle of April to the middle of July, with all birth weights after mid June above average and those of calves prior to that time below average. The variation in birth weight attributable to date of birth (as defined) was shown by Chen Zhihua *et al.* (1994) to be statistically highly significant ($P<0.01$).

Variation in birth weight with month of calving was also noted by Cai Li in Pien Niu calves (yak x cattle hybrids) born at Xiangdong farm in Ruoergai County of Sichuan. Average birth weight rose from 21.7 kg. for calves born in April to 24.3 kg. for those born in June.

However, calves born early in the season, March or April, have a longer suckling season ahead of them than those born later in the season. For example, Ma Zongxiang and Du Yaozong (1982) reported that calves born in March-April

Table 6.4. Effect of date of calving on birth weight (kg) shown as deviations from the least squares fitted mean (cf. Table 6.2) [source: Chen Zhihua *et al.*, 1994]

Period of calving (day and month)	Number calves	Deviation of birth weight
prior to 15.4	6	–1.28
16.4–30.4	29	–1.67
1.5–15.5	26	–1.49
16.5–31.5	23	–0.77
1.6–15.6	30	–0.98
16.6–30.6	18	1.08
1.7–15.7	14	4.02
16.7–31.7	12	1.09

reached an average body weight of 45.6 kg in October of that year, while those born in June had attained only 34.2 kg, on average. The calf's growth in the first 6 months of its life is very important to its subsequent survival over the first winter. Calves born later in the season have a poorer chance of survival over winter than those born earlier.

Seasonal growth of yak. Typically, gain in weight of healthy calves reared by their dam is almost linear over the first 6 months of life but declines with the approach of winter; this is followed by some loss in weight over the first winter and spring. Thereafter, in the second warm season, there is again rapid gain in weight followed by loss in weight over the next cold season.

Figure 6.1 illustrates growth from birth to 25 months old of 12 male and 12 female calves born in April at Longri breeding farm of the Pasture Institute of Sichuan. Daily gain for the male calves was nearly constant over the first 5 months and declined rapidly from November. For female calves, weight gain was somewhat more variable and started to decline (for reasons that are not apparent) one month earlier than for the males. In the second warm season after birth, weight gains from April/May to August/September were a little faster than in the first year, between a third and half a kilogram per day. The third warm season started again with substantial gains in weight after the losses in the previous winter.

Over the first winter, the weight loss of calves is around 12–15% of the weight reached before the onset of winter. Over the following summer and autumn young yak will regain their weight losses and may well double in weight before again losing, over the second winter of life, perhaps 25% of the maximum weight reached. The cycle of weight gain and weight loss continues throughout life as shown by further data with observations on 180 yak steers over a period of 4 years (Lu Guanghui, 1980). When the yak is adult, the weight lost in the cold season is roughly equal to the gains in the following warm season.

Effect of type of rearing on weight gain. The manner in which the yak calf is reared profoundly affects its growth. The 3 main classes are: 1) to give the calf exclusive access to the milk of its dam (the dam is not milked), 2) to milk the dam once a day and allow the calf the remainder, and 3) to milk the dam twice a day and

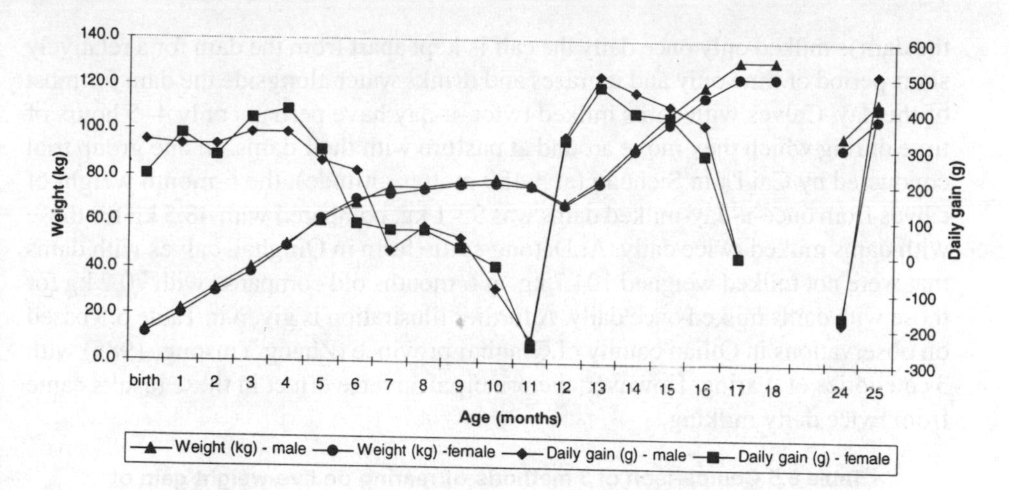

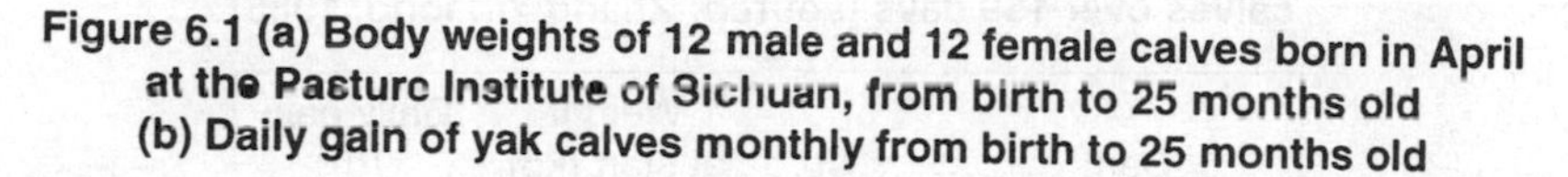

Figure 6.1 (a) Body weights of 12 male and 12 female calves born in April at the Pasture Institute of Sichuan, from birth to 25 months old (b) Daily gain of yak calves monthly from birth to 25 months old

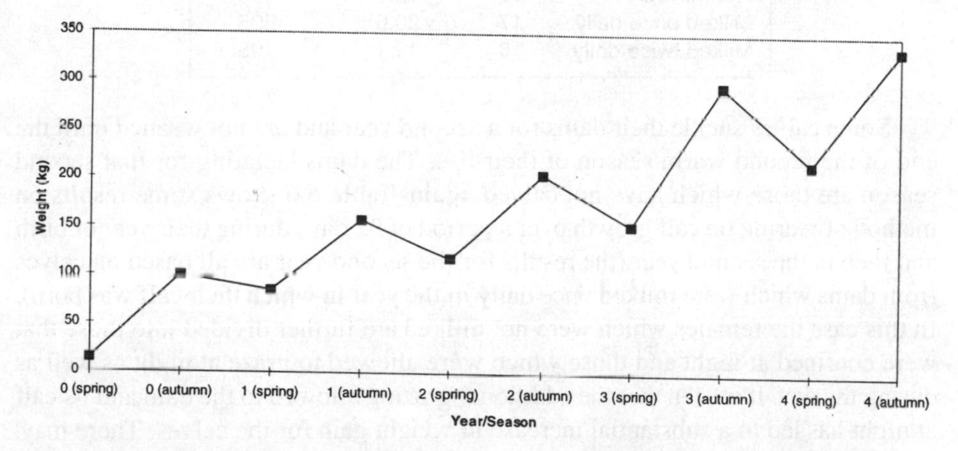

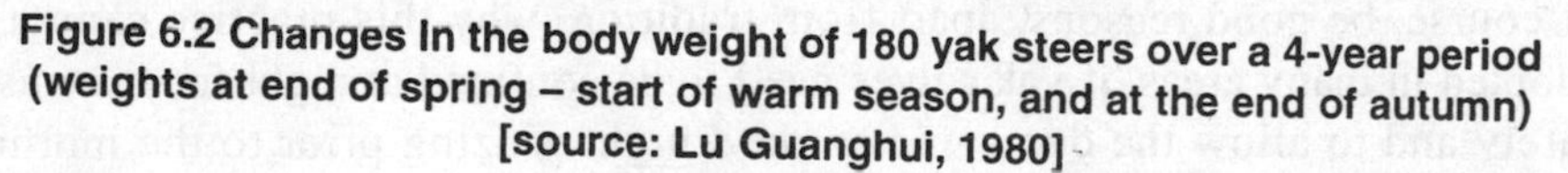

Figure 6.2 Changes in the body weight of 180 yak steers over a 4-year period (weights at end of spring – start of warm season, and at the end of autumn) [source: Lu Guanghui, 1980]

allow the calf the rest. An additional category (a sub-division of 1) is that dams which are not milked may a) be allowed to graze at night or b) not allowed to graze at night if kept restrained overnight with the yak females that are milked.

There are many studies bearing on the effects of these rearing treatments on calf growth. In general, the largest difference is between calves allowed access to dams milked only once a day compared with those reared by dams milked twice daily. Gain in weight under the former regime can be double that from the latter. This is not, however, a consequence only of differences in milk intake by the calf. When the dam is milked only once daily the calf is kept apart from the dam for a relatively short period of time only and it grazes and drinks water alongside the dam for most of the day. Calves with dams milked twice-a-day have perhaps only 4–5 hours of time during which they move around at pasture with their dams. In one group trial conducted by Cai Li in Sichuan (at 3 450 metres altitude), the 6-month weight of calves from once-a-day-milked dams was 93.1 kg. compared with 48.5 kg for those with dams milked twice daily. At Datong cattle farm in Qinghai, calves with dams that were not milked weighed 104.7 kg. at 6 months old compared with 70.2 kg for those with dams milked once daily. A further illustration is given in Table 6.5 based on observations in Qilian county of Qinghai province (Zhang Yinsong, 1985) with 3 categories of rearing. However, the principal adverse effect in these results came from twice daily milking.

Table 6.5 Comparison of 3 methods of rearing on live-weight gain of calves over 159 days [source: Zhang Yinsong, 1985]

Dam	No.	Weight at start (kg)	Daily gain (g)
Not milked	12	18.7	439
Milked once daily	17	20.6	395
Milked twice daily	10	19.1	195

Some calves suckle their dams for a second year and are not weaned until the end of the second warm season of their life. The dams lactating for that second season are those which have not calved again. Table 6.6 shows some results on method of rearing on calf growth over a period of 92 days during their year of birth and then in the second year (the results for the second year are all based on calves from dams which were milked once daily in the year in which their calf was born). In this case the females which were not milked are further divided into those that were confined at night and those which were allowed to graze at night as well as during the day. It is seen that the additional grazing allowed to the dam and its calf at night has led to a substantial increase in weight gain for the calves. There may, of course, be good reasons, apart from tradition, why this practice cannot be adopted in many areas, if yak calves need to be confined at night for reasons of safety and to allow the dams undisturbed night grazing prior to the morning milking. As was also seen in Table 6.5, milking the dam twice daily was a clear disadvantage for the growth of the calf in its first year but also to a lesser degree when the calf was already one year old. Milking the dam once a day had no significantly adverse effect on calf growth relative to not milking the dam at all.

Results shown earlier of the effects of feed supplementation of the dam over winter on subsequent calf growth (Table 6.2) may well be mediated through an improvement in the milk yield of the dam and hence analogous to the effects noted in Table 6.6.

Hand rearing of yak calves is restricted to situations where there is no alternative. Usually when a calf has lost its dam it is fostered on a cow that has lost

Table 6.6 Weight gain of yak calves in 2 successive years according to rearing method [source: Xu Guiling, 1985b]

Dam	Number	Weight gain [92 days] (kg)
Year calf born (calf age 0 year)		
Not milked	14	29.0
Not milked but grazing at night	17	60.8
Milked once daily	26	28.1
Milked twice daily	29	20.2
Year after calf born (calf age 1 year)*		
Not milked	32	28.8
Not milked but grazing at night	9	49.8
Milked once daily	27	29.7

her calf (see chapter 8). Data on the effects of artificial rearing on growth have not been obtained.

Breed and sex differences in growth. It is generally accepted that yak of the Alpine type, and especially the Jiulong breed (perhaps the best of the Alpine type), grow more rapidly than those of the Plateau type. The cautionary note has to be repeated that, normally, these different types and breeds are not at the same location at the same time and that yak type or breed differences are therefore confounded with location and the environmental differences implicit in that. This applies to the data shown in Table 6.7.

The faster growth of the Jiulong yak compared with the Maiwa yak (Table 6.7) appears to be a function not only a larger mature weight for the Jiulong but also a faster early growth rate relative to mature weight. Thus, by 3–3.5 years old the Jiulong males had reached nearly 58% of their 6–6.5-year-old weight whilst the Maiwa had reached only 41% (for females the corresponding percentages are 78% and 70% respectively). However, it is not known how these results may have been affected by the different environments in which the two breeds were kept. It is nonetheless clear, from Table 6.7, that, for each breed, the females made faster growth relative to mature weight in the early years of life than did the males. However, the growth of the females slowed down after they reached the age of about 4 years. The males still continued to increase in weight quite markedly after that age – to reach a substantially greater final weight than the females. These growth differences between the sexes are reflected by the practice of the herdsmen to regard females as suitable for transfer to the adult herd at the age of 4 years, whereas males are not regarded as "mature" (and at the height of their powers) until the age of 6 or 7 years.

The difficulty of interpreting data on size and other aspects of the performance of yak as presented here and in the literature on the yak at large, rests on the fact, as already noted, that conditions under which yak are kept vary from locality to locality and between years and that these factors are also often confounded with the type or breed of yak and with the management system. This point is further

Table 6.7 Estimated body weights* of Maiwa and Jiulong male and female yak (at separate locations) from birth to 6.5 years old and weight at each age relative to final weight (weights in October/November of each year). [sources: Maiwa: Chen Xiafei *et al.*, 1981; Jiulong: Cai Li *et al.*, 1980a]

	Maiwa								Juilong							
	Male				Female				Male				Female			
Age (yrs)	no.	Wt. (kg.)	[SD]	% of final	no.	Wt. (kg.)	[SD]	% of final	no.	Wt. (kg.)	[SD]	% of final	no.	Wt. (kg.)	[SD]	% of final
birth	77	13.4		3.2	71	11.9		5.4	27	15.9	2.3	3.6	24	15.0	2.5	5.0
1–1.5	84	65.9	2.2	15.9	82	67.0	11.3	30.2	34	145.3	20.8	30.7	35	124.9	25.2	40.2
2–2.5	33	120.1	19.7	29.0	35	119.6	28.5	53.9	18	208.6	25.5	44.0	21	189.6	29.4	61.0
3–3.5	30	170.7	25.8	41.3	61	154.8	28.5	69.8	3	272.6	25.6	57.5	11	243.1	23.2	78.3
4–4.5	15	302.3	49.5	73.1	73	181.9	21.2	82.0	11	312.5	19.2	65.9	26	269.7	18.3	86.8
5–5.5	10	375.3	69.8	90.7	40	188.7	42.6	85.1	7	386.0	20.1	81.4	9	283.1	33.9	91.1
6–6.5	17	413.8	67.0	100.0	21	221.8	25.9	100.0	38	474.1	38.8	100.0	10	310.6	26.9	100.0

*body weights estimated from linear body dimensions by the formula shown in footnote of Table 2.1

Table 6.8 Linear body dimensions and body weight of female, male and castrate (male) Maiwa yak at three ages (means and SD's based on a total data set of 711 animals) [source: results adapted from Chen Zhihua *et al.*, 1995]

	Sex:	Female			Male			Castrated male		
	Age (years)	1.5	2.5	3.5	1.5	2.5	3.5	1.5	2.5	3.5
Height at withers	mean*	87.2	96.2	105.2	89.1	100.4	114.4	–	100.1	114.2
	SD*	5.6	5.0	5.0	6.2	22.1	7.0	–	6.0	8.8
Body length	mean*	98.3	110.8	125.9	101.1	113.2	141.4	–	114.7	133.3
	SD*	7.7	6.6	8.4	7.7	8.5	10.8	–	8.5	13.6
Chest circumference	mean*	122.1	141.6	160.8	124.3	146.1	174.6	–	144.3	172.5
	SD*	10.1	9.3	8.2	11.1	8.6	12.5	–	12.9	15.9
Body weight	mean*	103.4	152.1	231.2	116.6	166.0	259.1	–	167.7	281.4
	SD*	20.8	16.1	31.8	25.3	36.9	112.4	–	33.4	72.9

*means and SD's are the averages of 4 randomised sub-groups in the original publication (Chen Zhihua et al., 1995)

exemplified by Sarbagishev *et al.* (1989) who note that yak in Kirgizia, for example, are considerably larger than those in neighbouring Tajikistan because in the former country yak are not milked, but kept exclusively for meat production. Under good grazing conditions on state farms in Kirgizia the authors recorded weight gains during 12-month fattening periods well in excess of 100 kg liveweight per year. These gains were made both in the second year of life (107 kg for 248 yak) and the third year of life (126 kg for 87 yak) and were only a little less in the year after that (92 kg for 11 animals). That these weight gains are markedly higher than those shown in Table 6.4 for Maiwa and Jiulong yak should occasion no surprise since the Maiwa and Jiulong were not specifically managed as "fattening" animals. The higher growth rates on the state farms in Kirgizia illustrate, however, that yak do have a higher potential for growth than is sometimes realised in the predominantly harsh conditions in which they are normally kept.

Linear body dimensions

A substantial body of data is available from the investigation at Longri farm (referred to earlier in chapter 5 and in this chapter, in relation to the effects of feed supplementation over winter and other environmental effects on birth weight). Table 6.8 shows linear body dimensions at three ages of female, male and castrate male yak. Body weights are also shown to indicate the relationship with linear dimensions.

The correlations among the body dimensions were reported to be of the order of 0.3–0.5 and those of the linear dimensions with body weight in the range 0.5 to 0.6 ($P<0.01$) (Wen Yongli and Chen Zhihua, 1994). Judged on body weight, the yak at Longri farm had grown somewhat faster than yak of the same breed, Maiwa, at the different location of the results of Chen Xiafei, Lei Deqian and Liu Shijie (1981) (see Table 6.7) since they are heavier at roughly corresponding ages. This further illustrates the importance of environmental effects on the performance of yak and the caution which must be attached to comparisons (such as breed comparisons) across locations.

As expected with linear body dimensions, these show in the yak, as in other bovines, less seasonal variation in size than does body weight (a cubic measure of size). Moreover, dimensions which are relatively early maturing and largely a function of skeletal size, such as height at withers, show less variability in size over the seasons than dimensions which are later maturing and also include in the measurement a greater proportion of muscle and fat (e.g. heart girth). This is illustrated by the results in Table 6.9 on yak at the Pasture Institute of Sichuan Province, where 12 male and 10 female yak were measured from birth over a period of 2 years.

It can be seen from Table 6.9, as might be expected, that height at withers showed no decline in size over winter, though almost certainly a slowing of growth, whilst heart girth, which is more affected by bodily condition, showed some reduction in size at the end of each winter period. Body length was somewhat intermediate between the other two measurements in its pattern of growth.

Table 6.9 Height at withers, body length, and heart girth of yak over a 2-year period (measurements in cm. are given for the unweighted average of 12 male and 10 female animals) [source: Pasture Institute of Sichuan Province]

Age (mth)	Ht. withers	Body length	Heart girth
birth	50.8	45.7	56.8
6	79.1	86.6	104.9
12	88.9	88.5	102.7
18	93.1	107.1	135.1
24	95.8	108.5	128.6

Results on body dimensions of adult Maiwa yak can be found later (Table 7.2) in a comparison with crossbreds.

Milk production

There is, at present, no breed or strain of yak developed especially for milk production. All breeds are kept to a greater or lesser extent to produce milk in addition to their other uses and products. Milk yield is closely related to pasture growth and quality and, in general terms, the amount of milk produced by the yak cow is considered as no more than the amount needed for the normal growth and development of its calf. In this respect the milk yield of yak is more akin to that of animals in the wild than to the milk yield of dairy cattle. None-the-less, even though the milk may be taken at the expense of the calf, milk of the yak is an important product for the herdsmen and their families – and in commercial terms perhaps the most important. Crosses with other cattle, the Pien Niu, produce substantially more milk than the pure yak – the actual amount depending on the cattle breed used in the cross. The Pien Niu has, therefore, considerable value to the herdsmen.

When considering estimates of the milk yield of yak, account has to taken of the milk consumed by the calf – which can only be estimated – and the quantity harvested by the herders. As a rule, yak females are not milked for the first month after calving, though perhaps only two weeks in some areas. During that time the calf takes all the available milk. Thereafter, it is estimated that the calf takes about a third of the available milk if the yak cow is milked twice daily and about half the milk with once-a-day milking. However, yak females give about a third more milk, in total, if stimulated by milking twice daily compared with once-a-day (39% more in a study by Cai Li in Sichuan, and 26% more in an investigation in Qinghai (Lei Huanzhang, 1983).

There is no generally agreed method of assessing yak lactation milk yield. Production over a lactation period of 180 days has been proposed, and estimated from the yield on 3–5 successive days and the use of coefficients based on the month in which the milk yield is measured. The coefficients, in turn, are based on the fact that yield is higher in months of high pasture growth than either at the beginning or end of the grass growing season. To the estimate of yield derived from hand-milking the cow has to be added an estimate of milk consumed by the calf. Though such methods of estimating yield are attractive in principle, the various methods suffer from the additional difficulty that the coefficients for different months vary greatly for different locations and dates of calving; hence the absence of general agreement on the use of these methods.

Milk yield and milk composition of different breeds at different locations
Table 6.10 provides estimates of daily milk yield from the amounts milked by hand with an adjustment for milk taken by the calf, and estimates for lactation yield.

The results shown in Table 6.10 indicate that, in general, the milk yield of the yak is low. The highest daily yield (2.6 kg.) recorded for the Bazhou yak in Xinjiang Autonomous Region, is associated with a sub-alpine area of vast grasslands with an ample supply of water and a low stocking density of yak at an elevation of 2 500 m. The yak in that region have, therefore, a plentiful supply of herbage. By contrast, the lowest daily milk yield of 0.9 kg is associated with Alpine yak in Tibet at an elevation of 4 500 m. where the pastures have a low yield of grass (225 kg per hectare of green grass) with a growing period of only 120 days.

Some of the studies included in Table 6.10 also provide a range in values for fat percentage. The widest range, from 5.0% to 8.2% was reported by Zhang Rongchang *et al.* (*in*: Research Co-op, 1980-87) from observations on the Tianzhu White yak in Gansu province.

Effect of age and parity
Lactation milk yield increases with the age of the female up to about 10 or 11 years old and also with the number of calvings (Zhang Rongchang *et al.*, 1983; Xu Guiling *et al.*, 1983) – although these two factors are rather closely associated with each other. Figure 6.3 illustrates these points.

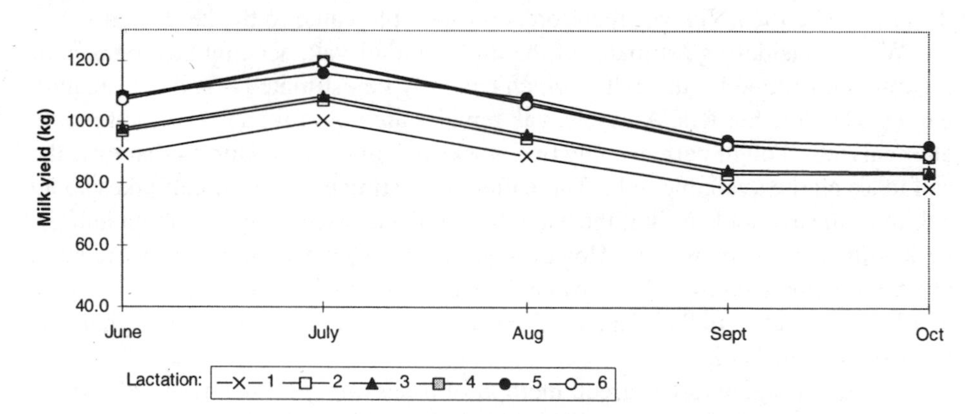

Figure 6.3 Milk yield (kg) of yak females in 5 (warm) months of the year in 6 separate lactations. (Number females per lactation: 1:20; 2:20; 3:13; 4:10; 5:10; 6:18)

There does not appear to be any evidence available to show whether yak cows have a lactation peak in relation to calving date – as in dairy cattle; an over-riding effect on milk yield in the yak seems to be that of pasture growth, reflected by month, in

Table 6.10 Milk yield of yak females of different breeds at various locations

Location	Breed	Month of measurement	No.	Av. daily yield (kg)	Estimated lactation yield (kg)	Fat %	Source
Sichuan	Jiulong	7	72	1.37	347 (150 d.)	5.7	Cai Li *et al.*, 1980a
Sichuan	Maiwa	4, 7	20	1.79	365 (150 d.)	6.8	Chen Xiafei *et al.*, 1981
Yunnan	Zhongdian	5, 7, 11	73		302 (210 d.)	6.2	Res. Co-op, 1980–87
Gansu	Tianzhu White	6 (end)	25	0.88		6.8	Res. Co-op, 1980–87
Gansu	Gannan	5 to 10	13	1.79	315 (177 d.)		Res. Co-op, 1980–87
Qinghai	Plateau	6 to 10	91	1.4–1.7	361 (150 d.)	6.4	Xu Guining *et al.*, 1983
Qinghai	Huanhu	6 to 10	5	1.68	385 (153 d.)	6.5	Lei Huanzhang *et al.*, 1983
Tibet	Alpine	8 to 10	41	0.92		6.4	Res. Co-op, 1980–87
Tibet	Yardong	8, 9	64	1.45			Res. Co-op, 1980–87
Xinjiang	Bazhou		23	2.56			Res. Co-op, 1980–87

Table 6.11 Percentage composition of fresh grass on meadow in different months over the warm season [source: Grassland Institute, 1982]

Date	Water	Dry matter	Crude protein	Crude fibre	Ash	N-free extract	Ca	P
June, 9	76	24	4.50	6.70	1.20	10.50	0.12	0.08
June, 30	72	28	3.29	8.37	1.43	13.64	0.12	0.07
July, 30	67	33	4.06	9.11	2.01	16.76	0.14	0.11
August, 30	62	38	3.88	11.67	3.11	18.15	0.23	0.10
Sept., 29	58	42	3.36	13.99	2.44	21.20	0.26	0.06
October, 31	38	62	2.98	21.58	3.10	33.16	0.33	0.10

each of the 6 lactations shown in Figure 6.3. Very similar trends in terms of the effects of parity and the month in which the cows lactate have also been shown for Jiulong yak (at an elevation of 3200m) in a substantial study by Wen *et al.* (1994) involving between 65 and 128 animals in each parity group.

Environmental factors affecting milk yield – the lactation curve

Herbage supply. As mentioned above, the most important influence on milk yield is the quantity, growth status and nutritive value of the herbage – and this, in turn, is affected by climate and season. All lactating yak, irrespective of age, parity, or breed type, and even location, tend to peak in yield in July and August when grass is at its best in terms of quality and quantity (cf. Figure 6.3). These months are known in yak-producing areas of China as the "golden age". Before July, though the grass starts to turn green and to grow, the amount of grass available is not high. After August, as air temperature falls, the nutritive value declines – as the grass seeds and then wilts, and the content of crude fibre of the grass is high. Table 6.11 provides some information on the composition of grass (but not on grass quantity) from samples taken on pastures at an elevation of 3 600 m. in Hongyuan County of Sichuan province. The pasture samples were representative of the herbage grazed by the yak.

Month of milking. In Hongyuan county, from where the data on grass composition in Table 6.12 are derived, the peak of monthly milk yield was in July for yak cows, and in June for crossbreds (both F1 [Pien Niu] and backcrosses to cattle [1/4-bred yak]). The monthly yields and the fat percentage of the milk are shown in Table 6.12.

Table 6.12 Monthly milk yield (kg.) and fat percentage of milk of yak, Pien Niu*, and 1/4-bred yak* in Hongyuan county of Sichuan

		No.	Jun	Jul	Aug.	Sept.	Oct.	Nov.	Total
Yak	Milk yield	13	40.4	40.6	37.3	27.0	20.0	11.0	176.5
	Fat %	6		5.6	6.6	6.5	7.6	7.8	6.8
Pien Niu	Milk yield	12	64.7	61.3	43.1	29.5	17.9	11.0	227.5
	Fat %	5		5.1	5.4	5.8	6.8	6.6	5.9
1/4-bred yak	Milk yield	10	48.5	40.9	40.9	29.5	19.4	6.7	185.9
	Fat %	7		6.0	6.0	6.0	7.0	7.6	6.6

* local *Bos taurus* (yellow cattle) bulls used for crossing with yak; the 1/4-bred yak are backcross offspring of the F1 (Pien Niu) dams mated to bulls of the yellow cattle.

The yields of the cows represented in Table 6.12 were lower than those in the sample represented by Figure 6.3 but the seasonal pattern of milk production is very similar. It is also seen that, as also found in dairy cattle, the percentage of fat in the milk increases as the season advances and the quantity of milk declines.

Similar results to those presented on the time of peak lactation have been obtained from various locations, all showing that the supply of grass is the major factor influencing yield and that parity of cow has a much smaller effect. A particular example of this, and from a more northerly region (the Vostochnyi Sayan area of Russia) derives from a study of Katzina (1993). It is reported that yak which calved early in the year, in April, attained their maximum udder volume in the third month of the lactation, whilst those which did not calve until June attained their maximum udder volume in the first month of lactation – thus both groups would have their largest udder volume around the same month of the year.

Month of calving. The study by Katzina (1993), quoted above, also showed that the yak which had calved in April had a maximum udder volume which was far greater (2.5 fold) than that of the yak which calved in June. The April-calving yak, in that part of Russia, lactated for 6–7 months to produce around 360 kg milk whilst those that did not calve until June lactated for only 4–5 months to produced 150 kg. milk on average.

An inter-relationship between the month of calving and the month of milking is shown particularly well in Table 11.M.5, with data from Mongolia. This re-affirms the month of milking as the most important variable for milk production – reflecting, as it does the growth and quality of the available herbage.

The weather. It has been recorded (Xu Guiling *et al.*, 1983) that the weather conditions on the day of milking affect yield on that day. Thus, in comparison with milk produced on a clear day, milk production on a cloudy day was 1.9% higher and on a rainy day 7.7% greater. It is not immediately obvious whether the small increase in milk yield is associated with increased intake of herbage or of water, or some other factors related to the environment.

Effects of winter and cessation of milking. As air temperature starts to fall after October and winter approaches rapidly, hand milking of the yak females is normally stopped. As indicated above, the yak does not, however, dry off in consequence of this and continues to secrete a little milk for its calf. This happens irrespective of whether the yak female is pregnant or not. Only a cow which has lost her calf during the warm season will dry off when hand-milking ceases. Similarly, a female which is pregnant, but has been isolated from her previous calf, will dry off when hand-milking stops. Other pregnant females with a calf still at foot, will not go dry until their one-year-old calf is removed prior to the next calving. Finally, a cow even though not pregnant at the onset of winter but still suckling a calf, will continue to lactate through the following warm season and, normally, will be hand-milked again. The half-lactating yak female will stop being milked at the end of her second warm season and will then go dry, irrespective of whether she is pregnant or not.

Supplementary feeding. Some trials have been conducted with supplementary feeding of conserved grass – silage or hay – during winter months. In one such trial (Zhou Shourong, 1984) 4 kg of silage was given per head per day. This resulted in a rise of milk output from 150 g.. to 350 g. after 7 days of feeding, and to 500 g. of milk after 15 days of feeding. However, the difficulties and costs involved in conserving grass (other material is not available), make such supplementary feeding uneconomic over the winter and spring as a means of promoting milk production at that time of year. Moreover, the yak cows are not in good condition during the winter and the additional strain of milk production may make matters worse for them. Also, herdsmen are reluctant to hand milk during the bitterly cold weather of winter.

None-the-less there is at least one theoretical reason why supplementary feeding over winter is worth further consideration even if milk is not taken from the cows at that time. This interest centres on the possibility that such feeding may improve the condition of the cows and lead to improved calf production, reproductive rate, and milk yield in the following warm season. The supplementary feeding carried out experimentally at Longri farm in Sichuan should be seen in that context. (The experiment was referred to earlier and involved provision of hay from mid-December to end of April or access to conserved paddocks for 45 days from the beginning of April). Results presented earlier referred to effects on calf survival (Table 5.10) and calf weights (Table 6.2). Results are now presented in Table 6.13 on milk yield, milk fat percentage and associated information on loss in weight of the cows over the preceding winter.

Table 6.13 Milk yield (kg) over 184 days, fat percentage in milk, and weight loss over winter of Maiwa yak cows of three groups: (a) fed hay from mid-December to end of April, (b) allowed access to conserved grass paddocks from 1 April for 45 days, and (c) unsupplemented, control. Least squares means and standard deviations (kg) [source: Weng Yongli *et al.* 1993]

Year	Treatment group	No. cows	Milk yield mean	Milk yield SD	Fat % mean	Fat % SD	No. cows	Weight loss mean	Weight loss SD
1989/90	hay	54	229.0	53.3	6.0	1.3	58	33.5	14.8
	paddock grass	55	220.6	54.7	5.8	1.6	58	34.5	15.5
	control	113	218.3	49.9	5.4	1.6	110	35.5	14.5
1990/91	hay	50	235.4	53.6	5.9	1.3	59	39.9	18.0
	control	137	224.1	47.6	5.4	1.2	150	42.7	17.4

As seen from Table 6.13, supplementary feeding had small but positive effects on milk yield ($P<0.01$) and, unexpectedly because of the increase in milk yield, there was also an increase in the fat percentage of the milk by approximately 0.5% (from below 5.5% to nearly 6.0%) ($P<0.05$). The estimate of milk yield is derived from measured amounts milked three times per month and does not include, as far as is known, milk sucked by the calves.

The cows given supplements lost slightly less weight over winter than the unsupplemented controls ($P<0.05$). However, the weighing at the end of the winter period was delayed until the end of May, by which time the cows may have started to recover some of their condition, especially because, in 1990, pasture growth at this farm had started exceptionally early. Weight loss alone also does not fully reflect possible differences in body composition, fatness in particular.

Milk production in a second year without calving again

Many yak do not conceive again in the year of calving. It is thus a common occurrence in yak for lactation to continue into a second year. The amount of milk given over the months from December to May is very low, declining to perhaps as little as 2–4 litres in the whole of April (in one set of observations – but see below). Yield then rises with the onset of grass growth and follows a monthly pattern similar to that already seen (cf.. Figure 6.3 and Table 6.12), but the amount produced in the second year is approximately half that given in the year of calving (sometimes up to two-thirds, and sometimes less); hence the name "half-lactating" commonly given to females milking into a second season without calving again – in contrast to the "full-lactating yak" in the year of calving. Parity differences are maintained in the second season at the lower level of yield. The fat percentage in the milk during the second "half-lactating" season is correspondingly higher than in the first "full-lactating" season, in line with the negative correlation between milk yield (quantity) and fat percentage in the milk.

Milk composition

Yak milk is dense and sweetish and greatly liked by the local people. Total dry-matter is around 17–18% during the main lactating period. Typically, fat percentage varies around 6.5 (see earlier Tables), protein and lactose each around 5.5%, and ash 0.8%. The proportion of essential to non-essential amino acids is 0.8 : 1 as observed in a full analysis of amino acids in the milk of the Tianzhu White yak (Zhang Rongchang *et al.*, 1986).

Milk composition varies with grass growth and climate as does milk yield. It was noted earlier (Table 6.12) that fat percentage increases as the quantity of milk given monthly declines with the advancing season. During the cold season when milk yield of yak females may be only of the order of 100 g. per day, the fat percentage of that milk can be as high as 14%.

However, the correlation between total 184-day milk yield and the average fat percentage was shown to be very small (–0.04) and non-significant in a study on 184 Maiwa yak by Wen Yongli and Chen Zhihua (1994) (at Longri farm referred to a number of times here). This is not a genetic correlation, but suggests nonetheless, if this lack of relationship is confirmed, that milk yield and fat percentage might be more readily improved simultaneously in the yak than is generally the case in dairy cattle.

Total dry-matter content of milk (and also the amino acid content) is at its highest in mid-lactation. This is shown in some results on Tianzhu White yak obtained by Zhang Rongchang *et al.* (1986) and presented in Table 6.14.

The yak udder

Yak udders are small and, by the standards of dairy cattle, not well developed. Measurements in Sichuan showed an udder circumference in pluriparous females of 55cm. and an udder depth of between 2 and 3 cm. Sixty females measured in Qinghai (Zhang Yinsong, 1985) had an udder circumference of 51.6 cm (SD 12.5), the mammary vein 0.94 cm (SD 0.38) in diameter, and the teats 2.2–2.3 cm in length and 1.1–1.2 cm in diameter. Usually (though not in all studies on the yak) the 2 rear quarters hold more milk than the 2 fore quarters; the fore quarters are generally reckoned to hold about 45% of the milk, but other ratios have been

Table 6.14 Composition of milk (%) of 10 Tianzhu White yak in Gansu province in 3 periods of lactation [source: Zhang Rongchang *et al.*, 1986]

	Early lactation (12 June)	Mid lactation (25 July)	Later lactation (20 Sept.)
Dry matter	16.06	17.77	16.31
Solids-not -fat	10.95	12.33	10.54
Fat	5.11	5.44	5.77
Protein	5.24	5.68	4.71
Lactose	4.88	5.86	5.02
Ash	0.79	0.75	0.77
Kcal/kg	839	870	902

reported (e.g. 47.6% [Zhang Rongchang *et al.*, 1983] and around 40% [Han Zhengkang and Lu Tianshui, 1980a]).

The sphincter muscle of the yak's teat is strong and hard squeezing is needed to extract milk. The teats are normally squeezed between the fingers. Especially among Alpine type yak, some one-third of the females are found to have particularly "tense" teats.

In Jiulong county of Sichuan an average yield of 1.4 kg needed almost 5 minutes of milking time at 80 squeezes per minute to extract the milk – a rate of 0.28 kg per minute (Zhang Rongchang *et al.* (1983) reported a rate of 0.42 kg/min). When a trial with machine milking was conducted, a negative pressure of 400 mm. Hg. was required to extract the yak milk.

Milk let-down. Normally, milk let-down does not immediately follow on squeezing the teats between the fingers but requires the presence of the calf to jolt the udder and to suckle briefly. If the calf has died, herdsmen will place the skin of the dead calf in front of the dam and allow her to smell and lick it, before milk let-down is achieved. However, experimentally, the use of a hot towel to massage the udder has been found to stimulate let-down and even to increase yield (Cai Li *et al.*, 1960). The time required to stimulate the udder into let-down is initially around 1 minute (SD 15 seconds) but a second somewhat shorter period of such stimulation is usually needed in the course of the milking process before all the milk can be extracted (Han Zhengkang and Lu Tianshu, 1980a).

The study of Han Zhengkang and Lu Tianshui (1980a) also indicated that the amount of milk in the udder cistern of the yak accounts for only about 6.5% of the milk produced at a milking and that the milk produced as a reflex to milking accounts for around 80% – of which four-fifths is let down as a result of the first stimulation of the udder and the remaining fifth after the second stimulation. Residual milk in the udder (that traditionally obtained by "stripping" in the hand-milking of dairy cattle) accounts for about 13% and is normally left by the herdsmen for the calf. The proportion of milk stored in the udder cistern was found, by these authors, to increase with the parity of the female to around 10% by parity 4.

Meat production

Meat from yak is derived from surplus males, often as castrated steers, and also from females, usually at the end of their useful reproductive life, or their time as milk-producers. In "efficiency" terms (meat output/feed input) the process of meat production in the yak cannot be regarded as "efficient", since, for the most part, the animals are not slaughtered until quite late in life after several cycles of weight gain and weight loss. Meat from the yak, however, represents an important source of sustenance for the herders and their families, and also an additional source of income from sales. Also, there are circumstances when meat production from yak should be regarded as an efficient use of resources, at high altitudes, which would otherwise not be utilised. In this sense, Smirnov *et al.* (1990) point out that, in a part of the Caucasus, to which yak were introduced only fairly recently, and with summer pastures at elevations of 3500–4000 m, the cost of a unit increase in liveweight was ten times greater for beef cattle than for yak. In fact, it is claimed that the annual expenditure on keeping a yak was marginally less than that on keeping a sheep.

Meat quantity

The major factor contributing to meat output is the body weight of the animal at the time of slaughter. Thus, the factors associated with variation in growth, discussed earlier in this chapter, all influence the amount of meat produced. Grass growth as affected by season and location is the major contributor, along with age and sex of the animal. Seasonal changes in body weight, shown earlier in this chapter, clearly affect meat output. In practice, however, animals intended for meat are slaughtered, whenever possible, only in the autumn when they are in good, fat condition. Just as July-August are termed by herdsmen concerned with milk as the "golden age" (see earlier), so in relation to meat production October is, for the local people, the month of "best fatness" (in Tibet this is considered to be in September [Ma Zongxiang and Du Yaozong, 1982]).

Breed and location

There is much variation in meat properties of different breeds of yak at different locations. Meat output in terms of dressing percentage, ratios of lean to bone, and loin-eye area are thought to be better from Alpine than from Plateau type yak – though this impression may be derived largely from the superiority of the Jiulong breed in Sichuan Province. Table 6.15 gives some of the results.

Liveweights at slaughter varied with breed and location from 116 kg to 576 kg. Dressing percentages of the groups ranged from 40 to 62%. In at least one case (Smirnov *et al.* 1990) the low dressing percentage was attributed to the slaughter of male calves at the wrong age – 2 years old. Trials are in progress in the Caucasus to determine the optimum slaughter age. The question of stage of maturity at time of slaughter is clearly of importance (some of this information may be available in the source references shown in Table 6.15), but the main criterion for timing slaughter is usually to leave it to the end of the grass-growing season when the condition of the animals is at its best.

Table 6.15 Meat production and carcass attributes of yak from different populations (animals at the age of 6.5 years or older – unless otherwise indicated)

Location	Breed	Altitude	Sex	No.	Live weight (kg)	Carcass weight (kg.)	Viscera fat % of LW	Dressing percent* (sq cm)	Ratio Lean:bone % of LW	Loin eye area % of LW	Heart weight % of LW	Lung weight	Hide+hair weight	Source
Sichuan	Jiulong	3 500+	male	2	576	324	1.22	57.6	4.8	87.3	0.58	1.09	6.56	[1]
			female	2	282	151	2.55	56.2	6.0	58.3	0.71	1.28	6.57	[1]
			steer	12	496	253	1.75	55.7	4.2	86.7	0.61	1.37	6.53	[1]
	Kangdin Liuba	3 500+	steer	25	409	222	2.44	56.6	4.0	86.0	0.46	1.47	7.23	[pers com]
	Maiwa	3 500	steer	2	372	208	2.81	58.6	3.0				7.21	[2]
			steer**	4	116	59	1.28	52.1	3.9	31.7	0.59	1.68	6.59	[Cai Li]
Gansu	Tianzhu	3 000	male	2	288	146	1.32	52.0	2.7		0.63	1.42	8.28	[3]
	White		steer	3	262	133	1.72	52.7	3.6	50.3	0.55	1.29	7.68	[3]
	Gannan	3 000	steer	8	223	112	1.81	51.6	4.1		0.79	1.23	5.92	[4]
Qinghai	Plateau	3 700	steer	12	368	194	1.56	53.2	4.1	60.6	0.47	1.23	5.88	[5]
	Huanhu	3 000	steer	5	226	110	1.62	50.3	3.9	66.3	0.57	1.25	6.31	[5]
	Gangcha	3 500	female	11	362	154	1.36	43.9			0.51	1.39	6.26	[4]
			steer	17	465	216	0.96	47.5			0.60	1.19	6.44	[4]
Caucasus	(from Tuva)	3500	female	3	287	130	3.21	48.6	5.0					[6]
			male"	3	205	81	0.81	40.3	3.9					[6]
Tibet	Laqu	4 570	steer	3	287	170	2.16	61.6			0.61	1.68	6.40	[7]
	Dangxiong	4 400	male	4	264	133	1.09	51.1			0.43	1.34	5.57	[4]
			female	2	153	66	1.35	44.2			0.49	1.17	5.68	[4]
Xinjiang	Bazhou	2 500	steer**	2	156	72	0.32	46.6	3.7	35.4	0.50	1.15	6.75	[8]
			steer***	4	221	123	1.65	57.2	4.2		0.60	1.45	5.39	[8]

*viscera fat included in dressing percentage; **steers of 16–17 months old; " males 2 years old; ***steers 2.5 and 3.5 years old.

Sources: (1) Cai Li *et al.*, 1980b; (2) Chen Xiafei *et al.*, 1981; (3) Pu Futang *et al.*, 1987; (4) Research Co-op, 1980–87; (5) Lei Huanzhang, 1983; (6) Smirnov *et al.*, 1990; (7) Jia Huaigong, 1966; (8) Wei Ronglu *et al.*, 1981.

The quantity of viscera fat weight differed substantially among the groups, but much less so in relation to liveweight. There were marked differences between the groups in ratios of lean to bone and in loin eye area. The data in Table 6.15 provide a useful initial insight into the available range of variation in carcass attributes of the yak The numbers in individual groups are, however, small, and may not be fully representative of their classes, nor do they allow firm conclusions to be dawn about the causes of the differences. Some other studies, referred to below, provide more information on specific effects.

Effect of age

In a trial in Sichuan province, entire male yak from the age of 1.5 to 4.5 years and, thereafter, yak steers to the age of 20.5 years were chosen at random from yak herds in the same area, and kept under all-year-round grazing without supplementary feeding. All the animals were slaughtered at the Animal Husbandry and Veterinary Station in Kangdin county of Sichuan at the end of autumn, when in their fattest condition. The results, in Table 6.16, show clearly that dressing percentage increased with age (and liveweight) up to 6.5 years and declined somewhat thereafter – however the castration of males and the use of steers after the age of 4.5 years could be an important factor in the increase in dressing percentage between the age of 4.5 and 5.5 years. Variation among the steers above the age of 16.5 years showed no clear trends (the data for these ages have been pooled).

Table 6.16 Dressing percentage (carcass weight/liveweight [as %]) of yak males and steers according to age at slaughter

Age (years)	Sex*	No.	Liveweight (kg.)	Dressing percentage
1.5	m	2	55	37.0
2.5	m	2	105	44.0
3.5	m	2	182	47.6
4.5	m	2	234	49.6
5.5	s	2	370	55.8
6.5	s	3	401	56.2
7.5	s	4	407	53.9
10.5	s	1	409	51.7
11.5	s	2	417	55.0
14.5	s	3	406	52.3
16.5–20.5**	s	10	413	53.4

* m = entire male s = castrated male (steer); ** weighted average for the older steers

Composition of meat

Yak meat is fine textured and scarlet in colour. It is regarded as very palatable, but muscular marbling is poor. It is rich in myoglobins and has a flavour akin to game. Among local people yak meat has been prized above that of ordinary cattle since ancient times. Table 6.17 provides some evidence on composition of the meat for different locations, breeds and ages of yak steers (the rib sample from the Tianzhu White steers was unusually fat).

Table 6.17 Composition of yak steer meat (%)

Location	Breed	No.	Age (years)	Meat from:	Dry matter	Protein	Fat	Ash	Ca	P	Source
Sichuan	Maiwa	7	1.5	rib 9–11*	25.8	21.5	3.3	1.04			Cai Li *et al.*, 1984b
Xinjiang	Bazhou	2	2.5	rib 9–11*	24.7	21.2	2.0	1.07			Wei Ronglu *et al.*, 1981
Gansu	Tianzhu White	3	4.5	rib 9–10*	33.8	20.0	11.9	0.87	0.019	0.138	Pu Futang *et al.*, 1986
				loin eye	23.7	21.3	1.4	1.05	0.018	0.202	Pu Futang *et al.*, 1986
Qinghai	Qinghai	?	4.5	back, rib	25.9	22.1	2.1	1.61	0.029	0.200	Lei Huanzhang *et al.*, 1983
			over 6	back, rib	26.8	22.3	2.8	1.68	0.019	0.237	Lei Huanzhang *et al.*, 1983

* meat sampled between the ribs

Table 6.18 The total yield of fibre (coarse hair and down) (kg.) in adult yak of different breeds at different locations according to sex of animal (conditions of harvesting not uniform)

Location	Breed	Male			Female			Steer			Source
		no.	mean	SD	no.	mean	SD	no.	mean	SD	
Sichuan	Jiulong (fibre line)	19	13.9	2.4	16	1.8	0.7	10	4.3	0.9	Cai Li *et al.* (eds), 1987*
Yunnan	Zhongdian	21	3.6	0.3	139	1.3	0.3				Duan Zhongzuan *et al.* **
Tibet	Alpine	7	1.8		50	0.5		4	1.7		Qi Zhenkun *et al.* **
Qinghai	Plateau				5	1.2	0.5	8	1.9	0.4	Lei Huanzhang *et al.* **
Qinghei	Menyuan	4	3.6	0.7	11	1.6	0.6	15	2.6	0.6	Chang Yingsong *et al.* **
Gansu	Tianzhu White	9	4.0		24	2.9		7	2.1		Zhang Rongchang *et al.* **
Xingjiang	Barzhou	2423	1.7	6765	1.3						Yu Beiyuan *et al.* **

* Cai Li 1979 results, in larger report
** in: Research Co-operative Group (report), 1980–87

The amino acid content of meat from different muscles of the yak has been analysed in a number of studies (Pu Futang *et al.*, 1986; Zhao Yibin *et al.*, 1986, Wei Ronglu *et al.*, 1981). The ratio of essential to non-essential amino acids was found to be around 0.7 to 1.

Fibre production and hides

Yak produce two types of fibre, coarse outer hair and a fine down fibre which grows prior to the onset of winter as additional protection for the yak against cold. The down fibre would be shed in early summer if not harvested. Since the 1970's the down has been used extensively by the textile industry as an alternative fine animal fibre. Fabric made from yak down has better lustre than wool and handles well. It provides a high degree of heat insulation. The income the herder receives from yak fibre is, at present, small relative to the income that can be obtained from yak milk and meat. However, the economic value of the down is none-the-less leading to consideration of developing strains of yak with improved fibre production.

The amount of fibre produced by individuals and the proportions of coarse hair and down varies with the region where the yak are kept and the associated climate, with breed, sex, age, and the season and method of harvesting the fibre.

Breed, sex, age and location

In general, yak of the Henduan Alpine type have a higher yield of fibre than those of the Plateau type. The highest amounts are obtained from a "fibre line" of Jiulong yak, especially selected for greater fibre production. Exceptional individuals of that breed can produce as much as 25 kg fibre, of which 50% is down fibre. This is tenfold the yield of most ordinary yak (Cai Li *et al.*, 1980a). Table 6.18 provides some results from different breeds at different locations for adult male, female and steer yak.

The results in Table 6.18 suggest considerable differences in the amount of fibre harvested at the different locations. The hair was, at all these locations, harvested by first raking the fleece to extract down fibres and then shorn to harvest remaining down and the other hair. The conditions of the animals was not, however, uniform and is likely, therefore, to contribute to some of the variation. The outstandingly high fibre yield of the Jiulong males is consistent with the yield expected from this line of Jiulong yak specially developed for fibre production. The yield from the same type of females, however, is lower not only on account of smaller body size and other sex-related differences in hair growth, but also because, in common with all females coming into lactation, they start to lose quantities of fibre with the onset of lactation. Similarly, steers tend to lose fibre when used for work. The differences in yield between the sexes therefore reflect more what happens in practice than something solely attributable to biological causes.

A study by Chang Yingson *et al.* (*in*: Research Co-op, 1980-87) (Table 6.19) showed that the total yield of fibre harvested increased as the animal became older and bigger and showed, in particular, that the proportion of down in the fleece declined from nearly 70% in one-year-old male yak to less than 20% in those of 6 years old. For females the reduction in the proportion of down was less.

TABLE 6.19 Total yield of fibre (kg.) and proportion of down at different ages in Menyuan yak in Qinghai province [source: Chang Yingson *et al.*, in : Research Co-op, 1980–87]

	Male				Female			
Age		Total yield		Down		Total yield		Down
(years)	No.	mean	SD	(percent)	No.	mean	SD	(percent)
1	2	0.80		68.8	7	1.10	0.25	60.0
2	20	1.84	0.64	48.9	27	1.47	0.38	54.4
3	13	1.97	0.61	40.6	24	1.50	0.52	46.7
4	15	1.99	0.68	43.2	11	1.39	0.58	43.2
5	3	2.65	0.38	21.9	11	1.60	0.58	53.1
6	4	3.60	0.70	18.6	8	[0.83 *]	[0.32 *]	{ *]

* only the down fibre was harvested in the milking females

Method of harvesting

Combing out of the down hair prior to shearing can increase by about 10% the yield of down in the total fleece compared with shearing alone. In one study (Wang Jia *et al.*, 1984), the percentage of down increased from about 50% to 61% between these two methods.

Fibre and staple

Fibre types have been examined in a number of studies (Wang Jia and Ouyang Xi, 1984; Wang Jia, 1984b; Zhang Rongchang, 1975, 1977; Lu Zhonglin *et al.*, 1982; Wu Guoying *et al.*, 1983; Xu Jiying and Yu Zhengfeng, 1981; as well as studies by Cai Li). The results can be summarised as follows:

Staple shape. This varies with the part of the yak body on which the fibre grows and differs between the coarser hair and the down.

- *Flat-topped type*. This is characteristic of down fibre of the best quality and is found especially in yak calves
- *Micro-braid type*. The fibres are even in thickness and relatively fine but less so, and longer, than the flat-topped type. This is found mostly in one-year-old yak
- *Sub-braid type*. The lower part of the staple is composed of down fibres and the upper part of mid-type and coarse hairs. This is seen often in the frontal parts of the body of one-year-old yak
- *Braid type*. The staple is composed largely of coarse hair and is typical of the hair on the yak's belly.

Fibre types. The fibres of the yak can be divided into 3 main types: down, mid-type, and coarse. (In practical production, there is often a dividing line drawn only between "down" hair – fibres of less than 35 μ diameter – and "coarse" hair with a greater diameter.)

- *Down fibre*. Short, unmedullated fibres of less than 25 μ in diameter, with irregular crimps and a soft lustre

- *Mid-type hair*. Diameter between 25 and 52.5 μ. These hairs have a few large crimps. Some of the fibres have a latticed medulla. The hairs are longer than the down fibres and have a good lustre
- *Coarse hair*. Diameter exceeds 52.5 μ. The hairs have no crimps and are long. A proportion of them (18% [Lu Zhonglin *et al*. 1982]) are medullated. They have strong lustre and poor textile quality.

Fibre density. The density of fibres per unit area varies greatly with the position on the body of the yak. Some results are shown in Table 6.20. The density of down fibre per unit area is far higher than that of the coarse hair. Particular note should also be taken of the high degree of variability in density among the 30 yak sampled. The coefficients of variation range from 23% to 64%.

Table 6.20 Fibre density (fibres per square cm of skin) of coarse hair and down hair on two different parts of the body of 30 adult yak [source: Li Shihong *et al.*, 1984]

Position	Hair type	Density mean	[SD]
Shoulder/Back	Coarse	182	117
	Down	1468	473
Belly	Coarse	201	94
	Down	757	403

Length of fibre. There are considerable differences in the length of stretched fibres, depending on the type of fibre and the part of the body. Thus, coarse hairs from the tail can reach 50–60 cm, from the fore-legs, belly and thigh 15–30 cm, from the shoulder and rump 10–20cm,and from the back 8–11 cm. Stretched down fibres are typically 4–7 cm long on shoulder, back and rump, and 3–5 cm long on fore-leg, belly and thigh. The corresponding lengths are greater in the male than in the female.

Fibre diameter. Diameter varies greatly with type of fibre, part of the body, sex, breed, etc. Average values (μ) from Tianzhu White and Gannan yak in Gansu, and Maiwa yak in Sichuan are as shown in Table 6.21.

Table 6.21 Fibre diameter in 3 breeds of yak

	Tianzhu White (μ)	Gannan (μ)	Maiwa (μ)
Coarse hair	68.6	83.5	86.9
Mid-hair	43.4	43.1	40.6
Down	27.8	25.2	22.7

The down tends to be more uniform in diameter along its length than coarse hair fibres. In one study (Wang Jie *et al.*, 1984) the diameter was measured at the upper (outer end), middle and lower part of the fibre. Approximately 100 coarse hair fibres and a similar number of down fibres were examined from each of 4 yak. Results are shown in Table 6.22.

Table 6.22 Fibre diameter at different parts of the fibre

	Part of Fibre	Mean (μ)	[SD] (μ)
Coarse hair	upper	83	15.8
	middle	75	16.6
	lower	77	4.8
Down	upper	21	3.3
	middle	20	3.7
	lower	20	3.1

Fibre strength. One of the useful properties of yak hair – both the coarse hair and the down – is its strength. Results from a study by Xue Jiying and Yu Zhenfeng (1981) were as follows: Down fibre (diameter 16.8 μ) strength (breaking load) dry 9.8 g, moist 6.9 g; corresponding values for coarse hair (49.8 μ) were 32.8 g and 25.1 g, respectively. Wang Jie *et al.* (1984) reported a breaking load of 12.9 g for down hair with a diameter of 22.7 μ. These breaking loads are remarkably high relative to those quoted for typical sheep wool (Ryder and Stephenson, 1968), if the methods used for determining the load are the same. Results from yak (Wang Jie *et al.*, 1984) also suggest that the stretched length percentage of wet fibres (the limiting extension on the load extension curve – *see* Ryder and Stephenson, 1968) is of the order of 60% for both down and coarse hair fibres. This appears to be in the same range as for sheep wool.

Other attributes of yak hair

Moisture retention. This is lower in the down hair of yak (1.9–2.7%) than for the wool of sheep (Xue Jiying and Yu Zhengfeng, 1981).

Grease content. The lanolin content of yak hair is low. For Gannan yak this has been estimated as 2.7% and 1.7% of the shorn fleece for male and female yak respectively (Lu Zhonglin *et al.*, 1982). Another study (Wang Jie *et al.*, 1984) suggests that the grease content varies with the part of the body of the yak – 3.8% on the back, 2.2% on the rump, 1.5% on the belly, and only 0.3% for hair from the tail. The melting point of the lanolin ranges from 37 to 43° C (Xue Jiying and Yu Zhengfeng, 1981).

Specific gravity of yak down hair is around 1.32 g/cm³ – similar to that of sheep wool (Xue Jiying and Yu Zhengfeng, 1981).

Static electricity. Under similar conditions the down fibres of the yak suffer less from static electricity disturbance than cashmere fibres from goats, thus giving yak fibres an advantage in processing (Xue Jiying and Yu Zhengfeng, 1981).

Amino acid content. The strength and resilience of yak down fibre has been attributed to its content of high sulphur proteins. The total amino acid content of down fibre from female yak has been measured as 79.8% of dry weight, with cystine, proline, and serine accounting for 19.4% – higher than the 15.9% of local sheep wool with which it was compared.

Other structural properties. The structural property of yak hair differs from that of sheep wool not only in respect of the greater strength and stretching capacity already referred to. In the yak, the angle between scale and hair shaft, on the external surface of the fibre, is small, so that the scale virtually sticks to the shaft – making the hair fibre relatively smooth. This gives yak hair poor felting qualities.

Shedding of fibres. Down fibres and mid-type hair begin to shed as the weather becomes warmer in the spring and early summer. Observations by Ouyang Xi *et al.* (1985) showed that shedding towards the end of May, in their locality, was greatest from the belly of the yak (nearly 20%) and less from the back and rump (just over 12%). Lactating females also start to shed fibres with the onset of lactation.

In July, when air temperature is at its highest, down fibre will twine around coarse hair or will fall on pasture and shrubs if not combed out or sheared. Shedding of the coarse hair has not been observed. As the length of coarse hair increases, the growth rate of the hair declines until it virtually stops.

Hides

For unspecified types of yak, average weights of hides per 100 kg. body weight were 6.1 ± 0.5 kg for female yak, 6.6 ± 0.6 kg for steers and 6.8 ± 1.3 kg for entire males. There are no direct results available on the skin thickness of different breeds of yak in different parts of the country, but there are suggestions that the fresh hide weight per 100 kg. body weight varies somewhat among breeds.

Draught performance

The yak is widely used for draught purposes at the high altitudes where it makes its home – and not only as the pack animal for much publicised Himalayan mountaineering expeditions, known world-wide. The yak has strong limbs, small, solid hooves with hard edges and a narrow hoof fork. These attributes help the yak to walk in dangerous places and marsh land and to climb over steep mountains. It can open up a path with its head and its hooves for people to follow and it can swim across rapids. In difficult terrain a yak is said to be safer to ride than a horse, as the yak will not readily panic, for example in swampy ground. Since ancient times the yak has been known in the mountainous regions of China and surroundings as the "boat of the plateau".

Most of the yak used for draught are steers. Male Pien Niu (yak x cattle crosses) are also chosen (they are sterile and cannot be used for breeding). The draught animals are used mainly for riding and as pack animals. Yak races are one of the games at folk festivals much loved by Tibetan people. In semi-agricultural areas they are also used for ploughing and other cultivation. Joshi (1982) also refers to the use of yak and crosses for threshing grain, in parts of Tibet, by driving muzzled animals backward and forward over sheaves spread out on a hard floor.

Yak have great endurance; they will, for example, walk carrying loads over long distances for two or three days without water or feed. In other circumstances the yak may be required to carry loads during the day, with the opportunity to graze only at night, for as long as a month at a stretch.

Direct observations (Liu Qigui, *in*: Research Co-op, 1980-87) have shown the yak to walk 20–30 km per day carrying loads weighing 60–80 kg. In Sichuan, observations on Maiwa yak recorded 75 kg loads (18 % of the body weight of the animal) carried over 30 km in 6.2 hours (4.84 km/hr). Respiration rate, pulse rate and body temperature were found to have returned to the pre-work level within 50 minutes of stopping work. Maiwa yak steers in medium condition weighing 480kg have been recorded as carrying as much as 390kg for short periods. Two Maiwa yak are expected to plough, in a day, one-third of a hectare of land suitable for cultivation.

Records from the grasslands of Qinghai province at an altitude of 4 100 m show pack weights up to a maximum of 300 kg (on top of a saddle weight of 11.5 kg), which is equal to 82% of the body weight of the animal (Lei Huanzhang *et al.*, 1985). Three Plateau-type yak were ridden on fairly even grassland at an elevation of 4 400 m for 500 metres in 2.13 minutes. Their respiration, pulse and body temperature recovered in just over 25 minutes.

Figure 6.4 Two yak ploughing

Figure 6.5 Pack yak (both yak and crosses are used as pack animals) [photo courtesy of D.D. Joshi]

7 PERFORMANCE OF CROSSES OF YAK WITH *BOS TAURUS* AND *BOS INDICUS* CATTLE

OVERVIEW

Crossing of yak with *Bos taurus* cattle, and in some countries also with *Bos indicus*, occurs both by using ordinary local cattle and using semen from "improved" breeds like the Holstein Friesian (and many other breeds) in artificial insemination (to produce "local" or "improved" crossbreds, respectively).

Female crossbreds, especially those with "improved" breeds of sire, reach sexual maturity sooner and are first mated a year earlier than the average yak. F1 females can return to heat several times in the same season, if not pregnant, and will generally calve every year. Calf survival is similar to that in yak. Consequently, overall reproductive rate of the crosses, especially the "improved" ones, is higher than in yak.

Male crossbreds are sterile. They function sexually but their semen does not contain sperm. The reasons for this are still under investigation, although there are a number of known possible causes. Sperm production does not resume until the third backcross at the earliest (15/16 yak or cattle), and often not until the fourth backcross is reached. In practice, there are few backcrosses after the first, since they have no role in the livestock economy.

The first cross (F1) generally grows faster and becomes larger than the yak – and also larger than some of the local cattle. Backcrosses to yak, or to breeds of local ordinary cattle, are smaller than the F1. "Improved" crossbreds are larger than the "local" crossbreds.

Larger size of crossbred animals also leads to greater meat production from the crosses, although dressing percentages and other attributes of the carcass are usually fairly similar to the yak. The crossbred animals, from mating yak females with "improved" breeds of cattle, however, are capable of slaughter at much younger ages than the traditional yak steer, or the "local" crossbred steer.

Milk yield is higher in crosses than in the pure yak and often higher than in the local types of cattle (for example the small hill cattle in some of the countries). Milk yield of the crossbreds is especially raised if their sires are from "improved" breeds. Backcrosses give less milk than the F1. Fat percentage of the milk of crossbred females is usually lower than that of yak milk.

Strict interpretation of this and similar results in terms of heterosis is, however, difficult, since the different types of crossbred, the pure yak and cattle breeds are not usually, if ever, kept and managed together under identical conditions. This applies with even greater force when "improved" breeds of cattle are involved. Holstein Friesian cattle, for example, are not kept at high altitudes alongside the yak, or managed in the same way. Nor are the reciprocal crosses made by mating females of, say, the Holstein Friesian breed to yak bulls. The presence of both the reciprocal crosses is necessary for any strict interpretation of the role of heterosis. None-the-less, the circumstantial evidence for heterosis from crossbreeding of yak and other species of cattle, both local and "improved breeds, is considerable. The strongest part of that evidence is the poorer performance of the first backcross (to yak or to other cattle bulls) relative to the F1, which is as expected if heterosis plays a part in enhancing the productivity of the crossbreds.

Introduction

As indicated in chapter 3, the crossing of yak with cattle of other species has been practised since earliest times. Originally such crossing occurred with cattle of the local breeds, generally referred to as "yellow cattle" (*Bos taurus*) in China and with cattle of both *Bos taurus* and *Bos indicus* cattle (zebu) species elsewhere; this practice is still extant. However, in recent decades, encouragement has been given by scientists and in the field, to the use of "improved" breeds of cattle for such crossbreeding which has been facilitated by the introduction of artificial insemination and the use of frozen semen. However, as referred to earlier (chapter 3), the use of AI is, inevitably, restricted to more accessible areas. Moreover, the expense, to herdsmen, of having bulls of the "improved" breeds of cattle (as well as their poor survival) means that, except in a few localities, most crossbreeding of yak continues to be done with the locally available cattle.

Interpreting the results of crossbreeding (the question of heterosis from yak x cattle crosses)

The purpose of any crossbreeding is to combine some of the good qualities of the breeds or species being crossed (from additive genetic effects) and to anticipate the possibility that the performance of the crosses will exceed the average of the two parental types (from non-additive genetic effects, described in performance terms as heterosis – or hybrid vigour). In the case of crosses of yak with *Bos taurus* or *Bos indicus* cattle there is a difficulty in apportioning credit between additive effects and heterosis. This arises because the purebred animals of *both* species, as well as the reciprocal crosses between them (i.e. progeny of yak female x cattle male *and* of cattle female x yak male) are rarely, if ever, all kept together under *identical* conditions of environment and management – as is required for a correct assessment of the magnitude of heterosis.

In general, the crosses occupy a different niche from that of the pure yak in the economy of the pastoral mountainous regions. As shown in chapter 3, the crossbreds are also more prevalent in environmentally more favoured areas and at the somewhat lower elevations in the range of yak territory. Local types of cattle, in turn, are most prevalent in still less demanding and agriculturally mixed areas of these regions. As for females of the "improved" breeds of cattle (e.g. Holstein Friesians), they do not survive and are not kept in typical yak country, nor are such females mated to yak bulls to provide the reciprocal cross. Moreover, as noted in chapter 5, crossbreeding is often done early in the breeding season so that, on average, crossbred animals are born earlier in the year than are the pure yak. Date of birth affects the subsequent performance of the animals because they have a better start before the following winter. Such an advantage can be seen over the first 2 years of life, but possibly longer.

None-the-less, the comparisons of the performance of crosses with that of yak, and, where possible, cattle, are highly suggestive of a part played by heterosis. This arises because the performance is not only better than that of the yak when kept alongside them (although without absolute certainty that they are treated alike) but also, in some cases, better than that of the local cattle (again with reservations about the similarity of treatment of the cross and the local cattle).

In relation to crosses with "improved" breeds of cattle, the argument for the occurrence of heterosis is stronger, if rather academic. It arises from the assumption that females of the improved breeds would not survive for long under the conditions tolerated by the yak at high altitudes (any more than did the bulls of these types – see chapter 3). Further it must be assumed that females of such breeds of cattle (e.g. Holstein Friesian or Simmental) would not lactate satisfactorily without a lot of additional feeding, even if they were to survive for a time. Therefore, the presumption is that purebred females of the improved breeds would yield effectively nothing if kept like typical yak. On these assumptions, the performance of their crosses with yak is clearly above the average of the parental types (in fact, providing a good example of what geneticists call "over-dominance"). This, result, however, has its roots in genotype-environment interaction.

Further, less controversial, evidence for heterosis arises from the poorer performance of backcrosses relative to the F1 – though again it is rare to find results on adequately large numbers of animals involving both the reciprocal F1 crosses and both types of backcross (both types of F1 mated back to both yak bulls and to bulls of the other cattle species). However, the reported results from backcrosses are as expected if heterosis is a feature of this inter-species crossbreeding.

Some results from inter-species crossing will now be presented. Although they show, without exception, that the crosses between the species out-perform the yak, any interpretation of the results in terms of heterosis should bear in mind the considerations discussed. Figures 7.1 – 7.3 illustrate different crosses (see also Figs. 3.1 and 3.2).

Figure 7.1 "Ordinary" and "Improved" Pien Nius (Both F1 animals have yak dams. That on the left has a yellow cattle sire; the one on the right has a Holstein sire. The animals are castrates, saddled as pack animals)

(a) (b)

Figure 7.2 "Improved" Pien Niu. (a) steer (b) female (F1 from yak dam and unspecified breed of exotic cattle sire)

Figure 7.3 "Black" Pien Niu (F1 from yak dam and Holstein sire)

Reproduction and fertility

The female crossbreds – first-cross and backcross generations – have normal fertility. The males, by contrast, are sterile until there have been several generations of backcrossing to either the yak or to "ordinary" cattle.

Female

Oestrus. Oestrus in the crossbred (Pien Niu) female is seasonal, as in the yak, and is affected by climate and nutrition. Sexual maturity in the F1, however, occurs at least a year earlier than is typical for yak. Thus the F1 females are usually mated at the age of 25–28 months (in the third warm season of their life) and they calve for the first time around the age of three years. Breeding a year earlier does, however, occur under more favourable conditions and was noted, already many years ago, as a potential advantage enjoyed by such crosses in Kazakstan (Denisov, 1938)

Importantly in terms of overall reproductive rate, oestrus can occur several times in a season if the crossbred female has not already been mated, or is not pregnant. This differs from the majority of pure yak cows in China – although repeated display of oestrus in yak is more commonly reported from some other countries, e.g. Mongolia (see chapter 5). Also, signs of oestrus in the F1 cross are more obvious than in the pure yak.

Conception rate. Among 211 F1 females on heat, Cai Li found, by rectal palpation, that 185 had normally developed follicles – a proportion slightly higher than in contemporary yak (see chapter 5). None-the-less, in ordinary mass mating with yak bulls, the conception rate (75%) of Pien Niu cows (F1 from yak dams and yellow cattle sires) was somewhat lower than that of yak at the same location (shown in Table 5.5). However, in a specific trial conducted by Cai Li using yak bulls, 155 female Pien Niu (F1) had a conception rate of 70% at their first oestrus of the breeding season, but a further 25% conceived at a second oestrus. When using frozen semen from Holstein Friesian bulls by AI, the overall reproductive rate of the Pien Niu was found to be substantially better than that of pure yak.

Gestation length. This has been recorded by Cai Li in crosses of yak with ordinary local cattle as 278.0 (SD 9.7) for 110 F1 cows with male calves and 271.3 (SD 11.1) in 98 such cows with female calves. Denisov (1938) reported an average gestation length of 282 days for F1 females mated back to Schwyz cattle bulls and 265 days for those mated back to yak bulls.

Reproductive and survival rate. Survival to the age of 6 months is very similar in F1 and first backcrosses (B1) as it is in pure yak. Thus, relative to the yak, the F1 cross has a better overall reproductive rate over a lifetime. This arises from a combination factors: the greater probability that the F1 cross will re-mate in the same season following failure to conceive at an earlier heat period, its greater capacity to calve every year, and these two things combined with similarity in survival.

The equally good survival of the first backcross (B1) in observations by Cai Li requires comment since it contrasts with the views expressed by herdsmen who regard this backcross as having poor survival. This viewpoint, however, has to be seen in the context that herdsmen generally wish to retain or sell as much as possible of the milk from the F1 dams. Accordingly, the B1 calves are neglected by their owners and often allowed to die. Encouragement for this practice is also provided by the complications of systematic backcrossing programmes and by the reduced performance of backcrosses relative to the F1.

Male

The external sex organs of the crossbred male are normal and so is its sex drive. Mounting and serving of females on heat is normal, but there are no sperm in the seminal fluid. The crossbred is, therefore, a "natural" teaser bull.

First and second backcross generations are also sterile. By the third generation of backcrossing (15/16 yak or cattle blood) some spermatocytes are usually present and the occasional male is found to be fertile. Fertility is not assured until the fourth or fifth generation of backcrossing (for a number of references on this aspect, see Zhong Jingcheng [1994]). In practice, however, entire males of the backcross generations are rarely seen, since there is no good reason to keep them. Therefore, precise proportions of bulls showing normal spermatogenesis in successive generations of backcrossing are not available.

The precise causes of this sterility have been, and are still, the object of much investigation and speculation. What is certain is that no spermatogonia are found in the seminiferous tubules of first crosses and early generations of backcrosses. Possible causes for this have been considered in the structures of the X and Y chromosomes – these structures differ in certain respects in the crosses from those found both in the pure yak and in pure cattle (Guo Aipo and Huang Wenxiu, 1983). In particular, the arm ratios differ, most notably for the Y-chromosome. It has been pointed out in a recent review of the subject (Li Jiyou *et al.*, 1994) that the chromosome arm lengths and the relative lengths of the chromosomes also vary among breeds of cattle. This has led the authors to suggest that fertility of the male yak hybrids might be restored by selecting a *Bos taurus* cattle breed with similar Y-chromosome arm length as that of the yak. This is clearly open to investigation.

A rather more tentative hypothesis is advanced by Zhong Jingcheng (1994) suggesting that male sterility may be due to an unbalance at many chromosome loci, including autosomal.

It has also been found that the proportions of different types of cells in the anterior pituitary gland differ in the crosses from those in yak or ordinary cattle. A consequence is a reduced production of FSH – an essential hormone for the satisfactory function of the tubular epithelium of the testes. Simple, frequent injection of FSH and LH into the blood stream of well-fed crossbred calves (investigated by Cai Li with 10 calves between the ages of 2–6 months) did not, however, result in the production of sperm – just a high libido in the calves at the age of 12 months.

Production characteristics

Body size

Birth weights of crosses of yak with yellow cattle can be as much as 50% heavier than pure yak calves (as shown in Table 6.1). Reports from other countries (outside China) also suggest substantial increases in birth weight in crosses of yak females with males of local breeds – for example an increase of around 15% for Buryatia (Katzina *et al.* 1994) and 30–40% for Mongolia (Zagdsuren, 1994a). The actual results will depend greatly on the types of yak and the breeds of *Bos taurus* or *Bos indicus* used and, of course on the local husbandry conditions. However, the universally accepted, substantial increase in birth weight is responsible in large measure for the increase in calving difficulties in yak cows with crossbred calves compared to those with pure yak calves – as referred to in chapter 5. These difficulties are further accentuated by the even bigger size of calves which have sires of the "improved" breeds of cattle (Table 7.1). Future results might show whether sire breeds differ in the incidence of dystokia caused in the cows to which they are mated – as the experience of crossbreeding among cattle breeds elsewhere would suggest.

Table 7.1 Birth weights of calves of yak and different crosses of yak at various locations differing in elevation and environment and body weight of local yak dams (average of male and female calves).

Sire of calf	Xinjiang [1]		Longri Sichuan [2]		Gannan Gansu [3]		Shiqu Sichuan [4]		Ganzi Sichuan [5]	
	n	kg	n	kg	n	kg	n	kg	n	kg
Local yak	25	14.8	25	12.4	91	14.0	71	11.5	40	9.4
Local cattle									19	12.2
Holstein Friesian			32	23.4	40	22.0	59	19.1		
Simmental	10	26.9	9	19.5						
Charolais	18	27.2	6	24.7			20	19.1		
Hereford	16	24.1	7	20.3	17	22.5	18	16.4		
Aberdeen Angus					22	23.1	17	17.9		
Shorthorn			9	18.2						
Body weight of yak dam (kg)	257		222		210		200		179	

Sources of data: (1) Agric. Exploit. Acad. 1984; (2) Cai Li *et al.* 1984b; (3) Zhao Bingyao *et al.* 1984; (4) Zhang Jiachuan 1984a; (5) Hu Angang *et al.* 1960.

Within locations (Table 7.1) there is a marked difference between the birthweights of the pure yak calves and the F1 crosses from "improved" breeds. There is relatively much less variation among the breeds of sire in the average birthweights of their crossbred calves. There appears to be a clear trend of increasing average birthweight of calf with increasing average body weight of the yak dam. However, caution is required in drawing that conclusion, since the different body weights of yak dams are confounded with the different locations – although, in itself, the result seems to show, for yak, a relationship between size of dam and birthweight of calf which would be generally accepted for cattle.

Body weights and linear body dimensions of adult females and steers are shown in Table 7.2 for yak and different types of crosses, derived from observations in small herds in several parts of Sichuan province.

Table 7.2 Body weights and linear body dimensions of adult Maiwa yak, F1 crosses from Maiwa yak females mated to bulls of yellow cattle or Holstein Friesian (or 75% HF + 25% yellow cattle) and backcrosses involving these types – in Hongyuan, Ruoergai and Ganzi counties of Sichuan [pooled data from several farms – source: Cail Li]

Type of animal	Sex	No.	Adult weight (kg)	Height at withers (cm)	Body length (cm)	Heart girth (cm)	Cannon bone circumference (cm)
Local yak	f	73	249	118.3	138.1	160.3	16.9
	s	12	443	128.7	161.5	198.0	20.6
Yak (f) x HF* (m)	f	42	357	121.8	125.3	182.7	18.5
(improved F1)	s	7	580	144.0	178.3	215.6	21.3
Yak (f) x yellow cattle	f	47	292	118.3	148.0	167.9	17.0
(m) (local F1)	s	14	477	128.7	173.0	197.3	20.3
F1 (f) x HF* cattle (m)	f	19	262	116.4	136.6	165.6	18.1
(improved B)	s	6	521	150.0	174.5	206.5	22.5
F1 (f) x yellow cattle or yak (m)(local B)	f	10	177	100.5	118.9	146.1	14.1

f=female; s=steer (castrate male); HF*= Holstein Friesian or (75% HF + 25% yellow cattle)

It is apparent from the results in Table 7.2 that the F1 crosses from Holstein Friesian bulls (or grade HF) were the heaviest and largest followed by the crosses of yak with bulls of yellow cattle. The backcrosses were smaller than the F1. The backcrosses to yellow cattle bulls were actually smaller than the local yak which suggests that the cattle involved in the cross may have been very small indeed – but in the absence of the data, this is speculation (however, see below). The larger size and weight of steers relative to females corresponds to what was reported in chapter 6.

Similar results are shown in Table 7.3 but with data from all three types of animal, yellow cattle, Maiwa yak and their F1 crosses (yak female x yellow cattle male), cohabiting in another area of Sichuan.

As seen from Table 7.3, the yak in the Ganzi area were larger and heavier than the local, yellow cattle and the first crosses between them were bigger than either. This certainly suggests a substantial effect of heterosis, greater among the males than among the females. Unfortunately, the results preclude a strict estimate of the magnitude of heterosis because of the absence of the reciprocal cross (the "counter-hybridisation" – cattle female x yak male) from these trials, and the lack of certainty that treatment of all the classes was identical. Again, if speculation is in order, one might assume, on the evidence of the adult size of the local yak and the local cattle, that crossbred offspring borne by local cattle females might, if anything, be smaller than the crosses borne by the yak females. If so, estimates of heterosis (expressed as a percentage deviation from the mid-parent levels) would be *lower* than the values which might be inferred directly from Table 7.3 (these range for females from 2.3% for height at withers to 12.3% for body weight, and for males from 10.7% to 53.3% respectively).

Table 7.3 Body measurements and body weight of contemporary adult animals of Maiwa yak, local yellow cattle and F1 crosses in Ganzi county of Sichuan [source: Hu Angang *et al.*, 1960]

Type	Sex	No.	Body weight (kg)	Height at withers (cm)	Body length (cm)	Heart girth (cm)	Cannon bone circumference (cm)
Local yellow cattle	m	10	189	102.8	113.2	134.4	14.2
	f	22	170	97.7	108.7	130.0	13.5
Local yak	m	11	209	104.7	125.3	154.4	17.3
	f	127	179	102.1	121.6	145.0	14.9
F1 individual (yak dam)	m	6	305	114.8	134.7	179.7	18.5
	f	98	196	102.2	121.0	152.1	15.7

Evidence from other studies shows that crossbreds vary in size and body weight from district to district according to differences in the environment and in the types and breeds of yak and local cattle extant in different areas (Zagdsuren, 1994b; Research Co-op, 1980–87; Qiu Huai, 1957; Zhao Zhangrong, 1957). Such evidence is also provided by the differences between the two locations represented in Tables 7.2 and 7.3.

In the case of crosses of yak with "improved" cattle, the breed also has an effect – as illustrated in Table 7.4 overleaf.

The animals shown in Table 7.4 are the same as those at the Longri location of Table 7.1, where birthweights are given. In relation to birth weight, therefore, the pure yak calves had increased their weight ten-fold by 17 months old, whilst none of the crosses did as well as that. However, in absolute terms the crosses all gained much more in weight than the yak. The differences among crosses from different breeds of exotic sire were small by comparison, although such differences can be seen – with the Holstein Friesian crosses the best of those tested. Intermediate weights, at 3-monthly intervals, were also available (not shown here). From them it is of interest to note that weight losses over winter were of the same order of magnitude (11–12%), relative to weight at the beginning of winter, in the crossbreeds as in the pure yak.

Meat production

A number of studies have also examined the meat output, at slaughter, of crosses of yak derived from mating of yak with both local cattle and different exotic breeds of the types shown earlier (Table 7.3). Numbers in the breed groups examined tend to be small and there are no consistent differences between the breeds of sire in dressing percentage or the yield of meat. Nor do these differ from pure yak. There are differences in carcass weight, but only in so far as this is related to slaughter weight.

Table 7.4 Body weights (kg) and linear body dimensions (cm), at 6 and 17 months of age, of yak and crosses with different "improved" breeds of cattle at Longri, Sichuan (means and [SD]) [source: Cai Li, 1989]

Yak female mated to male of:	Sex	n	6-mth weight mean	6-mth weight [SD]	17-mth weight mean	17-mth weight [SD]	17-mth linear body dimensions: Height at withers mean	Body length mean	Heart girth mean
Yak	m	14	68.9	7.4	129.8	11.0	95.3	107.8	135.4
	f	11	68.5	11.9	121.0	16.7	89.6	104.8	132.9
H. Friesian	m	11	123.0	11.0	234.6	18.6	114.6	128.8	158.4
	f	21	111.6	13.6	202.4	17.3	110.8	123.7	154.3
Simmental	m	3	115.2	13.0	210.0	24.1	105.8	118.0	143.7
	f	6	77.5	15.6	162.8	24.6	102.3	114.0	133.8
Charollais	m	3	93.0	7.0	184.5	18.8	98.8	112.3	133.0
	f	3	81.3	5.7					
Hereford	m	3	81.2	10.7	181.3	12.8	100.7	109.0	139.3
	f	4	88.6	6.6	182.8	11.5	101.4	109.3	143.8
Shorthorn	m	2	86.0		162.0		102.5	112.5	139.0
	f	7	86.1	5.0	169.2	15.3	102.9	113.4	138.1

In spite of the small numbers involved, however, it is very apparent from these studies that there is a potentially very large difference in growth rate during the first and second summer of life between yak on the one hand and its crosses from the "improved" breeds of sire on the other. Thus, when slaughtered at 17 months old, the crosses reached slaughter weights around 50% greater than yak at the same age. This had the important consequence that crosses had attained an adequate degree of finish to provide a proportionately much greater yield of meat from the carcass than the (immature) yak at 17 months old. The loin-eye area was also two-thirds greater in the crosses than in the yak at that age. When slaughter occurs at the more normal age for yak steers – above the age of 8 years – there was little or no difference between yak and F1 crosses (with local cattle as the sires) in meat production in a study conducted in Sichuan. However, Zagdsuren (1994a) has shown that F1 steers from yak cows mated to local Mongolian (cattle) bulls had higher carcass weights and dressing percentages than either of the parent breeds. Carcass weights of these F1 steers were 49 kg heavier than those of pure yak and 19 kg heavier than those of pure Mongolian cattle.

Katzina *et al.* (1994) also report slaughter weights of crossbred animals at 18–20 months old which are 25–30% heavier than for yak at that age in the Buryatia region of Russia. They report further big increases in the growth of the crossbred if slaughter is delayed for a further year. The Schwyz breed (cf. Brown Swiss) has been used in this crossbreeding with the yak in addition to the use of local breeds of cattle – and a more recent use of the Jersey and Galloway breeds (see chapter 11).

Like the yak, crosses of yak with cattle show similar responses to the seasonal cycles of grass growth, with rapid growth during the warm season followed by severe loss over the winter and recovery the following year (Xiao Zhiqing, 1984). Also, the crossbreds are subject to the same seasonal effects on birth weight. For example, the birthweights of F1 crosses from yak mated to Holstein Friesian at Xiangdong livestock farm in Sichuan increased as the season progressed. Thus, 25 calves (sexes pooled) born in April weighed 21.3 kg [SD 2.6] on average at birth, 28 born in May weighed 23.5 kg [4.0] and 31 born in June weighed 24.3 kg [3.6].

Supplementary feeding of corn meal, urea and bone meal during summer, in addition to grazing, and supplementary feeding of concentrates during the winter, have both been shown to give a marked response in weight gain and in the proportion of meat (including fat?) in the carcass of crosses of yak with, for example, the Holstein Friesian. Under similar circumstances, pure yak showed very little such response (Li Xuewen *et al.*, 1983; Langjie Zeren *et al.*, 1987). However, it is questionable whether such supplementary feeding is economically worthwhile in terms of meat output alone – the answer must depend on market circumstances. It is considered that supplementary feeding over winter is not cost-effective (but see below for effect of supplementary feeding on milk yield).

Milk production

As noted in chapter 3, one of the main purposes of crossing the yak with cattle of other species is to provide the herdsmen with additional milk for their own use, or for sale. The larger quantity of milk made available is a consequence of the higher yield of such crosses relative to the yak but also because all or most of the milk from the F1 is taken by the herdsmen. (As noted earlier, the progeny from the F1 females (the backcrosses) are reared for meat production and not for further breeding – and in some cases are (or used to be) taken from their mothers at, or soon after, birth.)

Table 7.5 shows the daily milk yield and its fat percentage for different types of F1 crosses (yak females with local cattle and yak with Holstein Friesian or part-Holstein Friesian). (The source of the information is the same as for Table 7.2.)

Table 7.5 Daily milk yield and fat percentage of yak cows and F1 and backcross cows involving the yak and its crosses with bulls of local cattle and with Holstein Friesian (or 75% HF and 25% local cattle) bulls – in Hongyuan and Ruoergai counties of Sichuan province – 10 females per group

Type of animal	Daily milk yield (kg) (at peak period)	Fat %
Local yak	2.0	6.3
Yak (f) x Holstein Friesian (m) (improved F1)	8.0	5.4
Yak (f) x local (yellow) cattle (m) (local F1)	3.0	6.0
F1 (f) x Holstein Friesian cattle (m) (improved B)	5.5	
F1 (f) x local (yellow) cattle (m) (local B)	0.5–1.0	6.2

B = backcross, f = female, m = male

The first crosses from predominantly Holstein Friesian bulls are seen (Table 7.5) to have yielded a much higher daily amount of milk than the yak, but the backcrosses in this case have fallen back in yield as might be expected when part of the hybrid vigour is lost. In the case of the ordinary Pien Niu (F1 involving local cattle) the yield is higher than that of the pure yak, but the backcrosses, perhaps surprisingly, gave less milk per day than the yak cows. However, no milk yields are reported for the local cattle which, as in comparable results of Joshi (1982) from Nepal, may themselves have had lower milk yields than the yak. In the data presented earlier (Table 6.12 to illustrate seasonal changes in milk yield), the monthly and the total yield of the 1/4-bred yak (B1[C]) was very similar to that of the yak itself, but in another respect the two sets of results support each other in showing a similar proportionate difference between F1 and pure yak milk yield – an increase of the order of 50%.

The question of how much heterosis is shown in respect of milk yield by crosses of yak with *Bos taurus* or *Bos indicus* cattle is, however, confusing from the literature – quite apart from the over-riding problems referred to at the start of this chapter. Whilst the reduced yield of backcrosses relative to the F1, as in the results shown here, is consistent with heterosis in the F1, Zagdsuren (1994a), for example, has presented results from Mongolia of F1 cows (yak x mongolian cattle) which yield substantially more milk than those of either of their parent species (heterosis indeed, if the different groups are treated alike) – though with a fat percentage almost average between the two. In contrast, Jain and Yadava (1985) present results from F1 crosses of yak with zebu hill cattle in Himashal Pradesh which suggest that the daily milk yield of the crosses was only half-way between that of the parent species (no heterosis) – but no information is given on whether the 3 types of animal (10 animals in each group) were treated alike. It is quite possible that they were not, as all the animals were not from the same place. Surprisingly, the milk from this F1 cross had a significantly higher fat content (7.32%) than that of the yak (6.45%) (in spite of a higher daily milk yield in the cross) and much higher fat percentage than that of the hill cows (4.17%). This result is difficult to explain.

Some further results from Honyuan county in Sichuan show that F1 crosses from yak dams mated to Holstein Friesian bulls (by AI) can produce milk in significant quantities – and much more than contemporary yak. Moreover, they start to do so a year earlier than typical for yak – at the age of 3 instead of the age of 4 years. If calving of the F1 females is, however, delayed by a year to the age of 4 years, the first lactation yield is higher. Results for Holstein Friesian and a mixture of other crosses are shown in Table 7.6.

It is also of interest to note from the results of Table 7.6, that the crossbred, like the yak, has the capacity to give milk in a second year without a further intervening pregnancy – although, again as in the yak – the yield in the second year is reduced relative to that in the first.

Supplementary feeding of crosses of yak with the Holstein Friesian with urea, minerals and some ground corn during the warm grazing season led to an increase

Table 7.6 Milk yield in 149 days of different types of first cross by age at calving (and parity) [sources: Cai Li 1984b; Xu Guiling *et al.*, 1983]

Cross of yak female with:	Age (yr)	Parity	No.	Milk yield mean (kg)	SD	Fat % mean
HF	3	1	26	689	93	5.3
HF	4	1	15	809	130	5.2
HF	4	2	3	919	207	5.2
HF (half lact)*	4	1	4	494	28	6.5
Various**	3	1	7	576	(194)	4.9
Yak	4	1	6	226	54	7.3

HF = Holstein Friesian or crosses of HF with local cattle breeds
* "half-lactation" – a second lactation in the year following first calving without a further pregnancy.
** various breeds of exotic cattle sire used

in milk yield of 10% in full-lactating animals (those that calved that year) and 20% in "half-lactating cows (those that had last calved in the previous year). This was considered to provide an economic return on the feed (Wen Yongli, Wu Kang and Zhang Zhongming, 1987). Experiments with winter feeding, with silage, hay, roots, concentrates and minerals also raised the milk yield of Holstein Friesian x yak crosses but the costs of this winter feeding were too high in relation to the extra milk obtained (Grassland Institute, 1985). Moreover, the availability of supplementary feed in winter would be severely restricted in practice to localities where pastures have been improved and where agricultural products are also available.

Some exceptional F1 cows (from Holstein Friesian sires) when housed and well managed on Institutional farms have been recorded as giving up to 1800 kg milk (5.7% fat, which suggests that a potential for higher yield from yak crosses exists given the right circumstances.

Milk let-down. This is more easily and quickly achieved in the crosses than in the pure yak. About 70% of crosses, and especially those with sires of the "improved" breeds like the Holstein-Friesian, do not need the presence of the calf for milk let down – the remainder do. Milk from the crossbred females is reported by Zhang Rongchang *et al*. (1983) to come out of the udder about 50% more quickly than from the yak cow and that the pressure required to extract the milk is lower. As in the yak (see chapter 6) and in most cattle, the rear quarters of the udder of the crossbred develop better than the fore quarters and provide, according to one study (Han Zhenkang and Lu Tianshui, 1980b), about 54% of the total milk.

Concluding comment on milk yield

Milk yield of crosses of yak with local *Bos taurus* or *Bos indicus* cattle and also those with "improved" *Bos taurus* breeds is very dependant on the breeds used for the specific cross and on the location and conditions of production. For that reason, the results presented here are intended as examples only. The common factor of nearly all the results is that the "local" Pien Niu (using the local cattle breed for crossing with the yak) yield more milk than the pure yak under, what are assumed to be, similar conditions and that the "improved Pien Niu (when, for example, the Holstein Friesian is used as the crossing sire) gives more milk than the local Pien Niu.

Figure 7.4 Ploughing with a "false" Pien Niu (F1 from local yellow cattle dam and yak sire)

Draught

First crosses of yak females mated to bulls of local cattle (Pien Niu), and the reciprocal crosses, are widely used for draught – both for ploughing and as pack animals. The crosses are easily tamed and have better heat tolerance than pure yak, which make them very suitable for work. The crosses produced from mating yak bulls to female (local) cattle ("false Pien Niu") are used mainly for ploughing (see Figure 7.4).

Liu Gunqi *et al.* (*in*: Research Co-op, 1980–87) have shown that with a traditional-style plough making a furrow 15 cm wide, 2 ordinary Pien Niu steers can till around 0.13 hectare per day. With a more modern plough (24.8 cm wide furrow) 2 mature crossbred steers in medium fat condition were observed to plough 605 m^2 in one hour on moderately moist, flat ground. Per unit body weight, the maximum draught power of mature crossbred steers in reasonably good condition has been measured as exceeding that of the pure yak. After ploughing was finished, respiration and pulse rates returned to normal in less than half an hour.

The Pien Niu has an excellent memory, which makes it good as a pack animal and for riding. It can find its own way home to the campsite, like an old horse, without a person in attendance. Herdsmen will ride a Pien Niu without saddle when, for example, herding sheep, but if the animal is wanted for riding for long distances, a saddle is used.

In tests of the Pien Niu as a pack animal on grassland, the Pien Niu has been found to carry 75 kg, equal to 16.3% of its body weight and to cover 30 km in 6 hours – not unlike the performance of the pure yak (see chapter 6). On reaching its destination the respiration and pulse rates had returned to normal in 53 minutes.

8 MANAGEMENT OF YAK

OVERVIEW

Management systems for yak follow, predominantly, a traditional pattern which is dictated by the climate and seasons, the topography of the land and by cultural influences. Methods of keeping the yak vary, however, from the primitive, where herds are allowed to roam virtually at will, to the technologically advanced. In general, a transhumance form of management predominates. During the warm season of summer and autumn, yak are on pastures at high elevations and the herdsmen live in campsites which are moved quite often. This gives way in winter and early spring to the grazing of winter pastures at lower elevations which are nearer to the more permanent winter abodes and villages of the herders and their families. The summer grazings are much the more extensive of the two.

Usually, the yak of several families or of a whole village are pooled for purposes of management, but subdivided according to function into a dairy herd, a dry-cow herd, a herd of stock replacements and a herd of steers, the pack animals.

Grazing traditions are based on accumulated experience in the different areas which includes knowledge of different types of pasture vegetation, each with their own particular properties as feed or for medicinal purposes. Overgrazing has become a recognised problem, especially on the winter pastures, because an increase in the yak population has occurred, at least in China, due to official encouragement of extra food production combined with the fact that many herders, perhaps most, still equate numbers of animals with wealth and status, irrespective of the intrinsic merit of the animals or their productivity.

To assist in the management of yak at pasture, there is a small range of fixtures, mainly at the winter quarters, in the form of pens and enclosures usually made of mud, turf or faeces. Wood, because of its scarcity, is used sparingly in the Plateau yak territory, but in the country of the Alpine yak, wooden enclosures are found more often. Pens are usually associated with a tunnel-like passage for restraining animals during vaccinations or other treatments. A pit for dipping both yak and sheep is normally available, and a crush to restrain cows for mating is seen where hand-mating is practised.

Herdsmen train yak to obey commands both by voice and by use of small stones which are either thrown or projected with a sling. The purpose is to allow one person to control a large herd. The herder normally stays with the herd, partly to protect it from attack by wolves, especially at times of calving, and partly to prevent the herd from straying onto another's territory.

During the warm season on the summer pastures, herdsmen send yak out to graze early in the morning and bring them back to the campsite as late in the day as possible. In winter, the reverse happens with late out and early back. Milking, which occurs only during the warm season, is done once a day or, in some herds, twice. The method of calf rearing revolves around the frequency of milking of the cows. Milking three times a day is also practised for cows which do not have a calf at foot.

Apart from the important task of controlling the grazing and protecting the herd, the other main tasks of the herders involve: calf rearing – controlling the amount of access the calf has to its dam and to rear artificially when required; milking the cows – done either with the cows tethered, sometimes in a stall but usually tied to a long rope, or free; supervising matings; giving help at calving to yak cows giving birth to crossbred calves (yak x "improved" breed of cattle) which tend to be too large for unassisted delivery; harvesting the fleece – which is, most often, either a combination of combing the down first, followed by shearing, or of shearing alone followed by separation of the fine down from the coarse hair. Other routine jobs include dipping animals against external parasites, vaccinations, castrating males, training of pack animals, and so on.

In areas where grazing is combined with land suitable for tilling, yak and crosses of yak with other cattle are also used for ploughing, for between 8–10 hours daily during the season. Such animals are given supplementary feeding of straw and grain. Animals used for ploughing may also be used later in the year for carrying loads on long journeys over often difficult terrain. When working, such animals may walk continuously for 7–10 days before a rest of 1–2 days.

Introduction

There is no single management system which applies to all yak over the large area of its distribution. Methods differ according to country and region, influenced by altitude, climate and topography. There are differences in management related to culture and religion. Proximity to centres of population, which provide a market for yak products, also has an effect on management, since it determines whether products are used primarily by the families herding the yak, or whether certain products, like milk, are exploited more for the sale of, for example, butter or cheese. In some countries, for example Nepal, tourism provides outlets for products from the yak, including handicrafts, usually made from the "wool". In yet other countries, for example Mongolia, meat from yak is an important commercial product with slaughtering at centralised, but often distant, abattoirs, again affecting management practices. Generalisations about the management of yak, and the uses to which yak are put, are bound, therefore, to oversimplify the situation when any specific case is considered.

Management of yak ranges from the most primitive, seemingly unchanged by the passage of time, to the technologically quite advanced. At one end of the scale are herds which are left largely to roam and where herdsmen will go, in autumn, to hunt and shoot well-grown steers or bulls for meat. At the other end are herds where modern technology has taken firm hold. This will include supplementary feeding, rotational grazing, disease control and other management aids, artificial assistance for mating, and artificial insemination to create crosses with "exotic" breeds of cattle – though the inseminators are not usually the herders. Most herds are somewhere between these extremes in terms of management, with varying degrees of 'technology' making some impact in reducing disease and mortality and increasing productivity.

At experimental stations concerned with the yak, most techniques familiar to modern cattle husbandry are under consideration, though not always found to be appropriate to yak husbandry, or the associated environment – and not therefore necessarily enacted. Multiple ovulation and embryo transfer are appearing on the scene, but only as an experimental tool in restricted circumstances. Similarly, at the scientific level, the concepts and development of new pasture management techniques are clearly recognised (e.g. Ren Jizhou and Chu Cheong Ping, 1993) Miller (1990) has taken the view that, for the vast grasslands of the Qinghai-Tibet plateau, a great potential exists for improving the herbage productivity of the rangeland and its livestock output, provided improved rangeland management policies are developed and implemented.

With so wide a spectrum of local environments and management practices, all that will be attempted here is to provide an overview of what must still be regarded as standard practice for most yak, at least in the areas of China, including the Tibetan autonomous region, where the majority of the yak live. Where countries outside China differ in major ways in their yak husbandry practice, or in specific aspects of yak production, this will be referred to in Chapter 11. However, in all areas, the climate and the seasons dictate to a large extent what happens to yak.

Activities according to seasonal cycle

- *Early summer*. Supervising births and protecting calves; adjusting and sub-dividing the herd; castrating.
- *Middle of summer*. Combing out the down fibres and shearing; prophylactic vaccinations and dipping against external parasites.
- *Late summer and autumn*. Milking and processing milk; arranging mating; harvesting and storing grass for winter supplements (usually, mostly for sick and weak animals).
- *Early winter*. Culling surplus or unwanted stock; slaughtering animals for meat; counting the herd; repairing pens and enclosures for yak.
- *Middle of winter*. Milking of cows stops (in order to allow priority to be given to the developing foetus in the use of nutrients and body reserves by the pregnant females); taking measures to protect the body condition of the yak; sheltering the animals in pens.

- *Spring*. Providing small amounts of supplementary grass as available (hay or possibly silage) and taking other measures to prevent death, particularly among the females.

Yak pastures and grazing habits

A survey and details of the many different plant species (grasses, sedges, shrubs and trees) found in the plateau region is given by Chai Zhaoguang et al. (1986). Miller (1990) records that the meadows at high elevations are dominated by sedges of the genus *Kobresia* and that purple feathergrass (*Stipa purpurea*) is one of the most common grasses. Other grasses referred to as of common occurrence are *Littedalia racemoa*, *Roegneria kokonorica*, *Ptilagrostis dichotoma* and *Koeleria cristata*. Near settlements, in fenced areas, to provide emergency winter grazing, Miller noted a wild rye grass, *Elymus nutans*, as one of the dominant grasses. Miller (1990) further states that of the 5 main vegetation zones of the Qinghai-Tibet plateau, the two which predominate are "the moist high-cold meadow and low shrub in the east" and "the arid and high-cold steppe in the north and central region"

In the pastoral areas of the Plateau yak, the grassland itself, as used by the herdsmen of a village, can be broadly divided into two categories: that used in the warm season (summer-autumn) and that used in the cold season (winter-spring). The local climate and character of the land determines precisely where each is located and for how long in the year each is grazed. In general, however, the warm season grazing is at the higher altitudes, often on the northern slopes of the terrain and furthest from the settled homes of the herdsmen and their families. The cold season grazing is then closer to "home" and in more sheltered, south-facing parts at lower elevations.

The areas where the Alpine type of yak predominate are more varied, because of the topography. The area of grassland occupied by the yak of a village can be quite large and is likely to be distributed across several mountain ridges separated by valleys. The ridges may well be above 4000 m. in altitude and the valleys at a much lower elevation. In consequence, the grazing areas are more sub-divided than on the plateaux. In the alpine regions there is a separate grazing area for each of the 4 seasons of the year. The summer pastures are the extensive alpine meadows at the top of the mountain range. The spring and the autumn pastures are occupied for relatively short periods only by the animals in transit between summer and winter grazing areas. For that reason, the spring and autumn grazing areas tend to be small and are mostly on the hilly ground. The winter pastures, or "winter house" as it is called by the herdsmen, is situated in the gullies and, when available, at the side of a forest for additional shelter.

When yak are kept in areas with swamps, there is a further variant in the use of grassland. The actual swamps or semi-swamps turn green relatively early in the year because they are generally at the lower altitudes. The yak therefore have an opportunity to graze fresh tender plants (with a high proportion of *Kobresia* and other *Cyperaceae* spp.) in the areas reserved for grazing in the spring. Summer-autumn pastures are then again at higher elevations and the winter pastures on lower ground nearer the settled areas of the herdsmen's families.

Traditionally, the nomadic way of herding yak was to keep the entire herd together, irrespective of age and sex, and to allow the yak to graze together with sheep and horses. The herdsmen would live with their animals and would, during the growing season, move with them as necessitated by the availability of grazing and water. Miller (1990), in a vivid account of the grasslands of the Tibetan plateau, regards the pastoral grouping and management of yak as well-adapted responses to different range and environmental conditions and ecologically sound and sustainable.

The traditional use of different pastures at different seasons and the periodic movement of the animals to new grazing sites (see below) represents some of the elements of "modern" rotational grazing systems. The use of fencing to control yak grazing more closely, in order to optimise pasture utilisation and reduce parasite infections, is rare, because of the high cost.

Since the 1950's, in China, encouragement has been given to a more settled existence for the herdsmen and their families. This has brought with it a division of the herds into different categories of yak and the separation of different types of stock and there is a more deliberate choice of the grazing areas – differing, of course, as before between the warm and cold seasons.

Herd ownership in relation to management

In China, the land itself is owned by the state, but the animals are usually owned by the herdsmen. Several families or even all the families of a village jointly share the same pastures. If stocking rate in a particular area of the country is low, the number of yak which can be owned by a family is not restricted. However, in most parts of the country this is not so. The number of yak allowed to each family depends on family size, and the rights to grassland are fixed by agreement. There are penalties for transgressing the rules. Not withstanding this, the encouragement given to increased food production in China in recent years, combined with the traditional view of yak herdsmen to equate number of animals with status and wealth, has led to an increase in yak numbers in many areas of the yak territory and, as already alluded to above, raises concern of overgrazing (see later). Increasingly, nowadays, the yak of several families or of a whole village are managed together, but, for this purpose, the herd is sub-divided.

Sub-division of the yak herd

At least in China, the total yak herd, as merged from the animals belonging to different families of the village, is usually divided up into component herds. There is, 1) the lactating-cow herd (dairy herd); 2) the dry-cow herd (the "Ganba" herd); and, 3) the group representing the younger replacement animals – those that have been weaned and separated from their dams (the "Yaer" herd). The herd of replacement animals is further divided to separate the males from the females. Finally, there is, 4) the steer herd (pack yak). There is no special herd for the bulls which live with the breeding females during the breeding season and at other times live mostly alone. Also, there is not usually a separate group for animals intended for slaughter for meat. Usually, the "meat" animals are merely the cull females and any chosen as suitable from among the steers and the bulls. (This would differ in countries where large-scale commercial fattening and slaughtering of yak is practised – see chapter 11)

Young calves remain with their dams up to weaning – which is most often in their second warm season of life, when they are between a year and eighteen months old, but it can, of course, be sooner. After weaning, whenever it is, the young animals are incorporated into the "Yaer" herd of replacement animals. First crosses (F1) of yak with other types of cattle are kept apart from the yak, if there are enough of them, and they constitute a second dairy herd. If there are only a few such crosses they are kept with the yak cows. The F1 and backcross steers are distributed, as appropriate, among the groups used for riding, or as pack animals, or for draught.

Yak herds vary in size. For the Plateau yak, which live in vast areas of open country, herdsmen find it convenient to aggregate yak into larger herds than in the more contained alpine regions. Herds of the different categories of yak also tend to differ in size. The dairy herd (of the lactating yak) is normally used as the standard against which to compare the size of the others. In the plateau country, the dairy herd of yak cows tends to number between 100 and 150 head, and in the mountainous alpine regions perhaps 50–100. The dairy herd of Piennius (F1 females) usually has fewer animals than a herd of lactating yak. The non-productive female herds (the replacement herd and dry-cow herd) are generally larger in number than the dairy herd – a point to note when reflecting on the efficiency of yak production. Similarly, the herd of steers can be very large, as these animals are not usually slaughtered until they are quite old – depending to some extent on the use to which they have been put.

The divisions described above, and relevant to large parts of yak territory in China, can be seen primarily during the day-time grazing in the warm season. At night, the yak tend to be divided again by family ownership and the different types of yak mixed and kept near the family tent. During the cold season, the yak from several families are grazed together and the sub-division of the animals may be only into a herd of adult yak females, a dairy herd of crosses (if appropriate) and the rest of the animals all together in a mixed herd. As ideas based on newer concepts of feeding and management are accepted by herdsmen, it is likely that new systems of management will develop. This process is already apparent in some cases where specialisation of production is emerging.

Utilisation of grazing

In early summer each year, usually in May – but depending on the particular location – the yak are still grazing the winter pastures. As soon as the season allows, however, the herd is sub-divided into the different production categories described above, and taken to the summer pastures (via the spring pastures where appropriate). The yak are back in their winter territory by early winter and not usually later than November.

During the warm season, a yak herd will typically be moved every 10 to 40 days depending on the state of the grass and the size of the herd. The direction of movement of the herd and the route chosen is usually the same every year. The distance between campsites is generally less than 20 km. There are two ways in which the move can be made. One procedure is to move the livestock and the people, with their tents and belongings, all together in one move, until the new campsite is reached. Under those circumstances the animals get virtually no chance to graze on route. The other way is to move the people and belongings to the new campsite first, establish the site and then move the yak gently in the course of a day's grazing toward the new campsite, which they reach at night. The former procedure is prevalent when the distance between the sites is great, the second method is more common when the distance is relatively short.

During the cold season, movements from one site to the other are few – not more than 2 to 5 over the whole period. However, if the yak herd is small, or if yak are kept in pens with supplementary feeding, there may be no move at all over the whole of the winter and early spring.

Yak are versatile grazers. As already noted (chapter 3) they will take a variety of different herbage and are equipped to do so by their different feeding habits. This ability of the yak contributes to a better utilisation of the total grazing. As pointed out by Cincotta et al. (1991), from a study of diet selection on the Tibetan Changtang, yak consumed a variety of forages avoided by sheep and goats, but these other ruminants in turn took large quantities of some types of browse largely ignored by yak. As reported from many other situations, complementary grazing by a mixture of livestock species generally leads to a better overall utilisation of the total grazing resource.

Grazing traditions. Much of the grazing management of yak is part of the ingrained tradition of the herdsmen, developed through a long history of experience going back over the centuries.. Much of this tradition has a sound scientific basis and is an effective means of utilising the resources of a hostile environment to best advantage. Thus, herdsmen know well how to exploit changes in grass growth. There is the use of swamp areas for early grazing in spring followed by a period on grassland with *Ophiopogon japonica*, said to cause de-worming and stimulate oestrus. Bog-meadows in June with yellow-flowered herbs of *Kobresia*, *Trollius* and *Caltha* spp. increase milk yield and turn the raw butter a desired orange in colour. In the autumn, grazing on seeded grass is used to build up body condition to withstand the winter and early spring. In the cold season, yak are pastured in the most sheltered and warm, south-facing areas with as much wilted grass as possible, to allow the animals some sustenance, which they obtain by scraping through the snow and ice. Many of these practices are enshrined in local proverbs and sayings which tell succinctly what to do and when.

Problems of overgrazing

Notwithstanding the great local experience of the herdsmen in exploiting their grazing territory to best advantage, serious problems from overgrazing are developing in the utilisation of the yak pastures in some regions. As referred to earlier, yak numbers have been increasing over the years, at least in China. An important factor in this has been the demand for economic growth and the increasing demand for yak products – mostly milk and meat. This has created a market and cash economy for these products. Another contributory factor to the increase in stock numbers is that the number of animals is still widely equated with wealth by the herdsmen. Herdsmen are not restricted in this respect and encouraged to take personal responsibility for their actions.

The resulting increase in stock numbers has put increasing pressure on the pastures, but particularly the winter grazings. The winter pastures cover a smaller area than the summer pastures, but also have to sustain a larger number of animals, because numbers are always at their highest after the calf crop of that year. The winter pastures in particular, therefore, tend to be increasingly often overgrazed. This has been accentuated by the fact that the income from sheep meat and wool has declined and that from yak milk and meat has increased – with a consequent decline in sheep numbers relative to yak. This in turn has created a further imbalance in the utilisation of the land.

In Ruoergai county of Sichuan, to take this area surveyed by Cai Li as an example, yak numbers increased between 1979 and 1984 by 95 thousand to 325 thousand, while over the same period sheep numbers fell by 87 thousand to 532 thousand. An optimal ratio of cattle to sheep for that particular area was calculated to be 1:2.9 (more commonly 1:3.2) (Lei Huangzhang et al., 1986) but had been reduced to 1:2.2 by 1984. Thus, not only had stocking density (per adult animal unit) increased but the stocking had become unbalanced in terms of the different contributions to grazing selection made by yak and sheep. If procedures were adopted to optimise the population structure, as recommended by Cai Li et al. (1986), it should be possible to increase overall productivity from the land whilst decreasing the total number of animals required. Measures would include the earlier slaughter of steers and culls, and changing management procedures so as to increase the proportion of the productive animals (the lactating cows and the crossbred dairy herd) and reduce the proportion of the unproductive animals. The same conclusions were drawn by Zhen Zhongchao (1994) using linear programming to obtain an economically optimum structure for yak herds. This ideal of optimising herd structure is not yet in sight. But the matter of overgrazing is one of great concern which requires action before permanent damage is done to the grasslands.

A particular example, attributed to a consequence of overgrazing, was reported by Winter et al (1992, 1994), and highlights the wider problem. The report relates to widespread deaths, among yak in Bhutan, which were found to be due to pyrrolizidine alkaloid poisoning. The plants causing this (most especially some species of *Senecio*) are not very palatable and are normally avoided by yak, or taken in only small amount. However, the plants had become prevalent through overgrazing and the yak, through hunger it was thought, consumed the plants in lethal quantity.

Supplementary feeding

There a few opportunities for supplementary feeding of yak, except perhaps in the agricultural areas (see below). Surplus herbage for hay or silage is not widely available, nor the equipment to make it – at least in the major yak-producing areas. A little hay is usually made but it is normally given only to sick or very weak animals towards the end of winter. Additional feeding when given can, however elicit a response, in terms of reduced weight loss (over winter) or increased growth or milk yield, as noted from a number of trials, quoted in chapter 6 and also in a recent study which involved winter feeding, under shelter, of hay and mineral licks (Liu Qian and Cheng Wending,1994). The cost-effectiveness of such feeding still requires investigation both in respect of home-grown and purchased feed. In Buryatia, however, as reported by Katzina (see chapter 11) it is customary to give supplementary feeding to yak calves over their first winter of life and, in consequence, these animals do not lose weight over that period. This may well account for the fact that the yak females subsequently breed for the first time a year earlier than in most other situations and that the steers are slaughtered at an earlier age. It is important, therefore, to judge the effectiveness of feeding not only by immediate responses, but also in terms of any long-term effects.

Equipment, enclosures and pens

Generally, there is little equipment to assist the herdsmen in the management of yak on range. The most usual provision is a dipping pit used for both cattle and sheep; there may be a silo or silage trench for use mainly by the sheep, there is likely to be a corral with a tunnel-like passage to restrain animals for vaccinations or other treatments; and there may be a simple crush to hold cows which it is intended to mate to particular bulls or inseminate artificially. Pens are also created to provide shelter. Such pens and enclosures are used only at night and usually only during the winter and spring. They are always at the campsite, or close to the habitation of the herdsmen and their families. The pens can be of various types of construction with differing degrees of permanence.

Mud enclosure. This is a relatively permanent construction built near the habitation of the herdsmen, or at the winter campsite. It is used primarily for the cow herd, including crossbred females, and it is also used for the replacement females. The area is usually 15 x 15 m. with a wall 1 – 1.2 m. high, but the size can be as large as 30 x 20 m. Most of the mud enclosures, though not all, have an additional shelter area constructed at one side of the enclosure facing the sun and providing extra protection from the wind. This extra shelter is constructed from a layer of clay on wooden boards knitted together with wicker. Such an enclosure is illustrated schematically and in a photograph (Figure 8.1 a, b).

The mud enclosures can stand alone, but more usually there are two or more built together and often joined by a passage with mud walls or wooden fence. A gate or gates keep the stock apart in the different enclosures. If several enclosures are connected to each other, the last enclosure will end in a long tunnel-like passage used for restraining the animals for vaccinations or other purposes. The passage can be roofed or open (Figure 8.2 a, b).

Faeces pen. This is a temporary structure, built and used only during the cold season. Fresh yak faeces is piled up near the campsite in a layer of about 15–20 cm deep every day. The first layer freezes solid overnight before the second layer is added. Such a pen can be completed in a few days. There are two types of faeces pen. One has four walls to keep out wind and snow and provides a relatively large area used for adult yak. The other is smaller, built on a horseshoe-shaped foundation with a diameter of about 1 m and looking, from the outside, something like an upside-down earthenware jar. It is built up gradually to its final 1 m height and is used to hold calves. The open end has its back to the prevailing wind. A wooden stake is used to tether the calf. Hay is put inside the pen to make it warmer for the calf. When the temperature starts to rise in the spring, the faeces thaws and pens made from it fall apart, to be rebuilt in the following winter.

Turf pen. To build pens with turf, herdsmen select a position on the winter pastures which faces the sun and is relatively sheltered from the wind. The height of the turf walls is at least 60 cm., but usually higher This type of pen is used for giving some shelter to pack yak and also to some bulls. The structure is semi-permanent, but needs to be repaired each year.

Wooden compound (or corral). Wood is in short supply on the plateau where most yak live. Wooden enclosures are, therefore, often an adjunct to a mud enclosure and within its perimeter. The wooden compound may be roofed or not (Figure 8.3). In the areas of the country which are home to the alpine yak, wood is more abundant and the compound may be built independently. The structure is of small wooden bars and provision is made for holding hay. During the warm season, these wooden enclosures are used to keep the calves isolated from their dams at night, whilst the adults graze in preparation for being milked the following morning.

Other shelters. Tents made of yak hair are also used for calves in the pastoral areas. In the alpine parts, for example in Jiulong county of Sichuan, there are small shelters, called cattle shelters, found as part of the permanent buildings of the campsites. They are used by herdsmen and milkers and for processing milk and storing milk products. Such shelters can vary in area from 10 to 20 square metres and are surrounded by a stone wall 1.5 m. high. Boards or bark are used for the roof. These shelters are in use whenever the herd comes to the campsite. A campsite with such shelters is illustrated in Figure 8.4.

Management of yak herds on the range

Controlling the herd

Temperamentally, yak are both wild and timid, cowardly and yet aggressive. Another part of the yak's character is its strong herding instinct. All these aspects have to be taken into account in training yak to obey commands, so as to allow a single person to control and manage a large herd. Because of the yak's timidity, the herder cannot follow too closely behind the herd, for fear of the herd scattering. The practice of the herder is to select a high spot of ground, overlooking the herd whilst it is grazing, so that he can protect the animals from wolves and prevent the herd from straying onto grazing land set aside for other herds.

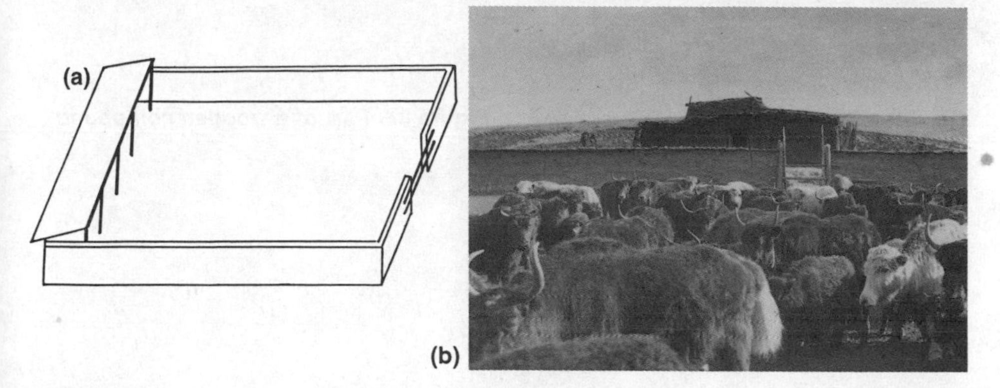

Figure 8.1 Mud (wall) enclosure with wooden shelter (a) schematic (b) photograph

Figure 8.2 Passage between mud enclosures
(a) open (b) roofed

Figure 8.3 Part of a wooden compound

Figure 8.4 Campsite with Jiulong yak, showing shelters used for processing milk and storing milk products

Figure 8.5 Sling of hair and yak down (or sheep wool) used to project stones used in herding yak

The herdsmen use special summonses to call the yak and they throw small stones to make straying animals return to the herd. Throwing a stone by hand may land it 10 m. away, but using a sling – as is a common practice in many parts – can project a stone more than 100 m in the hands of a skilled user. Both the sound of the stone flying through the air at great speed and the sound of the sling, like the crack of a whip, provide a warning signal to the yak. The direction from which the stone comes lets the yak to know which way to go and whether to advance, muster or disperse. The sling (illustrated in Figure 8.5) used for projecting the stone is woven from yak hair and down, or sheep's wool, it is 100–120 cm long, and has an elliptical net at its centre (7 x 15 cm) to hold the stone.

Daily schedules

The grazing schedule for yak differs with the type of herd and with the season. For herds of dairy yak there will also be a variety of different schedules depending on the frequency of milking and on the particular calf rearing practice. In sending yak out to graze, the guiding principle for the herdsmen is: "early out and late back in summer and autumn, late out and early back in winter and spring". The pack-yak herd and the herd of young animals – the replacement animals – are left out at pasture both day and night during the warm season and they do not return to the campsite over that period. Also during the warm season, the lactating females need to recover their body condition after the rigours of the previous winter and spring, if they are to give milk, rear calves and mate again. For that reason, the cows are allowed to graze both during the day and at night, while, as a rule, the calves are penned overnight (but cf. Table 6.6 for the effects on growth of calves grazing alongside their dams overnight).

The following are some examples of daily (summer) schedules for yak milked once, twice or three times a day in different localities.

- **Once daily milking (practice in Ninai township of Jiulong county, Sichuan). The calves graze with their dams and suckle them (except at night)**

05.00 – 07.00	yak cows recalled from their night grazing to the campsite, where they are mustered without tethering
07.00 – 09.00	milking; releasing calves from their overnight wooden enclosure
09.00 – 18.00	animals grazing the alpine grassland. Calves graze with their dams and suckle. Yak graze freely, drink water, rest and ruminate
18.00 – 20.00	end of grazing on alpine pasture, herd returns to campsite, calves enclosed in the wooden corral
20.00 – 05.00	yak cows allowed to graze freely on pasture near the campsite.

- **Twice daily milking (practice for lactating cow herd in Muye township of Mashu district, Ganzi county, Sichuan). Calves are reared artificially in some such herds**

05.00 – 07.00	animals grazing near campsite on grass with dew
07.00 – 09.00	yak called in for – first milking
09.00 – 13.00	yak driven to far-away pastures at high elevation, and allowed to walk slowly and gradually back downward whilst grazing
13.00 – 15.00	herd driven to a watering place, allowed to rest and ruminate
15.00 – 19.00	herd driven back to a point about half-way up the hill and allowed to graze at will
19.00 – 20.00	end of grazing, return to campsite with drinking water on the way
20.00 – 21.00	yak tethered at the campsite, second milking
21.00 – 05.00	yak cows released to graze near campsite.

- **Three times daily milking (practice from Xiangdong livestock farm in Ruoergai county, Sichuan). Calves suckle their dams**

05.00 – 08.00	first milking of cows
08.00 – 13.00	yak cows allowed to graze freely and have access to water at a distance from the campsite. Calves remain tethered at campsite, or are tied together in pairs and allowed to graze near camp
13.00 – 15.00	yak cows driven back to campsite, second milking (without tethering)
15.00 – 19.00	calves allowed to graze with their dams, away from the campsite in good weather and near the camp if weather is poor. The calves given the opportunity to suckle and also to have access to water
19.00 – 2100	grazing period ended, calves are separated from their dams after a further opportunity for suckling. The calves are then tethered to a long rope at the campsite (see Figure 8.6). The cows which have no calves – the "half-lactating" females and those which have lost their calf and are not fostering – are milked for a third time
21.00 – 05.00	calves remain tethered overnight. The cows may either be tethered or not, depending on the topography of the land and the ease with which they can be driven back to the campsite in the morning.

Management of the individual animal

The management practice and degree of technical input varies greatly between areas. A few of the most common practices are as follows:

Calf rearing

Normally, yak calves are suckled by their dams. Artificial rearing occurs only if the dam of the calf has died and no foster dam has been found, but in some cases also where twice-a-day milking is practised.

Figure 8.6 Tethering of yak calves to a rope

Fostering is attempted when a calf has lost its dam and another cow has lost its calf. Because of her strong maternal instinct, a yak cow that has lost her calf can be persuaded to accept another by smearing the calf to be fostered with her milk, or to place the hide of her dead calf on the intended fosterling. Smearing salt on the calf will also stimulate the foster dam to smell and lick the new calf and adopt it as her own.

Artificial rearing is accomplished with a feeding bottle made of yak horn without its tip, and with a teat, the size of a thumb, made of yak hide attached to the end of the horn. The "bottle" is filled with milk and the calf sucks normally. However, the timing and the length of time of such feeding has to take account of the normal suckling behaviour and also the need of the calf for young grass in order to establish grazing behaviour and rumination. Care is taken by the herdsmen to prevent calves sucking each other, as blockages of the *abomasum pyloris* can result from careless practice.

With normal rearing, the dam (or foster dam) is not milked for 10 days, or even a month, after calving, during which time the calf obtains first the colostrum and then all the milk from the dam. When the dam starts to be milked the calf continues to suck, to the extent permitted by the regime, and graze alongside its dam. Yak calves start to nibble grass at 7–10 days old, but have not been observed to ruminate before the age of 12 days. At night, as already noted, the calves are separated from their dams, except from those which are not milked because they give too little milk for that purpose or because they are ill.

During the cold season the cows are not milked and their calves stay with them all day and usually obtain a small amount of milk by suckling.

Weaning of calves is generally around the age of 12 months, though the calves of cows that have become pregnant again are weaned at 6 months old. To achieve weaning, the cows and the calves are separated into different herds (see earlier). In cases where the calf persists in trying to suckle, a piece of wood about 20 cm long, sharpened at both ends, is pushed through the nasal septum between the nostrils. This is removed only when the calf has stopped its attempts at suckling.

Milking

The teats of yak females are small and have to be squeezed between the fingers to extract milk. Milking takes place at the campsite. If the calf is tethered the cow will be tied up too, but not if the calf is kept in a closed corral. The cows which are not

Figure 8.7 A milking stall with stone slab floor, stone wall and pole for tying animal

Figure 8.8 Milking in progress

tethered usually graze all day and yield more milk than those which are tied up for part of the day.

Tethering is done by hitching a neck rope by a wooden peg to a long rope with many rings. The rope is fixed to the ground of the campsite. (Cows are accustomed to neck ropes from the time they were calves and to being tethered in the same manner). Milking the cow takes place where she is tethered. After a short time, the yak cows remember the position along the rope where they are to be tied – and they will quickly learn a new position, if given one after a move to a new campsite.

In some areas, milking also takes place in stalls. The milkers call to the yak using the charming, eloquent names given to them at their first milking. A little barley powder mixed with salt may be used as a further incentive to tempt the cows into the stall. Once there, the cow is hitched by her neck rope to a wooden pole and milked.

The milking stall is usually constructed with a left wall and a front wall of stone (100–120 cm long, 60–80 cm wide and 60–80 cm high) and the other sides open. The floor has stone slabs and there is a wooden pole for securing the animal (see Figure 8.7).

Yet another variation of milking practice occurs with yak cows which are not tethered at all. The milker goes to the cow, anywhere on the campsite, with bucket in hand and calf in tow. The forelimbs of the cow are tied with a short rope prior to milking.

The milking reflex is stimulated, in the first instance, by the calf poking the udder and being allowed to suck a little until milk let-down occurs. The calf is then removed a short distance but still within sight of the cow and hand milking starts. The reflex has to be re-stimulated a second time by the same procedure with the calf, after something rather more than half the milk has been extracted.

The milker normally squats on the right side of the cow with the pail hung from a hook on a girdle, as illustrated in Figure 8.8. The milker uses a little butter, which has been spread on the side of the pail, to lubricate the teats and milks at about 80 squeezes per minute.

A small number of cows are too ferocious and protective of their calf to be capable of being hand milked.

Mating of female yak

In pastoral areas, mass mating of the female herd is the normal practice with between 5 and 6 yak bulls to every 100 females – though more bulls may be used in some areas; for example, Dubrovin (1992) reports the use of 8 yak bulls per 100 females in the Caucasus. This system allows competition among the bulls for mates and is part of the selective process. In some areas, however, artificial assistance is given to the mating process. In such cases, when a yak cow is found to show oestrus, often through use of a teaser bull, she will be caught and her forelegs tied and a rope placed around her neck. The cow is then restrained in a breeding crate, or held by two men, one on each side of the cow. Three or more bulls are then driven toward the cow and allowed to compete for the mating. After the cow has been served twice (by the same bull, or once each by two different bulls), the bulls are driven away and the cow released after smearing her rump with fresh faeces to deter further mounting and mating. An advantage of such artificial restraint of the cow is that it also allows selected mating to be made, but a disadvantage is that accidents and damage occasionally occur to the cow in these circumstances.

In agricultural areas, only one yak bull is normally allocated to a cow, which is restrained for the actual mating. This is safer than the competitive mating procedure of the pastoral areas and can achieve the selection objectives of the herdsmen.

Artificial insemination is practised mainly for inter-species hybridisation, as referred to in chapters 5 and 7, and has been refined as a practice since the 1970s. Frozen semen is used from bulls of other cattle species, but is also now provided by yak bulls chosen for use in improvement programmes. By experiment and experience, techniques for collection and use of semen have had to be adapted to the yak situation and the climate. In particular, great attention has to be paid to the safety of the person undertaking insemination of yak. The yak cow has to be restrained in an insemination crate (see Figure 8.9). The temperature of the thawed semen has to be maintained to prevent cold shock since the ambient temperature in the earlier part of the morning can be as low as 0°C even in the warm season. For the same reason, particular attention has to be paid to the temperature of the inseminating tube and syringe.

Figure 8.9 Artificial insemination of yak

Training of bulls for semen collection

Because of a lack of information on the merits of young yak bulls, most of the semen collection is done from older bulls which are considered superior. The training of adult bulls is therefore an important aspect of the process.

The first step is for a herdsman, who knows the temperament of the particular bull, to use various means to try to eliminate the bull's hostility. It starts by holding the bull in a pen until the bull is used to being tied up and to being fed in a fixed place and, importantly, until the bull allows the herdsman to approach it. To obtain acceptance by the bull, the herdsman will initially tempt the bull in the pen with grass, and later he will stroke and scratch the bull from the front to the rear of the body and from the back to the abdomen. Yak fear most being touched on the head and, consequently, the herdsman avoids coming close to the head in the daily act of grooming. After some time, the herdsman will start to stroke the scrotum and testes of the bull and pull on its sheath and also walk the haltered yak bull to its feed.

Training for semen collection follows by first getting the bull accustomed to a female on heat, whilst she is restrained in a crate, and allowing him to mate her there. After that comes the process of guiding the sheath into an artificial vagina and allowing the bull to ejaculate into it. The temperature of the inner layer of the artificial vagina is kept between 39° and 42° C. Eventually, a dummy cow can be used for the yak bull to mount, as happens with other types of cattle. However, a yak bull appears to be more sensitive to its surroundings which have, therefore, to be kept quiet and familiar to the bull. The bull also has to be treated gently.

Pregnancy detection

Abortions and disease during pregnancy are rare. For that reason, herdsmen do not attempt pregnancy diagnosis. Yak cows are judged to be pregnant if they do not return on heat after mating at the next expected oestrus period. However, because a proportion of yak cows come on heat only once in a season, this negative way of assessing pregnancy has been found to lead to problems of unnecessary culling of cows which were thought to be barren, but are in fact pregnant. There is no visual early indication of pregnancy as there is no obvious outer swelling of the body, in the early part of winter. As an example of the mistaken culling of cows, because of lack of positive pregnancy diagnosis, was provided by an investigation, by Cai Li, at Xiangdong livestock farm in Sichuan. In one year, out of 38 yak cows which were culled, 17 were found to be pregnant, and only 5 of these 17 would have been culled anyway for other reasons. This mistaken culling, because of presumed barrenness, reduces calf numbers and production from the herd. Cai Li has found that rectal palpation would be an easy and quite accurate means of pregnancy diagnosis in yak under current methods of yak management (see also chapter 5).

Calving

A yak female leaves the herd shortly before she is due to calve and seeks out a sheltered, low-lying place in which to deliver her calf. By the time the calf is born and she has licked it, and it has started to suck, the herd has usually moved on. The calf is then in particular danger from wolves and other predators, which are prevalent around the time of calving. The herdsman, therefore, has to pay extra attention, from a distance, to guard against such attacks, even when other assistance with calving is not required.

Assistance at calving. Yak cows graze all the year round but their nutrition is particularly poor in mid and late pregnancy. They also have a somewhat shorter gestation length than *Bos taurus* cattle (see chapter 5). As a consequence of these factors, birth weights of pure yak calves are generally low and difficult labour is rare in the cows. Assistance at calving, therefore, is not normally required and would, in any case, be difficult to give, since yak cows are hard to approach during delivery because of their highly protective maternal instinct. However, assistance at birth is frequently necessary when a yak cow gives birth to an F1 (inter-species) calf. This is often too large for the cow to deliver unaided, especially when sires of large exotic breeds were used to produce the cross. Occasionally, a delivery by caesarean section may be required for a hybrid calf. Anaesthesia is provided by a method of electric acupuncture and local veterinary workers are readily trained in this technique. Such caesarean delivery takes between 1 and 2 hours to complete. The cow is conscious throughout, appears to suffer no pain and returns to normal activity immediately afterwards.

When calving is assisted, the navel cord is cut with a knife. In all other cases the cord is broken by the act of the cow standing up after delivery, or by the yak calf falling down. Although the broken cord is not sterilised, infections are rare.

Castration of males

Males not selected for breeding are castrated. Most of this is done between the ages of 1 and 2.5 years of age. It is usual to do the castrations on a clear morning in early summer or late autumn, when the risk of infection to an open wound is reduced. The procedure is first to catch the young bull in a pen and make him lie on his side and restrain him. The lower part of the scrotum is then sterilised with iodine and the bottom, held between thumb and index finger, cut off with a knife. The testicles are pushed out of the scrotum, the cords crushed and the wound sterilised with iodine solution and dusted with a powder to prevent infection. The scrotum is squeezed to close the cut end. The bull is then set free and walks away. The wound generally heals without complication within a week. The operation can take as little as 10 seconds. With older bulls more care is required, particularly in handling the cord and with sterilising the wound.

In some areas a different technique is used. For example in the Ganzi area of Sichuan the scrotum is slit vertically on the rear side, the testes are pushed out and totally removed. The other parts of the process are similar to those described.

F1 hybrid bulls, although sterile, are usually castrated at the age of 1 – 1.5 years.

A report by Feng Dagang and Su Lei(1994) indicates that problems can occasionally arise from the castration. They record cases of strangulation of the small intestine by the free *vas deferens*, which is thought to have been excessively stretched during castration. The *vas deferens* was found to have wrapped itself around the small intestine as a result of strenuous movement on the part of the animal during work or other activity, when high abdominal pressure had forced a section of the intestine into the urogenital fold which had previously been ripped open during castration. Once diagnosed, a simple operation rectified the problem in most cases.

Harvesting down and coarse hair

In China, shearing takes place usually once a year in May and June. Cutting and plucking are alternatives to shearing. The down hair can be combed out prior to shearing. Prior to harvesting the fleece, the yak is taken into a pen and the legs tied.

When shearing, the predominant method of harvesting the fleece, the long hair and the down are taken off together and are separated afterwards. The whole body is shorn, but only a little is taken off the tail, as long tail hair may be used later. Shearing is illustrated in Figure 8.10.

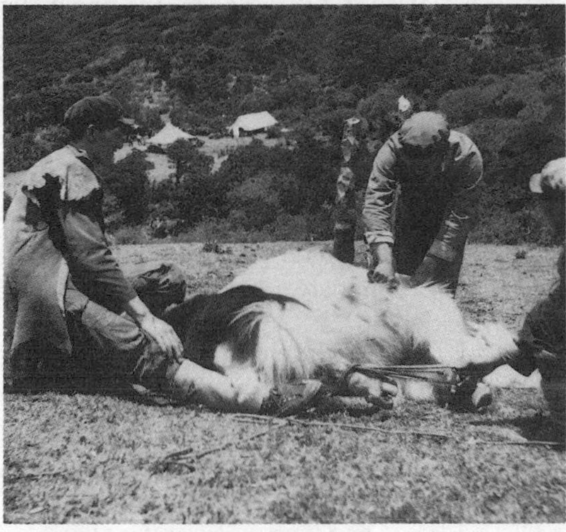

Figure 8.10 Shearing of yak

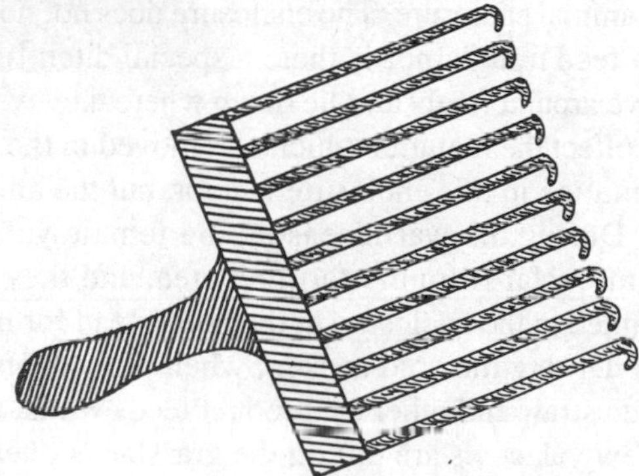

Figure 8.11 Comb used for harvesting yak down

The fleece can also be cut with a Tibetan knife, but in that case the fibre remaining on the yak is longer than after shearing and the total fleece yield and its down content are lower.

A plucking procedure of harvesting the fleece involves grasping little groups of hair at a time, twining these around a wooden, mallet-shaped stick and pulling sharply. The yak jumps with pain at every pluck, but this is thought, by the local people, to promote the growth of hair. The plucked hair contains little down and what is left behind may be gathered later or allowed to be shed.

With once-a-year harvesting, the content of down is low, irrespective of the method of harvesting used. The down hair felts readily and the quality is poor. With the increasing value of the down hairs for textiles, better methods of harvesting are being popularised. Combing out the down with a wire comb, with teeth 1 cm distant and 10 cm long (Figure 8.11), provides a greater yield and better quality. Shearing then follows some time after the combing.

If down fibre is not to be lost, combing needs to start before it begins to shed – this is about 20 days prior to the normal time for a single shearing. Although such separate combing and shearing involves the yak being caught and restrained twice, and uses more labour, it can be economically efficient if the price for the fine down fibre is high enough. Machinery for combing is being developed to increase both the speed of harvesting and the yield of down.

Management of yak in agricultural areas

In some of the areas of China with yak there is a relatively good micro-climate and some parts are suitable for tilling. This happens mostly in valleys at lower altitudes and near some streams. These are sub-alpine or agricultural-pastoral regions. Some pure yak are kept, but F1 hybrids (Piennius) predominate. Herds are small and the pure yak and the crossbred animals are mixed.

The farmers involved have a permanent house, usually two or three storeys high. The upper floors are for the family and the ground floor provides an enclosure for the animals – horses, cattle (including the yak), sheep, goats and pigs, all together. Usually, there is no window to the enclosure, and a single gate serves both people and animals. A small courtyard often supplies the light and ventilation for the animal enclosure. The enclosure does not normally have a separate bedding area or a feed trough, nor is there a special ditch for collecting the dung. The animals move around freely and lie down where they wish. Sometimes, weeds are put down to collect the manure, which is removed in the spring prior to cultivating the land. Sanitation in this enclosure is poor, but the animals keep warm.

During the warm season, the female yak and F1 hybrids are driven to the pastures, far from the farming area, and they are milked there. A few cows are retained in the enclosure at the homestead for milking and graze nearby during the day. During the cold season, when the yak and F1 females are housed, they are given straw and other by-product feeds whilst also grazing stubble during the day. A few yak cows are left on the grasslands over winter.

The use of the yak and the crosses as draught and pack animals is of particular importance, although they are also used for milk and meat. The males – both pure yak and crossbred – kept for work are castrated and have nose rings inserted at the age of one year. They start to be trained for work from the age of 2 years and start working around the age of 3 or 4 years.

During the busy period of spring cultivation, the animals used for ploughing are given supplementary feed, such as barley grain or peas. The animals plough for about 8–10 hours daily and receive the supplementary feed at night.

A typical ploughing schedule (as at the Tuobo township of Ganzi County in Sichuan) is as follows:

06.00 – 07.00	give grass and access to water
07.00 – 08.00	allow rest in preparation for work
08.00 – 10.00	ploughing
10.00 – 11.00	rest (at ploughing site), give barley straw
11.00 – 13.00	ploughing
13.00 – 15.00	resting; supplementary feeding of grass and other feed, provide water
15.00 – 17.00	ploughing

17.00 – 17.30	short rest; give supplementary feed and grass
17.30 – 19.30	ploughing
19.30 – 20.00	stop work and return to pen (or graze); provide water
20.00 – 01.00	provide grass and grain; and comb the animal
01.00 – 06.00	animals housed or allowed to graze outside.

During the busiest part of the season, ploughing may continue for 10 hours a day and the return for feeding and rest in the evening may be delayed for a couple of hours.

After the period of cultivation is over, the draught animals are driven to natural grazings and stay there until the winter, when they are housed. Some of the draught steers are used as pack animals, after a period of rest following the ploughing. Both yak and F1 steers are used as pack animals. The animals work all the year round with little rest, apart from the autumn when the grass is forming seed and the animals are allowed to graze and get fat. When working, the pack animals will walk continuously for 7–10 days and then rest for 1 or 2. The animals walk during daylight hours and graze and feed at night. A typical schedule is as follows:

04.00 – 06.00	muster the pack animals from their grazing, saddle up and tie on loads. The drivers have their breakfast
06.00 – 09.00	on journey (the loads may be re-arranged on the way)
09.00 – 10.30	rest with loads; grazing allowed on adjacent grassland
10.30 – 13.00	on journey
13.00 – 14.00	rest period without grazing
14.00 – 17.00	on journey
17.00 – 18.00	stop for night, unload animals, let animals on to grassland for grazing, drinking water and resting until 04.00 the following morning, when the procedure is repeated.

Yak and the crossbred animals used for carrying loads are also used for riding. They may be saddled for riding or not. They are not harnessed like horses; a nose rope is all that is required by the rider to control speed and direction. Figure 8.12 shows a yak with rider.

Figure 8.12 Riding (both yak and crossbred animals are used)

9 SOME OBSERVATIONS ON DISEASE IN THE YAK

OVERVIEW

Yak are prone to most of the diseases recorded for cattle world-wide. From specific studies and surveys it appears that the incidences of some of the diseases may be high and this is attributed to lack of economic incentive for prevention and treatment in many cases. Some important diseases have, however, been controlled or eradicated by vaccination.

Introduction

Most of the general literature on the yak highlights the remarkable ability of the animals to reproduce, survive and perform in an exceptionally harsh environment. The inference might be that the hardiness of the yak also reflects healthiness, in the sense of absence of, or resistance to, disease. It is important, therefore, to include a brief section in this book to indicate that yak are prone to most or all the diseases found in cattle elsewhere and that losses associated with such diseases are often quite high.

Information on the insidious losses of production from disease are not readily available, though the consequent economic loss could be high. Some records are kept at animal husbandry and veterinary stations of annual death rates, and clinical cases are recognised by herdsmen. Vaccines and other prophylactic measures, as well as curative treatments, are not widely used even when they are indicated and are known to be effective. Rinderpest is the exception where eradication schemes have been successfully practised.

The general paucity of treatment of disease is an unfortunate consequence of a several factors including the remoteness of much of the yak territory, the low cost-effectiveness of treatment (especially as treatment costs may often be relatively high), the traditional nature of much of yak keeping and, simply, a lack of knowledge on the part of herdsmen. However, the extent to which these factors operate differ from region to region and among countries with yak, because there are regional and national differences in the inputs of technical and veterinary advice to herdsmen and in the size and degree of organisation of yak herds. Moreover, in some countries and in relation to some diseases, vaccination is provided free by the State.

Only diseases which can result in high mortality, or are among the more commonly reported for yak will be listed here. The overall incidences of the diseases listed is not usually available, or known, from the specific studies quoted for the yak population at large; however, the prevalence of the conditions is sometimes inferred by the authors.

Contagious and infectious diseases

Anthrax

The disease has a long history in China. Herdsmen recognise the clinical symptoms of the disease and its danger to themselves and do not eat the meat of affected yak. Vaccination of yak is also used to control it in many areas. Lu and Ling (1985 a, b) record, from earlier years (1958, 1960), incidences of around 4% and mortality of 19% in a part of Sichuan and incidences ranging from low to high, but all with high mortality rates, for areas of Tibet.

Calf scours

Scours in young calves, mostly from birth to 4 days of age, are reported as a major cause of loss in two studies with yak. Both studies implicate *E. coli*. Yan and Ran (1981) reported an incidence of almost 80% within the first month of life falling to around 20% after that. In general, recovery rates are high if anti-bacterial treatment is given, but such treatment is not widespread. In a study by the Agricultural Research Institute of Ganzi (1977) a mortality rate of 67.5% among affected calves was noted. Clearly, this cannot be the normal situation, or too few calves would survive to replace the herds, but it does indicate that the problem of infectious diarrhoea can be very serious in yak calves. A high incidence of scouring in calves could, it is thought, be associated with the custom of tying up calves at the same place at the campsite for several months at a time, resulting in poor hygiene.

Contagious bovine pleuropneumonia

In some parts of the world this disease was regarded as the biggest killer of cattle next to Rinderpest. It occurs among yak between 2 and 10 years old, principally in winter and spring when the animals are more closely confined. In one such season, Hu and Cai Li (1960) recorded an exceptionally high incidence of 54% in Ganzi county of Sichuan province. Lu and Ling (1985a) reported an incidence of 1.9% for herds in Tibet and a mortality of around 17% among those affected. Though vaccination is an effective option for control it is not widely practised.

Foot and Mouth disease

This disease was well-known in yak in the past. In 1960 an outbreak was recorded in Ganzi county of Sichuan with an infection rate of 72% and a mortality rate of about 4%. Strain O caused the highest mortality. Joshi (1982) reports a number of outbreaks in different parts of Nepal both among yak and crosses of yak with local cattle. He states that quarantine of affected animals is used in alpine regions of Nepal with the intention of allowing the lesions to heal and that vaccination, though effective, is not widely used. Pal (1993a) refers to an outbreak in Sikkim in 1973 caused by the virus of strain A. Prasad *et al*. (1978) reported an outbreak among yak in the State of Himachal Pradesh. Virus of strain O, previously reported from Nepal, was isolated in that outbreak.

Keratoconjunctivitis

Moraxella bovis, a cause of conjunctivitis and keratisis in yak, is also known to be present in China.

Lymphadenitis

Joshi (1982) states that this is a disease of yak causing serious economic loss. He refers to its occurrence in Nepal, but quotes a report from southern Buryatia where the incidence there was more serious – at least in the 1960's from when the report dates.

Mastitis

Mastitis occurs in yak, but it is believed that the incidence is less than among dairy cattle, perhaps on account of the relatively low milk yield of yak and the suckling of calves. An outbreak in Hongyuan county of Sichuan was reported by Weggi (1983) to be due to streptococcal infection and similar in epidemiology, clinical symptoms and response to medication to that found in cattle. The outbreak affected some 10% of the yak recorded by Weggi and coincided with a period of hot, dry weather and overcrowding on pastures at that time.

Pasteurrellosis

This disease is reported to occur every year in yak-producing areas and takes the form of haemorrhagic septicaemia. Lu and Ling (1985a) noted an incidence among yak of 0.34% with a mortality rate among affected animals of nearly 36%, in parts of Tibet between 1976 and 1979. A higher incidence and mortality (2.3% and 88.5% respectively) was reported by Yang (1987) from Baiyu county (Sichuan). Joshi (1982) notes the occurrence of haemorrhagic septicaemia among crosses of yak with local cattle in many districts of Nepal, but makes the point that these are in the lower and middle hill regions where the disease can be virulent and result in high mortality, and that the incidence is much more limited in the higher alpine areas. Pal (1993) also quotes the occurrence of the disease among yak in India.

Pox

Joshi (1982) refers to the susceptibility of yak to both the cow pox and the buffalo pox virus, but states that the disease had not been recorded in Nepal. Similarly he notes that yak can contract vesicular stomatitis (with symptoms which can be confused with foot and mouth disease), but no data on incidence or distribution are given.

Rabies

Rabies is reported from time to time among yak in China and Joshi (1982) notes this also for Nepal, but states that cases in yak are very rare. He quotes one case of rabies in a pack yak which was bitten on its muzzle by a rabid dog, whilst the yak was carrying a load.

Rinderpest

When rinderpest occurs, yak are said to be highly susceptible and to die rapidly. In China, the disease has been eradicated, through vaccination, since 1955. Prior to that the disease was widespread (Liang Daxin, 1948) and around one million yak are said to have died of it in between 1928 and 1941 in the provinces of Qinghai, Gansu and Sichuan alone. A further outbreak in Qinghai in 1944, also reported by Liang Daxin, claimed 20 thousand yak within 7 months. Joshi (1982) refers to outbreaks with mortality rates up to 90% in parts of Nepal prior to 1966. Vaccination programmes such as those in Mongolia and the former USSR, as in China and elsewhere, may well have brought the disease under control.

Salmonellosis

This disease is common among yak in China, mostly among calves between 15 and 60 days of age (*S. Ttyphimurium*, *S. dublin* and *S. newport* have been isolated). Between 1960 and 1980 an incidence of 40% with a mortality rate of 35% has been recorded for 5 counties of Gansu province (Lu, 1986). Similar studies from 25 counties in Tibet (1976–1979) recorded 5.2% incidence and 26% mortality (Lu and Ling, 1985a) and 10.5% incidence with 56% mortality in Qinghai (Deng, 1983). Effective vaccines have been produced in several of the Chinese provinces, but are not widely used by the herdsmen.

Tuberculosis

Although the disease is known to occur in yak there is little information available and no control scheme. Lu and Ling (1985a) tested 1749 yak in Tibet with a single intradermal test and found 12.7% of animals to react positively but some of these showed no other visible lesions.

Diseases of the reproductive tract

Brucellosis

This infectious disease is common among yak and its crosses and the more important because of it is readily transmitted to man. In Sichuan, Qinghai and Tibet, sample groups of yak were tested over the period 1952–1981 and an average of 17.4% (1.8%–56.3%) tested positive (Local Disease Control Office, 1983). Wang and Yao (1984) reported that between 12.9% and 17.1% of yak in various groups, on Haiyan pastures in Qinghai province, had positive tests, and also that there was a significant reservoir of *Brucella* infection among wild animals as well as among sheep and dogs. These would help to maintain the infection among the yak provided the strains involved are the same. Yuan (1979) examined 49 Maiwa yak in Honyuan county (Sichuan) by serum agglutination test and obtained 12.6% positive reactions. Joshi (1982) also refers to a substantial incidence of positive tests and clinical disease in Nepal, countries of the former USSR and Mongolia. He noted the widespread use of vaccination programmes in both the latter countries.

Both *B. melintensis* and *B. abortus* have been identified as agents with the former the more prevalent in China with the latter more commonly isolated in the former USSR (Joshi, 1982). The strain of *B. melintensis* found most commonly was biovar 3, followed by biovar 2 (Chen, 1983; Peng, 1987). Diagnosis and testing, which depend on laboratory methods, is undertaken mostly for investigation purposes and not in practical yak production. Vaccination is sometimes used to reduce the spread and prevalence of the disease, but this practice is not widespread. Testing and slaughter are not considered to be viable options for control – at least not in the present circumstances of yak husbandry. The implications of Brucellosis in yak for human health may require consideration.

Enzootic abortion

Shuai Yongru *et al.* (1988) report that abortions in yak, in a part of Qinghai province, were diagnosed as caused by *Chlamydia psittaci* infection. Tests on serum samples collected on yak that had aborted resulted in 45 of 155 samples testing positive. This study shows in respect of this form of abortion, as for many diseases, that yak are susceptible and that the infection exists in yak producing areas. It does not indicate the overall incidence of the disease in that area of the country, or whether it is prevalent elsewhere.

Leptospirosis

This disease, which causes a generalised but serious illness in the animals, was reported to have occurred in parts of Sichuan in the period 1980–82, according to a report by Cheng *et al.* (1985). These authors recorded an incidence of 10–20% and a mortality of 30–50%. Agglutination and complement fixation tests on 187 serum samples were positive in 53 cases.

Camphylobacter jijunni

This infection has been recorded as a cause of infertility in yak.

Diseases and parasites of the skin

Various contagious skin diseases including ringworm (attributed to the fungi *Trichophyton* and *Microsporum*) and a chronic dermatitis, caused by the bacterium *Dermatophilus* congolensis, are reported to occur in yak.

Ectoparasites

Ticks, lice and mites have all been found in yak, though herdsmen do not, in general, recognise their importance or the irritant effect on the animals. A report by Biswas *et al.* (1994) documents infestations with ticks and lice among yak in tracts of Arunachal Pradesh of India and lists the types found and the sites of infection. Joshi (1982) refers to both mites and ticks among yak in Nepal and draws attention to the possible disease transmission caused by ticks among the livestock there.

Yak hypodermiasis (warble or gad fly)

On the basis of a study by Wang Yanhong (1994), yak hypodermiasis is a significant problem in yak. Tianzhu White yak are given special mention. Larvae, from warble fly (gad fly), cause damage to the skin as they burrow and emerge from the hide particularly on the back and loin of the yak. Apart from physical damage to the hide and loss of its value, there is irritation to tissues and secretion of toxins which retard growth and development in young yak and reduce milk yield and meat yield of adults. Death results in severe cases. Intra-muscular injection of a vermicide was fully effective in killing the larvae. In one trial, 110 out of 2393 untreated yak died, but out of 500 which had been injected only 2 died; the treated yak were also in better condition.

Internal parasites

Liver fluke

This is a common condition in yak in China and elsewhere where wet conditions exist. Infection rates of 20–50% are common. Shugin Cheng *et al.* (1994) refer to the disease caused by *Fasciola hepatica* as one of the major health problems of the grassland industry of China and provide references showing infection rates of up to 80% of yak on some pastoral farms. Zhu *et al.* (1986) collected more than 7000 snails in three areas of Sichuan and found the principal host snail to be *Galba pervia*. Herdsmen try to control infection by restricting grazing of yak on marshland in the spring to only half a day at a time and to prevent access to marshland after rain. Marshlands are also burnt in winter. Dosing with triclabenzadole is effective in yak (Zhu *et al.* 1982), but the extent to which it is used is not recorded.

Joshi (1982) notes significant infection by liver fluke of both yak and their crosses with cattle in many villages in Nepal.

Roundworms

A recent report by Liu (1994), from studies in Tibet, suggests that roundworm infestations and the associated larvae may be a common problem in yak, though not as extensive as among the sheep on the same pastures. Many genera of roundworm were isolated but the prevalence of different genera varied with the time year. Pal (1993) quotes one study on yak in Sikkim showing 62% of yak infected with helminths.

Miscellaneous

Botulism

This condition might also have been listed under bacterial diseases since the toxin which causes the poisoning, often followed by death, is produced by *Clostridium botulinum* (type C has been identified in Tibet). Botulism was common among yak in China prior to 1955, but since then the incidence has declined. However, Lu and Ling (1985a) recorded 9193 cases in some counties of Tibet between 1971 and 1979, of which 4048 were fatal. Vaccination is used as control in some areas. The bacterium multiples rapidly in dead carcasses and it seems likely that the access which yak have to these is accentuated by the custom of disposing of the carcass remnants and bones of slaughtered animals on pastures near the campsites of the herdsmen. Carcasses of animals which have died on the range are another source of infection. The yak may become infected either through direct chewing of bones of such carcasses, something they are known to do in cases of mineral deficiency, phosphorus in particular, or the infection may be picked up from polluted water.

Pal (1993) quotes the occurrence of botulism (strains B and C) from several countries with yak.

Pyrrolizidine alkaloid poisoning

Large numbers of deaths among yak in one part of Bhutan were found by Winter *et al.* (1992, 1994) to be due to Pyrrolizidine alkaloid poisoning. Several toxic plants were found to be involved, with species of *Senecio* predominating. It was concluded that the yak had been induced to eat these plants, which they would normally avoid, due to hunger arising from overgrazing of the pastures concerned. This matter was also been referred to in chapter 8.

Mineral and trace element deficiency

Problems of mineral or trace element deficiency or imbalance are not specifically reported in the literature from yak-producing countries. Such mineral-related problems, if they exist, are often difficult to recognise except in extreme cases – even though dietary mineral deficiency, excess or imbalance can lead to reduced animal performance. Herdsmen generally provide additional salt, and sometimes mineral mixtures, though whether from need, or as a means of attracting the animal, is not clear. Mineral-related problems would, in any case, be most likely to represent deficiencies or imbalances of dietary origin and not a particular attribute of the yak.

It is of interest, therefore, to record an observation from Whipsnade Wild Animal Park in England, where a small herd of yak have lived since the 1940's, which indicates that the yak there show several of the symptoms of copper deficiency on the same diet that other *Bovidae* and, local domestic cattle in particular, find adequate, or nearly so, in respect of copper content (Nick Lindsay, Curator, and Edmund Flack, veterinarian at Whipsnade, personal communication, 1994). In consequence, the yak require regular copper supplementation of their diet and occasional copper injection. Health, vigour and performance of the yak has improved as a result (E. Flack, personal communication, 1994).

The purpose of referring to this matter here is that it could be of wider concern to yak husbandry. Genetically controlled differences in copper uptake from the diet have been well established in sheep and more tentatively in cattle (for a review see Wiener, 1987). The report from Whipsnade Park suggests at least the possibility that yak may have inadequate copper uptake due to an inherently low capacity of yak to absorb dietary copper. If this were established to be the case in the native territories of yak, it could be of practical benefit in yak production. This is so because copper has an important role in the formation and function of several of the enzymes which are critically involved in animal growth, reproduction and health – and all of these can be impaired by copper deficiency. A remedy could be provided by suitable supplements, but care would be needed not to provide copper in excess.

10 PRODUCTS FROM YAK AND THEIR UTILISATION

OVERVIEW

Almost everything from the yak is used to sustain the life of the herdsmen and their families and is used either directly or sold to provide an income.

Milk in its raw state is used principally in tea, which is drunk liberally. Butter, made in traditional fashion, is the main product from the milk in most places, and has many uses apart from its use as food. Skim milk is used in a variety of ways, including a form of cottage cheese ("milk residue"). A Swiss-type manufactured cheese is made especially in Nepal.

Meat is obtained mostly from animals slaughtered before the onset of winter when they are in good condition. but animals which die accidentally are also used. Meat is used fresh, but for longer periods after being naturally frozen. Meat is also preserved by drying. Dried meat keeps longer than frozen. Sausage is made both from meat and from blood, or from a mixture of the two. Some parts of the viscera are eaten, others are used as casings for sausage or as storage containers for other products. Much of the viscera and the bones are not used and left on the pastures where this material can become a pollutant.

The hides are processed simply and dried before tanning locally or in factories. The leather has many different uses. Pelts of calves that have died are also processed and made into coats for children. The coarse hair and the fine down find many uses from making ropes to garments to tents. The yak tail is also used ceremonially and as a fly-whisk. Faeces of the yak after drying is used principally as a fuel by the herdsmen.

Introduction

The herdsmen and their families obtain nearly everything they need for their living from the yak. The direct products from the yak during its lifetime are milk, hair and down, draught power, and dung for fuel, and after slaughter there is the meat and various products from the organs and non-consumable parts of the body and the hide. Most of what is produced is used by the herdsmen and their families themselves, but some of it is sold. Income can be derived from most of the products and also from the sale of pack animals and animals for breeding. Where yak herds are in the proximity of hill towns and villages, there is a ready market for the products and a further cash value to yak production.

At present, most of the things sold from the yak are primary products, or close to primary, and so the economy based on the yak benefits only little from the added value that accrues from processing, or from the manufacture of more sophisticated products. Butter and various forms of soft cheese, made by the herdspeople, are sold or used in barter for other necessities – and sometimes, as in parts of India (chapter 11), used as a means of paying rental for grazing land. Factories built in Nepal for the manufacture of a Swiss-style hard cheese and in China for the manufacture of yak leather goods and textiles, are the beginnings of developments designed to provide new markets for the pastoral peoples. These developments arise from national concerns to raise the living standards of the peoples in these remote mountain areas and to improve the economies of these regions.

The rest of this chapter considers the products and describes briefly how they are traditionally and, for the most part, currently used. In general, what follows applies to yak-producing parts of China in particular. It is likely, however, that the traditional methods of making and using yak products are essentially similar among yak herders in most areas.

Milk and its products

Though the milk yield of individual yak females is low, there are many of them so the total quantity produced is substantial. Milk is used primarily in the areas of the country where yak are most widely distributed and in the regions of the mountain pastures. In areas where yak have only relatively recently been introduced, on the periphery of the main area, there is no tradition of using milk from the yak or from the crosses of yak males with the females of local cattle. The latter give little milk and are used mainly for draught purposes. In recent years the price of yak milk has become high in China and, as a result, is an important part of the herders' income.

Raw milk

Whole milk is usually drunk only by people who are ill or weak, but it is also given to children and old people. Some of this milk is drunk raw, being considered more nutritious that way, but mostly the milk is boiled first, as now encouraged on grounds of health and hygiene.

Yak milk yield, as evident from the results given in chapter 6, has a high content of solids – around 18%, including about 7% of fat. The milk has a fragrant, sweetish smell and whole milk also tastes somewhat sweet even without adding sugar – so when drunk by herdsmen sugar is never added.

Raw milk, as a drink, is used mainly for the beverage called "milk tea" – a mixture of tea and milk – drunk at all times of the year. This is a staple part of the diet of the herders and their families. In the warm season, when there is plenty of milk available, or when given to guests, the brew will contain 20% milk or even more; the colour of the drink is yellow. Herdsmen and their families themselves more usually drink a light tea with only 5% milk added and the colour then is milky white with a little yellow. The milk-tea is brewed from tea leaves (cut from a tea brick) which are added to water and boiled for a few minutes; raw milk is added in the proportion required and boiling continues for a further few minutes. Some people may add a little salt. Sugar is never added, but the milk itself has already, as noted earlier, a sweetish taste. Also, mostly Tibetan people, may add some Zanba to the brew, making it both a food and a drink for themselves and their guests. Zanba (also tsampa) is the staple food of Tibet. It consists of roasted oat or barley flour, or a mixture of the two, made into a paste with yak butter and usually rolled into balls for eating.

Normally, whole milk is used in the tea, but skim milk is also used so as to increase the amount of butter that can be produced from the available milk supply.

Milk when boiled up with mushrooms produces something regarded as a delicacy by the herdspeople. Salt is usually added to milk-mushrooms – and the boiling is thought to give protection from poisoning in case the wrong mushrooms have been used.

Raw milk is also sold to milk powder plants, which have been built in recent years to produce milk powder as well as butter and other milk products. Some milk is sold for direct consumption in towns and villages in the upland areas.

Raw butter

Raw butter is the principal product from yak milk and it represents one of the staple foods of the local people. The raw butter contains 12–15% water, 1% protein and the rest fat. (Old butter contains about 3% water.) Raw butter production is regarded as the yardstick by which to measure the quality of yak, and herdsmen pay great attention to it.

There are two main ways in which the herdsmen make yak butter in China. The traditional and still most prevalent method is to squeeze the butter in a bag made of hide. The other method is to make it in a churn. Milk separators are coming into use in some areas and reduce the amount of work needed to make the butter. Cream separated in this way prior to churning produces the best butter with a lower water content and longer storage life than the older methods.

Making butter by churning involves allowing the milk to stand for a day to ferment. The milk is then heated to about 20° C. The warm milk is poured into a churn set aside for the purpose and varying in size up to 80cm high and 60 cm in diameter. A stick for stirring is held in the centre of the churn by the lid. Figure 10.1 shows a medium-sized churn in use. The herdsmen (more often the womenfolk) rotate the stick until the fat solidifies and it is difficult to churn further. The churning takes between 1 and 4 hours depending on the size of the churn used and the quantity of milk. The herdsmen then remove, by hand, the lumps of milk fat floating on the surface and wash it in water. Next, water is squeezed out and the butter is formed

Figure 10.1 Butter making in a churn

into cylindrical or cube-shaped blocks by using a plank of wood. Lastly, the raw butter is wrapped for storage in a bag of calf hide or yak rumen. Each bag weighs approximately 50 kg. The butter will keep usable in this way for one or two years without going mouldy, but not usually for longer.

To make butter in a hide bag, the milk is first heated, as before, and poured into the bag made of calf or goat hide. The herdsman blows into the bag to expand it and closes the opening. The bag is then shaken until the fat solidifies into globules, when the contents of the bag are poured into another container. The rest of the procedure is similar to that already described.

Before using a milk separator, the milk is first heated to 30–35°C and then filtered. The separator operates by turning a handle at a standard speed until the fat has separated from the other components. The fat and skim milk are then put in separate containers, and the rest of the process of making the butter is as before.

Some herdsmen add a little sour milk as a starter to the raw milk in order to increase the amount of butter made.

Raw butter is used for number of foods including Zanba (see above), pancakes and dishes fried in butter. It is also added to milk-tea and consumed salted or unsalted according to the area. When milk is not available, butter is used in tea in some areas in place of raw milk. Some of the people, however, drink butter-tea from choice, particularly, it is said, herdsmen in North-west Sichuan and in Tibetan pastoral areas.

Another use, is to mix melted butter with roasted flour, in equal quantities. The mixture is then kneaded and stored until used. When required, this dough is melted into salted or sugared water and eaten in that way or further mixed with seeds such as peanut, sesame, walnut, soybean or mixed with Chinese dates. These ingredients add flavour and make the food a favourite among Tibetan people for welcoming their guests.

Butter is used also for many purposes other than food, including its use for tanning and for polishing fur coats. It is used as a fuel in domestic lamps and by lamas in sacred lamps, but also on family altars. Butter is also used by women on their skin, it may be used as hair grease, and it is used as a lubricant to assist in hand milking. Butter is a component of some Tibetan medicine. When mixed with different colouring materials, butter is also used to make moulded sculptures. Larrick and Burck (1986) describe some of these sculptures as huge – sometimes two or three storeys high – and fashioned by monks for religious ceremonies and New Year celebrations.

"Toffee"

Larrick and Burck (1986) also refer to a product the consistency of toffee (korani, in Sherpa) made by boiling milk very slowly to dehydrate it.

Milk residue

Some "milk residue" (as it is called by the herdsmen) is normally made from skimmed milk but occasionally from whole milk. Whichever milk is used, it is heated to 50–60°C and sour milk added to make the liquid curdle. The mixture is poured into a wicker basket or gauze bag to allow the whey to run off. The curds are then spread on a cloth to dry. The "milk-residue" from skimmed milk is white and hard, that from whole milk yellow and brittle. The protein content is around 55% and the lactose 21%.

The milk residue, which is a form of cheese, is served as a snack on its own or mixed with butter Zanba. It is also used in other ways such as fried or eaten with added salt and sugar.

Milk cake

This is a product mainly of whole milk, though sometimes skimmed milk is used. It is similar in production to "milk residue" but is harder and looks like "cake". It is usually eaten with butter and sugar to make it more tasty to the herdsmen and it is one of the dishes offered to guests.

Sour milk

Sour milk is a favourite among herdsmen and their families all year round but especially in the warm season when milk is being produced. Freshly boiled milk is poured into a pail and when the temperature has fallen to 50°C a little sour milk is added and mixed until the temperature has dropped to 40°C. The pail is then covered and wrapped in wool to keep it warm. Five or six hours later in the warm season, and longer in winter, the milk will have soured. This product can be made from either whole or skimmed milk – the former having more colour and taste. The sour milk is drunk alone or sometimes mixed with Zanba

Sharma *et al*. (1989) mention the use of milk to make alcoholic drinks in Mongolia.

Whey

After butter and milk-residue have been made, the whey is rarely used in the pastoral regions. But in the agricultural-pastoral areas it can be used to feed pigs. The whey is, however, also used in traditional processes for making leather.

Cheese

In Nepal, cheese factories have been set up by the government to make a valuable, high-quality Swiss-style cheese. This is sold in towns mostly to tourists on account of the high price for the cheese. In 1971–72 there were 8 cheese factories producing 230 000 kg cheese (Joshi 1982). By 1993, there were 9 such factories, but the quantity of cheese manufactured had trebled and, in addition, 30 000 kg of butter were made in these factories (Joshi *et al*., 1994). Sharma *et al*. (1989) also refers to cheese production in Mongolia.

Meat and its products

Yak are an important source of meat for the herdsmen and their families, but the meat is also sold. Even in areas and countries where religious taboos inhibit the slaughter of the animals the meat is eaten, but professional butchers, rather than the owners of the animals, do the slaughtering. As Joshi (1982) explains for the situation in Nepal, ordinary cattle there are protected by law, but the legal code is unclear in relation to yak. Larrick and Burck (1986) make a similar point in respect of parts of Tibet.

Animals that die accidentally are quite commonly eaten, even where killing is not the norm.

For the many yak slaughtered every year, this is done before the onset of winter when the animals are in their best condition. Some of the meat is consumed fresh and much else is frozen in nature's own "deep freeze" and stored in that way. Meat is also dried and keeps longer that way than when frozen.

The herders and their families eat meat mostly for the 4 to 5 months following slaughter. Yak are not slaughtered deliberately in spring or early summer because they are in poor condition and very lean at that time – though a few yak may die or be killed as casualties. Herdsmen therefore rarely eat yak meat from April to July, although dried yak meat is still available.

Over recent years, the Chinese government has built a number of small meat packing and storage plants in the cold pastoral regions. This has allowed more slaughtering of yak at the best time and has also extended the storage season for frozen yak meat and meat products, including some retail cuts of meat. Most of this is supplied to cities.

Commercial slaughter houses taking in yak also exist in Mongolia and some other countries.

Fresh yak meat

The quality of yak "beef" is at its best in the autumn because of the good condition of the animals at that time. The method of butchering and eating by the herdspeople is quite simple. The carcass is cut into large cubes and these are then boiled in fresh water for a few minutes and the pieces of meat eaten with salt with the help of a Tibetan knife. Milk-tea is taken at the same time. When guests are present, the meal is made more elaborate. Boiled rib-meat from the yak as well as from sheep will be put on a plate to be eaten with the hand. There may be a steamed bun stuffed with chopped yak meat to which salt, condiments and fat have been added. The casing of the bun is thin as the flour has not been fermented. Sausage (see below) may also be served to the guests. Thawed, frozen yak meat has the same flavour as fresh.

Air-dried meat

Prior to winter, the herdsmen living on the uplands cut yak meat into long narrow strips (approximately 4–5 cm wide and 30 cm long) and dry these suspended from woven-hair ropes. Drying takes only a few days. The air-dried meat will keep for one or two years either hung in a tent or stored in hide bags – this is longer than for the naturally frozen meat.

The air-dried meat is very dry indeed and has a distinctive flavour. Some of this dried meat is eaten as it is, only cutting or tearing the strips into smaller pieces; and milk-tea is drunk as an accompaniment. When cooking the dried meat, there are two main methods. One is to roast it by burying the meat in the stove, fuelled by yak dung, until the meat smells fragrant. It is then taken out, cleaned and cut into pieces with a knife. The other method is to soak the dried meat for several hours and then boil it in water. Salt and condiments are not usually added.

There is also "bacon-beef" which is similar to air-dried beef, but the fresh meat strips are first salted in a container for one or two days and then hung over the stove in the herdsman's tent to smoke. This again can be eaten either raw or cooked. The "bacon-beef", however, is a product of the warm and rainy season and is made from the meat cut by the herdsmen from yak that have died of old age or from disease, or have been killed by wolves.

Sausage

There are two main types of filling – blood and meat. The casing for the sausages comes from the cleaned, large or small intestine of the yak. Sausage, and in particular the blood sausage, is made at the time the yak are slaughtered.

Blood sausage. The blood used is that from the thoracic cavity of the yak. To maximise the amount of blood there, herdsmen do not use what would be regarded as the normal method of slaughter, but resort to a way of asphyxiating the yak. When dead, the yak is skinned and the heart and lungs are removed and the large quantity of blood in the thoracic cavity drained off and used for making the sausage.

Zanba and salt are added to the blood to make it into a paste before filling the clean, small intestine. This is then tied into segments (20–30 cm long) with sinew from yak, or with hemp rope. In some areas, a little yak meat is added to the sausage mix and this is considered the more tasty. The blood-sausage is boiled in water and eaten either at the time it is made or after it has hung in house or tent. The sausage may also be roasted on top of the stove fuelled by yak dung.

Larrick and Burck (1986) also refer to the occasional use, in an area of Tibet, of blood bled deliberately from the yak, ostensibly for the sake of its health. Joshi (1982) refers to a similar practice in Nepal. This blood, when solidified, is eaten fried or boiled, or mixed with Zanba and baked into a form of bread. Perhaps a litre of blood (maybe a little more or a little less) is taken from the jugular vein and the blood is then used for consumption as described.

Meat sausage. This is usually encased in the large intestine. It is composed of 50% yak meat, 25% visceral fat and 25% blood. The meat and fat are chopped into pieces and salt and condiment and the blood are added before the mixture is put in its casing. The filled large intestine is tied into segments as for blood sausage – though the segments are usually larger (about 50 cm long). In Tibet, the herdsmen usually consume the sausage fresh – it is boiled in water for about 2 hours, and the casing is pierced with a needle to prevent it bursting. The meat sausage can be stored for about one month.

In more recent years, herdsmen living on the cold grasslands have taken to filling the intestine of pigs with a mixture of diced yak meat, diced pork fat, salt and condiment. The sausage is tied, as before, into segments (15 cm long), small holes are pierced in the casing and then hung up in the house to be dried, prior to eating.

Viscera and offal

There are large quantities of viscera and offal from the animals that are slaughtered, but they are not all used. Much is lost and is left on the pastures, which is a waste of a resource and can become a pollutant. There is a potential for better utilisation – the problem arises from the likely further costs involved in such utilisation relative to the potentially low value of the product.

Viscera. Herdsmen divide viscera into edible and inedible parts. The parts regarded as edible are heart, stomach including rumen, small and large intestine, liver and kidney. The other parts of the viscera are classed as inedible by the herdsmen and, interestingly include the lungs and the pancreas which are eaten in some other parts of the world.

When yak have been slaughtered in meat processing plants more of the viscera are eaten. Viscera from these yak are also used for making medicine which is sold both locally and in the cities. The exceptions are the spleen and the pancreas, which if used at all are kept only as dog food.

Offal. By tradition, all inedible parts (apart from hair and hide) are regarded as offal and much of it is discarded on the grasslands. Some of it is cooked as dog food. The discard includes, in addition to parts of the viscera, the horns and hoof, the contents of the alimentary tract and blood, other than that in the thoracic cavity (used in sausage making). (The bones are also discarded in this way if there is no market for them). If not eaten by birds of prey, the discarded offal can become a source of pollution when it decomposes.

The thick horn of the yak bull, as already referred to, is used as a feeding bottle for rearing calves. The empty gallbladder can be used as a casing for sausage or as a container for butter or milk. The bladder and the male reproductive organs find a use in Chinese medicine. In particular, the penis of the male yak is regarded as a strong aphrodisiac.

Hide and pelt

Yak hide is generally inferior to that from ordinary cattle. It is loose and uneven in texture and often has holes from gadfly (warble fly) in it. There are large quantities of yak hide and pelt in the pastoral areas, which have great importance in the local economy.

The method of processing the hide is very simple. The herdsmen peel the skin off the yak after slaughter, or other form of death, and spread it on the grassland to dry. After drying, the skin is sold to a tannery or used by the herdsmen. Some fresh hides are also sold without being dried.

Raw hide which has not been tanned and with the hair still uncut is used mainly to pack raw butter. It is also used as a wrapping for the wooden box used by herdsmen to transport their belongings. For this purpose, the fresh hide is cut into long pieces, tied on the wooden box and allowed to dry. Sometimes the whole hide is used for this purpose. The hide makes the box easy to carry and more difficult to break in the frequent moves made by the herdspeople. Because of the cold climate, the raw hide does not quickly go bad and can be used over and over again, even if the box inside gets broken. Raw hide can also be cut into ropes.

This traditional use of raw hide is, however, getting less frequent. More often now it is the leather, made from the hide, which is used. This has improved the utilisation of yak hides.

Leather from yak is usually tanned by a traditional method. For this purpose, the herdsman soaks the hide, removes from it the connective tissue under the skin and then spreads old, rancid butter on the skin (fresh butter is not used in tanning). The skin is then rolled up to allow the butter to soak in. Sometimes the skin may be pounded with feet or hands to help the butter to soak in completely. When the hide is fully soaked and soft it is trimmed by the herdsman using a knife. As for most procedures, a number of local variants exist in methods of tanning.

The leather is used to make bags for storing food, including milk-residue, and to make felt boots and soles. It can also be cut into strips of differing width, depending on use, as an alternative to rope for carrying water or firewood, and to tie up animals. These leather ropes can also be used with the saddle in pastoral areas and as a form of carriage for people in agricultural parts of the country.

The leather from yak has other uses too. The sliding ropes across rivers and streams in the mountains and valleys are often made from yak hide. Boats used to carry goods on, for example, the Yanlung Zangbo and the Yanlong rivers, use yak hide. Herdsmen make bags from yak hide which are then blown up and a link of 10 or more such bags is fixed to a wooden plank to make this boat, which will be 4 m long and 2 m wide.

Most pelts are made from the hides of yak calves which have died. Herdsmen skin the dead calf, remove connective tissue, and soak the skin in milk whey. After the skins have soaked for a few days they are taken out and tanned with butter to make them soft. The hair is then combed to complete the process. These yak pelts are used traditionally to make children's' coats.

According to Siegfried Scheller (personal communication to 1st international congress on yak at Gansu agricultural University, 1994) yak is one of the species which has attracted particular attention from industrial-scale manufacturers of leather in the immediate vicinity of yak herds. Such factories have been set up in parts of China, especially for processing yak hides and sheep skins. Quoting Scheller (1993), it was said that: "The leather made from yak hides for shoes, leather goods and clothing is characterised by a unique handle, an interesting grain pattern, and good wear and performance properties."

Hair and down fibre

Yak differ from other domestic cattle in that the hair is of economic use and importance. Use of the hair goes back to the time that yak were first domesticated. More recent developments, and especially since the middle of the twentieth century, have brought the use of the down into contention for quality textiles, following trials of the materials in China. Products are made from the down fibre in Shanghai and Beijing, in Sichuan province and Tibet and elsewhere. The down is used in clothes and suiting, knitted garments and blankets. The textiles made from down are considered to have a better lustre and feel than those made of wool.

Generally, in traditional use of the hair, the coarse fibres and the down are left mixed together. The uses to which the mixed fibres are put then depend on fibre length, on the position of the body from which the hair is derived and on the down content.

The long hair which grows on the fore and rear ends of the body (the "skirt" hair – see yak in Figure 10.2) and on the legs is used to make rope for tying up the tent. The method of making the rope is as follows: The longer hairs are removed from the coat and made by hand into a roll of hair about 15 cm in diameter. A single spindle fixed into the ground is then used to spin the hair into yarn of thickness and length depending on different requirements. To make the strands, one person turns the spindle by use of a hide rope while another holds the ball of hair. A rope will then be made from either three or four strands of yarn, the latter being the stronger. Rope made of yak hair is durable and withstands rain, wind and sun. Rope made from black and white yarn is liked for its appearance and is used to enhance the appearance of saddle and reins.

Figure 10.2 A yak at the Government Breeding Centre, Arunachal Pradesh, India – showing the "skirt" hair (which can sometimes reach the ground) [photo courtesy of R.N. Pal]

In local use, down hair is most often processed mixed with coarse hair. What passes as down is shorn hair from which long fibres have been removed, This comes mostly from the "skirt" hair. Down hair from the neck, shoulder and rump of the animal is used less often and is allowed to be cast onto the grazing land.

The way that the down mixture is used varies among the nationalities keeping the yak. For example, Tibetan people use the hairs mostly to make tents whilst Yi people use it to make cloaks and short jackets. The procedure is first to weave the yak hair and down mixture into a blanket and then use blankets to make tents or to sew clothes. Processing procedure depends on what is being made. Blankets of 50 cm width, for example, are woven from 2-ply yarn made into a thread. The material for the blanket is loose, clean hair shorn from the belly of the yak, with long and coarse fibres removed. A tent (Figure 10.3) may be made up of two large hair blankets interspersed with several smaller ones. Each year it may be necessary to replace one or two of the smaller blankets. Blankets are also made into a rectangular bag, used locally, with an opening in the middle.

In Jiulong county of Sichuan, the herdsmen like to wear cloaks and short jackets made of yak down-hair mixture. It is waterproof and keeps the people warm – summer or winter. The clothes are also ornamented and turned into handicrafts since the advent of better knitting and processing methods. One way to make clothes is similar to that for making tents, from blanket, but with a higher content of down in the material. Another procedure is to felt the yak down, before making clothes. The felt of yak down and hair is widely used in the pastoral areas to make pads for saddles, cushions, bedding and insoles for boots. The felt pad made from the down-hair mixture is damp proof and helps people to keep warm in what is often a damp tent.

Hairs from the tail of the yak were historically used as a tribute. White tail hairs are the best for this – and now-a-days are sold to tourists. The major uses of tail hair are for clothing and beards used in Chinese opera and for wigs. The yak tail is also used as decoration and, more practically as a fly-whisk – well-known in India but valued as such even in ancient Rome to which it was taken by merchants from the East (Zeuner, 1963).

Figure 10.3 A typical large tent

Bone

Yak bones are now less often discarded on the range than they used to be and are collected and sold for the manufacture of bone meal and glue; the bone meal being used both in feed and as manure.

Faeces

Yak faeces is used primarily as fuel by the herdsmen, but, as described earlier, is also used to make enclosures for stock and is painted on wood fencing in the cold season to fill cracks (see chapter 8).

When used as fuel, the faeces is dried. The faeces for this purpose is collected daily at the campsite at the end of the day's grazing and brought in from the range in the warm season. A stick wrapped in yak hair is used to cut the faeces into thin (1 cm) slices which are exposed to the sun for a day or longer and turned until dry on the other side. When fully dry, the faeces slices are stacked in heaps up to 2 m high and "painted" with fresh faeces to keep out rain. A drainage channel is often dug at the bottom of the heap to take away run-off water. If the heap is to be used up before the rainy season it may not be painted. Completely dry faeces is also stored in the tent ready for use.

Bezoar

One unusual product from yak, as also from other cattle, are naturally cultivated bezoar stones. They have a high cash value when sold and therefore help the herdsmen to add value to their yak production. The bezoar stones are produced in parts of Sichuan, Xingjiang and other provinces by inoculating the gallbladder of the yak with a "nucleolus" around which the aggregate forms. To do this requires a small operation performed by the herdsmen. The bezoar is sold all over the country for use in Chinese medicine.

11 YAK HUSBANDRY IN DIFFERENT COUNTRIES (other than China)

OVERVIEW

This chapter introduces the distribution, production and husbandry of yak in countries outside China but deals primarily with those aspects of yak keeping which are particular to those countries. Although the number of yak outside China are relatively small, yak are very important in some of these areas. Experience in Mongolia and various countries of the Russian Federation in particular, and in other countries in general, highlight the special virtue of the yak in exploiting the natural resources of remote pastures at high altitudes. Herbage which might otherwise not be used is turned cheaply into meat and milk. More than one report notes that meat produced from yak is much less costly than that produced by other types of cattle; the principal reason for this appears to be that yak exploit lower-cost grazing and that other inputs of management or feed are minimal for yak.

Introduction

This chapter is intended to provide a brief overview of yak production and husbandry in most of the countries, apart from China, where these animals have a role in the pastoral economy. China, the country with most of the world's yak population, is excluded from this chapter because the descriptions of yak production and husbandry and of the products of the yak in earlier chapters have been based mainly on experience in China. Many of the aspects already described will be common to yak-keeping elsewhere, and, where this is so, repetition will be avoided, at least in detail. As regards the more basic biology of the yak, the earlier chapters concerned with this have already drawn on the relevant studies, irrespective of country of origin.

Some of the information in this chapter has been supplied direct by individuals in the countries concerned, in response to a request made to them, and this help is greatly appreciated. It provides an up-to-date record of yak husbandry for these countries. Unfortunately, in respect of some countries, replies were not received in time. For these countries, information about yak husbandry, and the importance of yak in their pastoral economy, has been assembled, whenever possible, from previously published sources.

AFGHANISTAN

It has not been possible to obtain topical information on yak production in this country, although it is known that yak have a role in the economy of the peoples in the Pamir mountains which extend into Afghanistan, but also form part of the territory of Kirgizia and Tajikistan. Yak are kept at high elevations (4000–4800 m) and wild yak were also found in this area – at least in the past. An earlier account of the area, including the part embraced by Afghanistan was given by Dor (1976) ("Note sur le yak au Pamir").

BHUTAN

(*Personal source of information from Bhutan: Dr Lham Tshering*)

The kingdom of Bhutan borders the Indian states of Sikkim in the west and Arunachal Pradesh in the east, both are home to small populations of yak (see section on India). West Bengal and Assam border on the south of Bhutan, and on the northern and north-western border lies the Tibetan autonomous region of China, the main territory of the yak.

The country is almost entirely mountainous. Southern foothills rise out of sub-tropical plains from an altitude of 300 m to around 1500m. A second land form, the inner Himalayas, then rises gradually to 3000 m. Above that, the land rises to the snowy peaks of the high Himalayas at more than 7000 m. About half the country is forested. Yak come into prominence in the northern region of the country – in the summer at elevations mostly above 4000 m. Bhutan is a small country – the maximum north-south distance being 170 km and the longest east-west distance 300km. The rugged territory of the country contributes to its relative isolation – many villages still being accessible only on foot. The economy depends heavily on agriculture and animal husbandry.

Yak play a significant role in the economy and in the social practices of the people of Bhutan. According to the 1992 Livestock census there were just over 30 000 yak in 9 districts of Bhutan, with the district around the capital, Thimphu, accounting for a third. Female yak accounted for about 17 000 of the total yak population, that is only a little over half of the total.

Yak are an integral component of the pastoral system of the northern areas of the country where the pastoral groups in the west are known as "Zhop" and as "Brokpa" in the east – both names meaning "yak herders". The groups in the east are dependant entirely on yak for their livelihood because there is no land suitable for cultivation. The Brokpa have a nomadic lifestyle without permanent abodes. The animals are herded in a transhumance pattern, depending on the state of the grazing. The alpine summer pastures, at around 5000 m, are grazed until late September or early October. Thereafter the herds begin to descend to winter pastures on lower ground in forest areas at an altitude of around 2500 m.

The Zhop people in the west follow a similar transhumance system, but the yak are part of their farming system as they also have significant cultivated land holdings.

Some of the herders own their pasture land, but most of it is owned by the community or the government. The community land is usually located near villages and everyone with a herd has the right to use it for grazing. Government-owned pastures are leased to herders for a nominal fee on a five-year basis. Usually, particular pastures are grazed for two weeks at a time, but if the supply of feed is plentiful the herd may be allowed to remain for a month.

A general description of the grasslands and some of the plant species found is given by Miller (1987).

As far as the herding of yak by nomadic people are concerned, the account of Turner (1800) (referred to in chapter 1) of his journey to Bhutan and Tibet in 1783, could almost have been written today. Thus in reference to the yak in Bhutan, Turner wrote: "… the southern glens afford them (the yak) food and shelter during the severity of winter; in milder seasons, the northern aspect is more congenial to their nature, and admits a wider range. They are the valuable property of itinerant tribes of Tartars, called Dubka, who live in tents, and tend them from place to place; they at the same time afford their herdsmen an easy mode of conveyance, a good covering, and wholesome subsistence." It appears also from the account of Turner that the herders moved freely among the chain of mountains that divided Bhutan from Tibet.

According to Dr Tshering, the yak in Bhutan are generally smaller than those in other countries and the yak in the west of Bhutan, the agro-pastoral area, are larger than those in the east of the country. A range of height at withers is given for adult male yak as 115 to 135 cm and for females 100 to 125 cm, with weight ranges of 300–450 kg for the male and 250–300 kg for the female. The normal breeding season is from June to September. Females are first mated around the age of 43 months to calve at 50 months old. Two calf crops in every three years is the norm. Bulls are first put into service when they are 3 or 4 years old. They are past their breeding peak from 7 or 8 years of age on. However, as described in chapter 5, the presence of older, dominant bulls, deters the younger ones from serving the cows.

Inbreeding among the yak in Bhutan is reported to be a serious problem since, for many years now, it has not been possible to obtain breeding bulls from across the border in Tibet.. To overcome this problem, the Department of Animal Husbandry in Bhutan has imported some yak semen from China, but, as reported by Dr Tshering, the usefulness of this is still in some doubt due to the inaccessibility of the yak females on most of the summer grazing areas, for purposes of artificial insemination. In the western region of he country exchange of bulls among herds with places further afield is also practised to reduce the harmful effects of inbreeding.

Milking of yak is done once daily. During the day, the calves run with their dams but in the evening they are separated and tied up for the night. The cows are milked once daily, in the morning. In some places the yak are tied up in a yard at night in the winter to prevent overgrazing of the winter pastures. Milk production drops off rapidly when the yak are brought to the lower ground for the winter. In spite of a low average milk production, estimated at 200 litres in a 7–8 month lactation, a good female yak will produce 4 litres per day during the peak grass-growing season of the summer.

Milk is used to make butter by the traditional methods described in chapter 10, but cheese is also made from the butter milk. The cheese so made is pressed between two large flat stones covered in muslin to remove the liquid. The resultant block is cut into smaller pieces which are strung up and dried in the sun or in smoke and called "chugo". The whey is consumed by the herders, or fed to calves. Because of the high fat content of the yak milk (7–8%) an average production from a yak cow is 25 kg butter and 30 kg cheese (and more from a crossbred). Butter and cheese are sold or bartered for food grain.

The hair and down fibre are both important for the herders, and used to make the products described earlier. About 1–1.5 kg of coarse hair and 2 kg of "wool" (down) are claimed as the average production per adult (but this appears to be rather high as an average for the down).

Although for religious reasons yak are not normally slaughtered by the herders themselves, the meat is in great demand (Winter and Tshewang, 1989) and, as reported by Dr Tshering, slaughter does occur, carried out by those permitted or willing to do so. Yak meat is prized above other meat in Bhutan and a yak sold for this purpose can fetch up to Nu. 6000–7000, the same as a good crossbred cow and much more than a yak cow (see later). (One Nu [Ngultrum] is approximately equal to one Indian rupee).

A number of diseases are reported by Miller (1987) as being important amongst the livestock of Bhutan but Dr Tshering provides evidence that gid is the main cause of death in yak calves. ("Gid" or "staggers" results from cysts of the larval form of the dog tapeworm lodging in the brain or spinal chord of the calf). In 1991 and 1992 some 9% of yak calves of 1 and 2 years old died from this cause..

Crossbreeding

Two systems of crossbreeding of yak are popular, but mostly in the east of Bhutan. In the western region most of the yak are bred pure. The crosses find a niche in the zone regarded as too low in altitude for yak and too high for cattle. The heterosis they are said to express, particularly in terms of milk production (see chapter 7) makes them popular. (It must be evident, from their predominant, if overlapping, distributions at different altitudes, that the crosses, the purebred yak and the pure cattle are not all treated necessarily alike and compared under identical conditions. This, as argued earlier, makes a strict interpretation of the superiority of the crosses in terms only of heterosis invalid.)

One form of crossbreeding involves Siri cattle, described by Mason (1988) as a zebu, hill type, probably with Tibetan blood used for draught and milk purposes. Mason also suggests that the Siri originated from crosses with Nepalese hill cattle. The crossing is done by using the yak bull on the Siri cows. Thereafter, the crossbred females are backcrossed to the yak. Different names apply to each of the crossbred generations and, as described in chapter 7, the first generation (F1) has the best performance. A good F1 is reported as capable of giving 7 litres of milk per day at her peak, but from twice daily milking, compared with the 4 litres (once-a-day milking) quoted earlier for a good yak cow in Bhutan.

The other cattle used for crossing with the yak is a *Bos taurus* type, described as the Goleng by Winter and Tshewang (1989), as well as by Dr Tshering. It is almost certainly the same as the Tibetan *glang*, listed by Mason (1988) and said to be synonymous with the humpless dwarf cattle of Tibet. The use of the Goleng breed in Bhutan is restricted to the Merak-Sakten region. The crossbreeding procedure differs from that with the Siri (where yak bulls were mated to the Siri females). In the case of the Goleng it is the bulls which are used on the yak females, but then also on successive generations of crossbred females. The procedure is reported in detail by Winter and Tshewang (1989) who also describe this part of the country as "... the most distant and inaccessible in the eastern region of Bhutan with distinct ethnic, cultural and economic characteristics. The people of Merak-Sakten depend for their livelihood almost entirely on the yak, its hybrids and to a lesser extent on sheep."

The use of Goleng bulls on successive generations of the yak crosses is unique to the Merak-Sakten region of Bhutan. This occurs because the herders of Merak-Sakten cannot obtain replacement Goleng bulls from Tibet – their formerly normal source of supply. They therefore resort to this grading-up procedure to reconstitute the Goleng breed for the sake of obtaining bulls – the Goleng females are not sought after. The usual crossing regimes elsewhere avoid successive backcrossing, because of the relatively poor performance of such animals. In terms of lost productivity, therefore, this system must be costly for the herdsmen. The backcrossing continues for 5 generations, when the name "Goleng" is applied again (only a negligible amount of yak blood remains in this fifth generation cross). The intervening generations each have their individual names (the F1 is call Zo for the male and Zom for the female). As with the performance of yak-cattle crosses elsewhere, the first cross is the best producer of milk and the most valued animal. Winter and Tshewang (1989) assign a commercial value to an F1 female which is twice that of a yak cow, but six times as much as the first backcross.

Dr Tshering reports that a trial has started in the Bumthang district of Bhutan of crossing yak females with Brown Swiss and Jersey bulls but results are as yet few and inconclusive.

(The major part of the above information on yak in Bhutan was kindly provided by the National Co-ordinator for FAO, Dr Lham Tshering (Office of the Assistant Chief Veterinary Officer, National AI Programme and Semen Processing Centre, Wangchutaba). Additional information, apart from the references quoted, has been taken from a report, by Mr Tim Win (UNV specialist) on yak breeding in Merak-Sakten – separately supplied by Dr Tshering.)

INDIA

(Personal source of information from India: Dr. R N Pal)

Yak in India are confined to the States adjacent to the Himalayan mountain ranges, but in two different zones distinct in environment and ecology. One is the north-western part of Himachal Pradesh and Jammu and Kashmir, which have a cold but arid climate, the other is an eastern zone which is cold and wet (>1800 mm rain). According to Pal (1993a) the yak numbers (to the nearest hundred) were as follows in the years shown: Arunachal Pradesh: 8500 (1988–89), Sikkim: 5400 (1989), Utar Pradesh: 300 (1988), Himachal Pradesh: 3500 (1992), and the Ladakh region of Jammu and Kashmir: 13000 (1990). Crossbreeding with cattle (*Bos indicus*) is common only in Arunachal Pradesh and in the Ladakh region – the two areas of India with the most yak. Crossbreds account for a further 6300 animals in the former and 7900 animals in the latter area. Yak are restricted to only the higher altitudes in these States and to a small proportion of the total land area. Thus, yak tracts occupy only 3% of the total area in Arunachal Pradesh, but 30% of the area in Himachal Pradesh.

Kalia (1974) produced an interesting theory about the origin of crossbreeding of yak with cattle in the yak tracts of India, adjacent to the former trade routes to the north. He claims that yak carrying merchandise from the north mingled with Indian cows carrying milk and other supplies from India to "exchange areas". The theory on the origin for the idea of this hybridisation might, however, be questioned, attractive as it sounds, on the grounds that castrated males are generally used as pack animals – though of course it may have been different on these trade routes. Kalia's study also provides some information on the now familiar better productivity of the crossbred in Himachal Pradesh compared with the productivity of the pure yak. Pal (pers. com. 1995), however, reaffirms in respect of India the point also made elsewhere in this book (see chapter 7) that the better performance of F1 hybrids between yak and other species of cattle, relative to the yak, cannot be attributed to hybrid vigour alone. Pal points out that the yak-cattle hybrids in India are kept at mid-altitudes (compared with the high altitudes at which the yak are kept in summer and autumn) and that the F1 females are managed better and given more feed than the yak. Only on the winter pastures are both yak and the crosses kept together in a similar way.

The point is made repeatedly in several articles (e.g. Pal, 1993b) that yak numbers in India have declined dramatically from a total of around 132 thousand in as recently as 1977 to the approximately 30 thousand now (with a further 14–15 thousand yak hybrids). This decline mirrors a corresponding fall in numbers in Nepal and Bhutan. The reason for the decline adduced by Pal relates directly to the closure of the border with Tibet in the 1960's. Prior to that time there were regular trains of yak transporting goods over the high passes from the north into India (and reciprocal trade from India). Work as transporters provided a good source of income for the yak herders in these areas – many of Tibetan and Mongolian extraction. This income supplemented that from their own yak. Now times are harder, with income restricted from what can be produced – mostly milk and fibre. A second consequence of the closure of the border has been a deterioration of the yak stock in India (as also noted for Bhutan and Nepal). Because new supplies of yak bulls are not available from across the border, inbreeding among the yak in India is said to have become a serious problem and has led to reduced performance of the animals (see also chapter 3). Attempts are now being made to counteract the inbreeding problem by encouraging farmers in areas otherwise isolated from each other to exchange yak bulls. Frozen yak semen is also being imported from China.

There are, however, according to Pal, other reasons for the reduction in the number of yak now in Indian States, relative to former times. There is said to be now a lesser willingness of younger people to face up to the rigours of high altitude life as yak herders. It is a story which has its counterparts in countless of the more remote rural communities across the world. As a result of a drift away from the higher regions, where yak have so special a role, there is now an under-utilisation of the high pastures and overgrazing of the middle and lower hills. This has been further exacerbated by cultivation of slopes on some areas that were previously forested.

Yak in India, as at most other locations for yak, play an important role not only in the rural economy where they are kept, but in the culture and religion of the people. Pal notes that some of the animal husbandry traditions can be traced back almost unchanged for hundreds of years. Grazing land near the villages, used especially in the winter, are owned by the local village clan and herders who belong to it pay no tax (or royalty) for the use of the grazing. Summer pastures are also owned by the village but herdsmen who do not belong to the local clan pay a tax for their use. The amount is fixed arbitrarily by the head of the village and is usually paid in the form of butter and churpi (a cottage-type cheese) because the herdsmen rarely have cash available. Grazing rights are generally renewed each year to the same client – unless a dispute happens to have arisen.

Pal has estimated that approximately 9000 households are involved in yak production. Herds vary in size from around 5 to more than 100 animals, but the average number of yak per household are perhaps 10 yak and 7 hybrids – the latter restricted to herds in Arunachal Pradesh and the Ladakh region. This number is said to provide a reasonable income (Rs 11 thousand). Pal, Barari and Biswas (1994a), however, also make the point that farmers are reluctant to disclose their actual income and expenditure (Indian farmers are not unique in this !). From a survey, these authors estimated that a farmer with 9 female yak and a bull was able to earn, over a 5-year period, twice the amount of his initial investment – after meeting expenses. Relative to some occupations, so it is implied, yak keeping is economically viable. Herding of a smaller number of yak, however is not economic, and owners with, say, 5 animals may offer these to a "tenant" herder who will collect together, from different owners, 50 or more animals to look after. The tenant pays the owner usually in butter or churpi (as in the case of the use of grazing land administered by another village). Pal reports that disputes over the verbal agreements made between owner and tenant herder are very rare.

Yak husbandry follows a similar pattern in the Indian States as described for other regions. Winter pastures tend to be at altitudes of 3–4 thousand m. They are often poor and the yak eat lichen, dry leaves and tree lopping where available. In the proximity of the more cultivated areas, crop residues may also be available for the yak and the crosses in the winter. But over the winter, the animals lose condition. Summer pastures at 4–6 thousand m. are of much higher quality and provide entirely for the growth and production of the yak.

Pal suggests four reasons for maintaining a migratory (transhumance) system of yak keeping in India. (1) to exploit the large fodder resources in the alpine areas, which are inaccessible in winter; (2) to conserve the grazing resources at mid (lower) altitudes for winter use; (3) to escape the intense summer heat at the lower altitudes, which is not tolerated by the yak; and (4) to avoid ecto-parasites, including leeches, which are prevalent in summer up to altitudes of 3000 m.

No shelter is provided for yak even in the coldest weather, except, occasionally, for calves in make-shift huts. As a rule, supplementary feed is also not given, but when available it will be given to lactating animals and in winter to the most emaciated animals. Winter temperatures can go down to as low as –30°C and in the summer the maximum is around 20°C and the minimum between 0° and 2°C. Snow and frost are not unknown in the summer months.

Some yak females, in India, breed annually, but having one calf every second year is more common. Recent investigations of herds in Arunachal Pradesh, on winter pasture, revealed high calf mortality – which was reduced by introducing to the traditional management some veterinary health control measures.

Pal (1993c) shows that in comparison with yak in China, Mongolia and the former USSR, the yak of India are smaller and less productive. More data are provided by Pal, Barari and Basu (1994c) with linear body dimensions of randomly chosen animals on summer pasture in Arunachal Pradesh. Height at withers is shown to be, on average, 128 cm for males and 115 cm for females above the age of 4 years, "oblique" body length (measuring points not specified) 113 and 109 cm respectively and heart girth 190 and 163 cm respectively for the male and female groups. Body weights (estimated from body dimensions) were 367 and 249 kg respectively for males and females above the age of 4 years.

In that study, Pal *et al.* (1994c) identified five different types of yak in India similar to the main types or breeds recorded for yak in China (see chapter 2). The same team of authors (Pal, Barari and Basu, 1994d) also record colour and colour pattern in Indian yak and note that wholly black animals represent 29% of the total, 40% were black with white patches, 14.5% were entirely grey, 1.6% wholly white and six other combinations accounted for the rest.

Milk yields are quoted by Pal and his co-workers, but in more detail by Jain (1989) who notes a daily milk yield of 0.4–3.8 kg for yak, 0.8–4.4 for yak hybrids with hill cattle and 0.5–3.9 kg for the hill cows themselves (see also chapter 7). Jain notes that milk is produced only from yak on pasture and that some hay may be given to them in stalls, but only in the worst part of winter weather.

Herdsmen and their families do not consume liquid milk (Pal *et al.*, 1994a) but convert it to butter and the soft cheese called churpi. Yak meat is held in great esteem and eaten, but slaughtering is infrequent and often associated with religious occasions. Commercial slaughtering is, however, also becoming more common as the meat is then more juicy, tender and well flavoured. The herdsmen generally preserve meat by salting and drying slices of it either in the open air, or over an open hearth.

Yak fibre provides only a small proportion of the total income from yak. The quantity of coarse hair varies from 0.3 to 3.0 kg depending on the type, condition and sex of the animal and the down fibre will amount to between 0.4 and 0.6 kg.

The yak in India, as elsewhere, is greatly valued as a pack animal capable of use in even the most difficult terrain.

In order to reverse the decline in the yak population in India and to improve the productivity and economics of yak keeping, the Indian government set up the Indian National Research Centre for yak in 1989. Its aims include a characterisation of the yak and yak production systems in the region; investigations to improve yak husbandry practices and to study the underlying scientific and practical factors and to establish a herd which may provide superior yak bulls to herdsmen (Pal, 1990). Extension services also now provide advice and help to overcome some of the current problems facing yak production in the Indian states. Inbreeding depression in performance and high calf mortality are identified among these. A recent survey by Pal (pers. com. 1995) suggests that in Arunachal Pradesh the decline in the yak population appears to have been halted and perhaps reversed. It will be of interest to see in years to come whether improvements in techniques of yak production, leading to improved income from it, will succeed in counteracting the social forces which make younger people reluctant to face the hardships required to herd yak throughout the year.

(Information for the above was kindly provided by Dr R N Pal, Director, National Research Centre on Yak (ICAR), Dirang, West Kameng, Arunachal Pradesh 790101, India, in the form of correspondence and additional reprints. Other information is readily available to English speaking readers from the sources quoted).

MONGOLIA

Mongolia, with more than six hundred thousand yak and yak crosses, ranks next in importance to China in terms of the size of its yak population. Although that number is only a small proportion of total yak population of China (12–13 million) it is arguable that yak play a more important part in the total economy of Mongolia and also in relation to the sizes of Mongolia's human and total livestock populations.

The following account of yak characteristics and yak husbandry in Mongolia has been kindly provided by Professor M Tumurjav and Associate Professor M Olonbayar. The contribution was received in the form of a self-contained paper and this is reproduced below, amended only, at Professor Tumurjav's request, to conform in style, to avoid duplication with matters referred to in other parts of this book, and to provide cross-reference (see occasional italicised comments).

Yak in Mongolia

by Professor M Tumurjav and Associate Professor M Olonbayar

Mongolia is a landlocked country in the central Asian plateau with an average elevation of 1580 m. Its territory extends over 1.5 million sq. km – extending 1250 km from Russia in the north to China in the south, having long borders with each, and 2400 km from east to west. In terms of its physical features, vegetation and livestock management, Mongolia can be divided into three main zones with different climatic features, as shown in Table 11.M.1.

Table 11.M.1 Features of three geographical zones of Mongolia

	Mountain	Forest steppe	Gobi desert
Average monthly temperature			
(Dec., Jan., Feb.) °C	from –20 to –30	from –20 to –25	from –15 to –20
(June, July, Aug.) °C	from +15 to +20	from +15 to +20	from +20 to +25
No. warm days per year	90	90–100	140
Annual rainfall (mm)	250–350	150–200	100–150
Depth of snow cover (cm)	15–20	10–15	2–5
Average pasture yield [as hay equivalent] (100kg/ha)	5–8	3–4	1–3

Snowfall varies from year to year but generally occurs in October. Particularly heavy falls in some years can be disastrous for the livestock, but even in normal years cold temperatures freeze up the rivers and harm can come to the animals through shortage of water. Most of the annual precipitation (70–80%) occurs in the summer, but in some areas and some years there is no rain, causing further problems for the stock.

Administratively, Mongolia is divided into 18 provinces (aimaks) which in turn are divided into districts (somons) – around 16–18 per province. Most of the yak are kept in the mountain areas and some in the Forest steppe zone extending over 13 of the provinces and including 130 of all the districts. Nine of the provinces (Arkhangai, Bayan–Ulgii, Bayankhongor, Gobi-Altai, Zavkhan, Uburkhangai, Uvs, Khovd, and Khubsugul) account for nearly all the yak in Mongolia with only small populations in other provinces. There is a tendency for the yak stocking density to increase with increasing altitude and also for the altitude to be lower (on average) the further north yak are kept. Thus yak in the Khangai mountain region at a latitude 44–46 degrees north (98–104 degrees east) are at altitudes from 3000 to 4000 m. In the Khubsugul mountain area (46–50 degrees n., 100–105 degrees e.) yak are distributed at 3200–3460 m. and in the Altai mountain region (43–47 degrees n., 91–100 degrees e.) the yak are at 3200–4200 m. The first two of these mountain areas contain more than 70% of the total yak population with most of the remainder in the Mongolian Altai mountains. The "average" stocking density of yak is very low. According to figures of the Mongolian Ministry of Agriculture and Food Industry (1990) stocking density of yak is 2.5 per square km in the Khangai mountains, 2.0 in the Khubsubugul mountains, 1.1 in Mongolian and Gobi Altai mountains and only 0.7 in the Khentii mountains. These low stocking densities are responsible for the freedom of access which herdsmen are allowed to have to the grazings (see later).

In the mountain areas where yak are actually kept, the average annual rainfall is between 350–500 mm. – higher than the averages quoted for the zones as a whole

(Table 11.M.1.). The ground is covered with snow for between 100 and 150 days per year; annual sunshine ranges from 2600 to 3600 hours; and winter temperatures can fall to as low as –40 oC. The different mountain areas where yak are kept differ from each other in situation and micro-climate and are separated from each other by distance. The yak in the different areas are also separately administered. It seems likely therefore that different types may have developed within the Mongolian yak population, but, if so, they do not appear to differ in conformation, appearance or performance characteristics, and no breed differences are officially recognised.

Yak are kept in Mongolia for all the normal products – meat, milk and fibre and they are also used as pack animals. Crossbreeding of yak with the local Mongolian cattle has been carried out since time immemorial. The F1 hybrids are called "khainag" and prefixed by "naran" if derived from female cattle crossed with male yak, and "saran" for the reciprocal cross. The total number of crosses represent, however, only about 10% of the total number of yak (in 1994). Table 11.M.2. provides an indication of numbers of cattle, yak and crosses over the years since 1940.

Table 11.M.2 Numbers of cattle, yak and their hybrids by year (in thousands)

Year	Total cattle yak and hybrids	Yak	F1
1940	2634.9	725.8	73.6
1945	2004.8	610.3	87.7
1950	1950.3	561.0	52.4
1955	1720.2	432.3	58.0
1960	1905.5	495.6	69.2
1965	2093.0	501.3	73.5
1970	2107.8	452.2	69.1
1975	2427.0	525.5	65.0
1980	2397.1	554.5	50.7
1985	2408.1	521.8	63.4
1990	2848.7	566.9	70.0
1994	3005.2	570.8	56.3

The decline in numbers from 1940 to 1955 was proportionately less marked in the yak than in the general cattle population but, conversely, the increase in the sizes of the populations since that time has been relatively greater among ordinary cattle than among yak, or the hybrids. Thus, in the earlier years, yak and their crosses with cattle accounted for approximately one-third of the total bovine population, but in 1994 that proportion was closer to one-fifth. Yak numbers can, nonetheless, be seen to have increased from their low point around 1970.

Crosses of yak with other cattle

What follows later in this account will deal with yak alone. It should therefore be said at this point that the performance of the F1 crosses in Mongolia displays heterosis, crosses exceeding the performance of both parental types for some traits. Some of the critical work was based on trials involving the reciprocal crosses of yak and Mongolian cattle and both parental types and reported by Zagdsuren (1994a). Results on crosses with European "improved" breeds of cattle were also quoted by Zagdsuren (1994b). *(Results have already been referred to in chapter 7 and are not therefore repeated here).*

Male crossbreds are castrated at 2.5 years old and mostly slaughtered for meat. Some are trained for draught purposes. F1 females are backcrossed to either yak or Mongolian cattle bulls, but the backcross progeny yield less milk than the F1 generation. Males of the later generations are, however similar in size to the F1. Herdsmen prefer crossbred oxen for transporting hay, water and wood from one campsite to another. The crosses of yak with other cattle are produced by natural service, apart from the recent crosses with "exotic" breeds of cattle where artificial insemination has been used in the trials (Zagdsuren, 1994b).

Mongolian yak

Appearance

A wide range of colours is found. Among nearly 64 thousand yak examined (Bat-erdene, 1977), 68.5% were black or black with white spots, 16.9% greyish brown or that colour with white spots, 8.9% were blue or tending to blue and 5.7% white (usually with small dark spotting). Polled animals are preferred by the herdsmen. Among large numbers of bulls sampled only 4.8% were horned – and none in some provinces. For female yak, the proportion with horns was 17.6%.

Conformation

The general conformation is as described in earlier chapters. For adult Mongolian yak bulls, the average height at withers is 123–128 cm., the oblique body length 137–152 cm., chest circumference 198–204 cm., chest depth 80.6 cm and liveweight 400–450 kg (up to a maximum of 550 kg.) Corresponding figures for the linear dimensions of adult females are 108–110, 119–123, 158–167, 65.1 cm. respectively and liveweight 270–280 kg (maximum 350) (Bat-erdene, 1961).

Meat production

As referred to also in chapter 6, yak muscle has a darker colour than meat from other domestic cattle due to a higher myoglobin content. The fat is bright gold in colour and there is little marbling. Soup made from yak meat has a sharp taste and smell. Yak meat is preferred in the Mongolian market place to meat from other cattle and fetches a higher price.

Liveweight and carcass weight of yak in Mongolia *(as elsewhere [see chapter 6])*, are greatly influenced by the conditions of rearing and previous weight gains and losses of the animals. Traditionally, castrated male yak are fattened on summer pasture and slaughtered at 2.5–3.5 years old, but also at later ages. The yak are generally taken to central slaughter factories at Ulan Bator or Darhan, involving treks for the animals of 500–1500 km over a period of 3 months. These long treks result in a loss of body condition reflected in a proportion of animals being in unsatisfactory condition. Some results are given in Table 11.M.3.

An experiment by Bat-erdene (1988) has shown that dressing percentage in particular could be improved (through an increase mainly in the proportion of fat retained) by slaughtering the animals in the district where they were fattened.

Table 11.M.3 Slaughter characteristics of yak trekked over long distances to slaughter houses [source: Bat-erdene, 1988]

Sex	Age (yrs)	Level of fatness	No.	Live-weight (kg)	Carcass weight (% Livewt.)	Viscera fat (% Livewt.)
Male	3.5 or more	> satisfactory	38	322	51.2	1.9
Castrate	3.5 or more	> satisfactory	5	322	51.6	2.6
male	2.5	> satisfactory	244	220	50.9	2.0
		satisfactory	195	175	47.8	1.0
		unsatisfactory	11	153	45.8	0.6
Female		>satisfactory	20	251	49.5	2.2
		unsatisfactory	6	209	44.9	1.7

Dressing percentage is taken as the sum of carcass wt % and fat %

Bat-erdene (1988) has also shown for Mongolian yak that between the ages of 1.5 and 5.5 years the bone content decreases as a proportion of carcass weight and that the proportion of fat increases. The dressing percentage also increased with increasing age. Furthermore, water content in the meat decreased with age of animal and the calorific value of the meat increased (*cf. Tables 6.16 and 6.17*).

Milk production

Milk production of yak in Mongolia, *as elsewhere*, is highly dependent on feed supply, age, season of calving, etc.

Table 11.M.4 provides some results which show that the earlier in the season that yak females calve, the longer the period of time they are able to suckle their calves and the higher the total milk yield before the onset of winter. The milk yield totals include an estimate of the quantity of milk suckled by the calf.

Table 11.M.4. Length of suckling period and total milk yield (both milked and taken by calf) of adult yak cows according to month of calving [source: State and Co-operative farms: Bat-erdene, 1993]

Month of calving:	March	April	May	June
No. cows:	34	26	12	11
Suckling period (days)	283 (232–331)	258 (210–300)	231 (180–285)	206 (171–280)
Milk yield (kg)	737 (635–1018)	673 (526–754)	607 (488–711)	564 (382–645)

In the mountainous areas of Mongolia, the late spring and early part of the summer are times of recuperation for the livestock as they start to graze the new green vegetation after the deprivation suffered during the long winter and early spring. Yak cows which calve in March to June have their maximum monthly milk yield in July, whilst those which calve in July, or later, have their maximum yield in the month of calving. Table 11.M.5, which is based on the same data set as Table 11.M.4, shows the results.

Table 11.M.5 Monthly milk yield (average and range, kg) of adult yak cows (based on quantity milked plus amount of milk taken by calf) according to month of calving and month of milking [month of calving = month 1 of milking]

[Data set as for Table 11.M.4; source: State and Co-operative farms: Bat-erdene, 1993]

Month of milking	Month of calving: March	April	May	June
1	65.2 (41– 91)	70.1 (49– 94)	70.1 (58–100)	112.6 (82–128)
2	63.6 (47– 85)	63.3 (48– 81)	101.5 (67–154)	118.3 (79–132)
3	64.3 (41– 90)	105.5 (71–130)	108.5 (78–146)	102.0 (71–111)
4	107.9 (76–158)	107.3 (93–132)	109.3 (80–153)	87.2 (62– 97)
5	115.8 (87–174)	99.8 (71–126)	82.0 (64–109)	65.6 (37– 94)
6	104.7 (73–151)	83.5 (68–107)	61.9 (44– 90)	48.1 (27– 84)
7	84.5 (59–119)	58.8 (40– 84)	40.5 (25– 75)	29.7 (16– 31)
8	60.4 (42– 90)	52.9 (25– 73)	33.5 (16– 48)	
9	44.7 (25– 84)	31.3 (16– 43)		
10	26.1 (16– 45)			

(It is clear from Tables 11.M.4 and 11.M.5 that the milk yield of the yak on these State and Co-operative farms is higher than the yields quoted earlier – chapter 6 – which were based largely on data from smaller, individually-owned herds in the mountainous regions of China. It is less clear to what extent this difference is attributable to differences in the pasture conditions, the management, or the breed type of yak.)

Milk yield, as shown in Table 11.M.5 peaked in July, around the time of maximum growth of vegetation of good quality. (*This seasonal peak was also noted in data from China – Figure 6.3 and Table 6.12*). The seasonal effects on milk yield are further borne out by consideration of daily milk yield in successive 10-day periods throughout the season, as shown in Table 11.M.6.

As seen in Table 11.M.6, the milk yield of first-calving yak heifers was only a little over half that of the older cows, but the heifers had a shorter milking period. The total yield for the cows in these data is lower than shown in the earlier Tables. This arises in part because of a shorter length of lactation over which the yield was estimated, and partly because the milk suckled by calves has not been included here, whereas it was before.

The calves at the State and Co-operative farms are allowed to suckle between one-quarter and one-third of all the milk produced by the dam (Bat-erdene, 1986). Calves reared in individual or private households are allowed to suckle more and the cows are not milked as intensively. There is, therefore, a correspondingly lower off-take of milk in private herds in Mongolia.

Table 11.M.6 Daily milk yield (litres) of 148 yak cows which had calved 3 times or more and of 116 first-calving yak heifers according to 10-day period over the milking season (milk taken by calf excluded from daily quantities shown) [source: state and co-operative farms: Bat-erdene, 1993]

Month	10-day period	Cows	Heifers
May	first	0.93	
	second		
	third	1.11	
June	first	1.53	0.96
	second	2.18	1.20
	third	2.32	1.40
July	first	2.41	1.76
	second	2.35	1.84
	third	2.55	1.88
August	first	2.35	1.56
	second	2.28	1.54
	third	2.20	1.23
September	first	1.79	1.02
	second	1.42	0.71
	third	1.19	0.44
October	first	0.75	
Milking period (days)		150	120
Total yield (litres)		273.8	155.6
Average daily yield (l)		1.83	1.30

Table 11.M.7 Average monthly fat content (per cent) of yak milk of cows according to month of calving and month of milking (month of calving = month 1 of milking) [source: state and co-operative farms: Bat-erdene, 1993]

Month of milking	Month of calving			
	March	April	May	June
1	6.0 (5.0– 6.6)	6.0 (5.5– 6.3)	6.6 (5.1– 7.6)	6.5 (6.3– 7.5)
2	6.0 (4.5– 7.0)	5.8 (4.5– 7.3)	6.7 (6.1– 8.5)	6.6 (6.3– 7.6)
3	5.7 (4.6– 6.8)	6.5 (5.4– 7.5)	7.0 (6.5– 7.5)	7.1 (6.4– 8.0)
4	6.3 (5.5– 7.3)	6.6 (6.0– 7.4)	7.0 (6.5– 7.6)	7.4 (6.9– 8.4)
5	6.5 (5.8– 7.2)	6.8 (6.1– 7.5)	7.6 (7.1– 8.3)	8.4 (7.1– 9.8)
6	6.6 (5.5– 7.5)	7.4 (6.8– 8.0)	8.6 (7.2–10.4)	9.7 (8.7–11.6)
7	7.5 (5.9– 9.6)	8.0 (7.3– 9.0)	11.3 (10.5–12.3)	10.9 (9.6–12.4)
8	8.6 (6.4–12.1)	9.6 (8.8–12.0)	11.9 (10.8–13.0)	
9	10.9 (9.0–12.2)	11.4 (10.6–12.5)		
10	11.5 (9.5–12.5)			
mean	*7.02 (6.2–8.0)*	*7.20 (6.3–8.0)*	*7.55 (6.9–8.2)*	*7.54 (6.8–8.1)*

The composition of yak cows' colostrum is very high in dry matter (36.4%, 33.8–42.3). The total protein content averages 17.9%, with albumin and globulin accounting for 12.7% (6.2–15.7), and the fat content is 14.8% (10.4–19.8).

The fat content of yak cows' milk, like the milk yield itself, depends on month of calving, but to an even greater extent on month of milking. This was shown by Bat-erdene (1993) studying the animals for which milk yields are presented in Table 11.M.4 and 11.M.5. The corresponding data for fat percentage are shown in Table 11.M.7.

The fat content of the yak milk, *as also seen in chapter 6*, is negatively related to the quantity of milk produced. The fat content of the milk of the yak increases sharply in September and is at its highest (9–12%) in the period from October to December when the quantity of milk produced is also at its lowest (cf. Table 11.M.5).

Reproductive characteristics

Yak heifers in Mongolia reach puberty at ages ranging from 18–32 months depending on their earlier development. Bat-erdene (1986) has found that calves with dams that are also milked grow less well and reach puberty in a later warm season (at 24–30 months) than those calves which have exclusive access to the milk of their dams. Yak females can, therefore, calve as early as 2.5 years. (*cf. puberty – chapter 5, and calf growth – Tables 6.5 and 6.6*).

The breeding season in Mongolia depends largely on the environmental conditions (*as elsewhere; cf. breeding season – chapter 5*). Normally, mating starts in June and continues to October. Conception rate appears to improve with altitude. Thus Purevzhav (1968) found that over a 3-year period yak cows at the rather low altitude of 1600 m had a conception rate of 77.5% whilst those at 2200 m had a conception rate of 90.8%. However, other environmental differences are likely to be associated with the differences in altitude. It has also been found that yak cows which calved in March came into oestrus again 140 days later and that this post-partum interval became less the later in the season calving occurred (April – 116 days, May – 105 days, June – 93 days, July – 78 days, August 35 days). *(These trends, although not the precise intervals, are similar to those reported, also for Mongolian yak, by Magash [1990] and shown in Table 5.3*).

Duration of oestrus can last for 18 hours and exceptionally up to 37 hours (*very short intervals are noted, from Mongolia, in chapter 5*). Conception following first oestrus is in the range 70–80% and most of the remainder become pregnant following a second oestrus which, in Mongolia, occurs, on average, 20 days (16–25) later in cows which did not conceive to first service (*cf. chapter 5*).

Gestation lasts on average 8.5 months. Calves weigh 15–16 kg at birth (range 7–18 kg) (*which appears to be higher – though not outside the range – quoted for China in Table 6.1*). The birth weight represents approximately 6% of the dam's weight. Sex differences in birth weight have not been recorded, but differences in size and weight between bulls and cows become very apparent from around the age of 2.5 years. At 5 years old, bulls are between 20% and 30% larger in linear body dimensions and anything from 50% to 100% heavier than females (Tumurjav, 1989). Growth continues to the age of about 7–8 years.

As for females, the age at puberty in Mongolian male yak depends on the conditions of rearing, most particularly whether the calf suckled the dam exclusively. With exclusive access to the dam, a bull calf will reach puberty at 16–18 months. If the dam was also milked, puberty of the male calf is delayed until the age of 2 years. Bulls are used for service between the ages of 2.5 and 8 years. On average, one yak bull is allocated to 15 yak cows. Annual conception rate is around 75–80 per cent on average, and cows can calve 8–10 times over an average breeding life which stretches from 3 to 13 years old, but sometimes older. *(From these results it appears that calving rates in Mongolia seem to be higher than those reported from ordinary herdsmen's production conditions in mountainous regions of China – see chapter 5 – and some other countries. This, in turn may be associated with the fact that, until very recently, most of the data on yak in Mongolia were derived from State or Co-operative farm enterprises where management practices might have been more controlled and production orientated.)*.

Artificial insemination, except under experimental conditions, is not used with yak in Mongolia, as it has been found that sexual activity of the yak is suppressed when man is present. Solutions to this problem are under investigation.

Grazing environment and yak husbandry

Mongolia's 120 million hectares of natural pastures contain almost two thousand different types of plant, of which over 600 are useful as animal fodder. Pasture growth starts in April and usually reaches a peak in August. If the year's standing vegetation is taken as 100%, then that present in the late autumn represents 70–80% of the total, that in winter (*mostly wilted herbage*) 50–60 %, and that in the spring 30–40% *(also mostly the previous year's herbage)*. From its peak, the quality of the herbage declines 2–3 fold in feeding value and the protein content declines 3–4 fold. (Tserendulam, 1973).

Mongolian yak, like other livestock in the country, get more than 90% of their annual feed intake from the pasture. During winter and early spring with grass dried off and quality poor, the yak's daily intake is only 40–60% of maintenance requirements. Weight loss of the yak over that period is between 25 and 30 % of their autumn weights (Gonchig, 1956; Bat-erdene, 1986).

Grazing management by Mongolian herdsmen depends on season:

- Late spring and early summer: yak recuperate from the stress of winter and from weight loss and graze on new, green vegetation.
- Summer: complete the period of recuperation
- Autumn: the yak deposit soft fat
- Late autumn and early winter: fatness is consolidated to build up the capacity to withstand the approaching cold
- Winter and early spring: measures to conserve fatness as much as possible (reduce rate of weight loss)

In accord with this seasonal classification, herdsmen take their herds and flocks to distant pastures, taking account of grass growth, and the supply of water and salt. The herdsmen move lightly and rapidly in an organised way following a nomadic (transhumant) tradition which is called in Mongolia "Otort yavakh" (translated as "to go a long way from home territory, looking for better pastures in bad season").

There are different ways in which the distant pastures are used. The methods include penning the animals at pasture, moving the base camp, changing the pasture used, long-distance camping and winter camping. Pasture land is made freely available in Mongolia. The population density in rural areas is very low, so there is no problem with land allocation to herdsmen for grazing their yaks. The herders can move freely from one place to another – even across districts and provinces – in their search for good pasture. This is particularly important in the hard winter time. Different yak herds may graze together.

Late spring: yak, along with other cattle, are first taken to distant pastures in April when the grass starts to turn green and sends out new shoots from old roots.

Summer: yak are kept on pasture as long as possible. Most herdsmen allow their yak to graze the pastures for 12–14 hours daily, very experienced herdsmen for perhaps 15–16 hours per day. A base camp is used for around 15–30 days, though some more experienced herders may change base camp every 7–10 days. During their stay at the base camp the herdsmen also work for profit by making milk products.
When pasture is well chosen, the yak will eat 30–35 kg of grass daily and gain weight at the rate of 400–600 g per day (Bat-erdene, 1988)

Autumn: In August, at the beginning of autumn, herbage quality and yield is at its highest, the sun's heat has weakened and conditions are at their best for the yak and other livestock to gain in strength and to deposit fat. Herding over that period aims to limit movement of the yak in order to increase their chances to lay down fat and build up their strength against the oncoming winter. Yak are kept at pasture for 10–12 hours daily. From mid-October, when it starts to get cold, herdsmen work to consolidate the conditioning of the yak.

Winter: the places selected for the winter camp are chosen for being relatively sheltered from strong winds and from dust, with as thin a snow cover as possible and with as sunny and warm a situation as can be found. In such conditions snow starts to melt early and grass grows well. In selecting the winter pasture it is believed that the grazing will be most nutritious if the grass looks brown from a distance – and not if it looks whitish.

Herdsmen are not in a hurry to move to their winter camp before it gets very cold, because they consider that if the campsite is used too early in the season the capacity of the pasture to maintain the yak will be reduced and the animals will lose endurance. They would then have to move again, Special heavy stockyards are not built for yak in Mongolia.

Herd size, herd ownership and production

The size of yak herds varies considerably depending on the area. In the Arkhangai and Uburkhangai provinces some herds number up to 40–50 yak; 20 yak is a more usual number. Many families keep yak only, but most prefer to keep yak as well as Mongolian cattle. In 1989, 75.7% of all yak were kept at state or co-operative farms and the remainder were privately owned. The average herd structure for the years 1977–87 is as shown in Table 11.M.8.

Table 11.M.8 Structure of yak herds (%) in Mongolia, averaged for the years 1977–87 [source: Mongolian Ministry of Agriculture and Food Industry, 1990]

	State farms		Private farms	
Age group	Male	Female	Male	Female
< 10 months	12.9	11.7	15.7	13.8
1.5 years	10.9	10.0	11.4	9.9
2.5 years	6.0	8.5	6.9	3.1
3.5 years old and older	1.0	36.0	2.9	34.7
Bulls: 2.5 years old and older	3.1		1.7	
Total	*33.8*	*66.2*	*38.5*	*61.5*

As seen in Table 11.M.8, cows and heifers accounted for 44.5% of all the yak of state farm herds but only 37.8% of the yak in privately owned herds. Part of the reason for this is that on state and co-operative farms only 58 calves were reared per 100 cows, whilst in the private sector this was 75 calves per 100 cows. The difference came about because the yak females were milked until the late autumn on the state farms, with the consequence that calf growth was poorer and calf losses higher, especially during their first winter of life. The lower proportion of calves in the state and co-operative farm herds meant that a higher proportion of the available calves had to be kept as replacements than in the privately owned herds and this, in turn, reduced the opportunities for selection.

None-the-less the total output from the yak on a co-operative farm could be very substantial. Thus, according to figures from the Mongolian Ministry of Agriculture an Food Industry (1990), the production of meat and milk from the "Yalalt" co-operative in the high mountain area of the Tariat district of Arkhangai province, with a herd of twenty thousand yak was 86.5 kg of meat (as liveweight) per cow, as well as 250–300 litres of milk per cow and over 100 tonnes of butter.

Since 1989, privatisation of state herds has been taking place, so that now all yak in Mongolia are owned by the herders themselves. In view of this period of transition and rapid changes in the price of animal products, no reliable, economic data relevant to the current yak production are available. Targets for yak herding have, however, been set. These are that the proportion of heifers and cows in the herd should not exceed 38% of the total yak numbers in the herd, that 75 calves should be reared annually per 100 yak cows, and that the meat output per cow (as liveweight) should be 160 kg.

Investigations on yak

The main centre for yak research in Mongolia is the Research Station for Animal Husbandry in High Mountain Area of Ikh Tamir somon, in the Arkhangai aimak. The principal scientist involved was Dr T Bat-erdene, with V Dagviikhorol and

Figure 11.1 Mongolian yak on a private farm [photo courtesy of Dr Doyoddorj]

colleagues concerned with yak husbandry and D Lkhagvajav concerned with pasture problems in relation to yak. Dr Yo Zagdsuren was, until 1990, concerned particularly with research on crossbreeding of yak with other types of cattle.

References

The following sources were used in the preparation of this paper:

Bat-erdene, T. 1961. Biological peculiarities of Mongolian yak and their hybrids. Synopsis of MS degree thesis, Moscow (in Russian).

Bat-erdene, T. 1977. The colour coat of yak. Agricultural magazine, no. 2 UB (in Mongolian).

Bat-erdene, T. 1986. Yak husbandry. *In* Cattle husbandry, UB (in Mongolian).

Bat-erdene, T. 1988. Biological and farming peculiarities of yak. Synopsis of doctoral thesis, Moscow (in Russian).

Bat-erdene, T. 1993. Milk productivity of yak. Uliastai (in Mongolian).

Gonchig, D. 1956.

Mongolian Ministry of Agriculture and Food Industry. 1990. Mongolian yak – breed characteristics (in Mongolian).

Purevzhav, Zh. 1968. Some questions on physiology and reproduction of yak. Synopsis of MSc degree thesis, Moscow (in Mongolian).

Tserendulam, R. 1973. Fodder resources of Mongolia. Synopsis of doctoral thesis. Moscow (in Russian).

Tumurjav, M. 1989. Mongolian Ikvgl breeds of animals – performance and biological peculiarities. UB (in Mongolian).

Zagdsuren, Yo. 1994 a&b (*as given in main references of this book*).

(Professor M Tumurjav, who kindly provided the above article, is President of the Mongolian Agricultural University, Ulan Bator, Mongolia. Associate Professor M Olonbayar is a member of the Department of Animal Husbandry of that University.

They in turn wish to acknowledge help of other colleagues in the preparation of the material.)

NEPAL

(Personal source of information from Nepal: Dr D D Joshi)

The kingdom of Nepal borders India to the south and the Tibetan autonomous region of China to the north. From south to north is little more than 160 km, but over that relatively short distance the land rises from only 100 m altitude and tropical and sub-tropical climate to the highest parts of the Himalayas (6000–8000 m), including Mount Everest on its border, with a mixture of temperate and arctic climate. Yak are confined to the northern districts of Nepal at the higher elevations and many crosses of yak with domestic cattle are kept on neighbouring somewhat lower ground. Joshi (1982) states that without yak and yak hybrids it is doubtful if people would live in much of northern Nepal. In total, according to Joshi (1982), there were between 8 and 9 thousand yak and about double that number of yak-cattle crosses spread over some 20 or so districts. Paudyal (1993) quotes the 1991 census of the Central Bureau of Statistics of Nepal showing more than double that number – over 19 thousand yak and nearly 41 thousand hybrids – but with some large changes over that ten-year period in particular districts, with some showing a large increase and some substantial drop in numbers. It is possible that differences in the procedure for the census may account for some of the difference. However, it appears that the numbers have declined from an estimated 200 thousand yak and hybrids in 1961.

Joshi also describes in some detail the villages and Kharks (or Goths) – the latter being the temporary settlements usually on the summer pastures – in each district and in the several Himalayan ranges which strike off in various directions. Thus, from east to west Nepal, the Himalayas have numerous valleys, glaciers, ridges, peaks and rivers. For each village Joshi gives an estimate of the numbers of each type of livestock – yak and crosses of yak with local cattle, sheep and goats, and horses and mules – thus providing a full picture of the relative importance of the different classes of stock. Joshi also describes the peoples of these various districts, often isolated from each other by the different mountain ranges and differing in some cases ethnically, in culture and in dialect.

Joshi says that Nepali yak are smaller than those in various parts of China (cf Tables 6.7 and 7.2 – but see also Table 11.N.2) and provides the following data from animals in 3 districts in Nepal:

Table 11N.1 Weights and linear body dimensions of yak in Nepal [after Joshi, 1982]

	Male yak	Female yak	Castrated yak
Number of animals	15	25	10
Live-weight (kg)	245	215	337
Height at withers (cm)	105	102	116
Length – pins to shoulder (cm)	110	105	124
Heart girth (cm)	140	130	157

(In order to clarify a possible confusion arising in the literature on the size of yak in Nepal, it should be noted that Joshi (1982) also quotes in his book some larger average values than those shown above, for what are described as 'well-grown' yak in Nepal. These larger average values are the same as those given by Epstein (1977) in relation to Nepal, but they, in turn, are identical to values also given by Epstein (1969) but for yak in China – with the male and female figures attributed to a personal communication (Chen Lin-feng, 1963) and those for castrates to another Chinese source.)

Most of the yak are black or black with some white markings. Pure white yak are rare, but highly prized. Most yak are horned, but a few polled yak are found and not as greatly valued. Polled bulls are always castrated and then used for riding.

Milk is the main commercial product from yak and from the crosses of yak with cattle. Nepal differs from China in respect of one important use of this milk. In Nepal, in addition to the butter and other products made by the herdspeople from milk, large quantities of are sold and made into a Swiss-style hard cheese, in processing factories built in the yak milk-producing areas. According to Joshi *et al* (1994) the production from the various factories in 1993 was over 91 metric tonnes of cheese and nearly 30 metric tonnes of butter. The cheese, especially, fetches a high price and is sold, principally to tourists in Kathmandu. On the basis of a marketing report quoted by Paudyal (1993), the demand for yak cheese still substantially exceeds the supply. Although the yak cheese commands a higher price than cheese made from cattle or buffalo milk, the costs of production are high also, principally because production is only seasonal and the factories do not therefore work the year round. In addition, transport costs are high. Paudyal also refers to a Winrock research report on cheese production in Nepal which suggest that as a consequence of the profitable sale of milk for cheese making, yak calves are being deprived of milk to the extent that calf mortality has increased.

Yak meat is eaten in Nepal, although for religious reasons slaughter is usually undertaken by butchers and not the herdsmen. The fibre and the hides of the yak are used as elsewhere.

Crosses with yak are made with the type of cattle similar to, or the same as, the humpless dwarf cattle of Tibet known here as Kirko (or Khirko), but also as zo-lang (and referred to earlier as Goleng or glang in Bhutan but also in some parts of Nepal). The so-called Lulu cattle, used in some districts, are almost certainly the same type (K. P. Oli, personal communication). Crosses are also made with the Siri hill cattle, a zebu type. Crosses may be made either by mating the cattle bull to yak females (Dimjo or Dim-dzo) or the other way around (Urang).

Table 11N.2 Performance characteristics of yak and yak-hybrids in Nepal [adapted from Joshi *et al*, 1994]

	Female yak	Hybrid (Dimjo)	Hybrid (Urang)	Hybrid Brown Swiss cross
"Average" age at first calving (month)	44	35	44	48
that is to say, calving at age:	some at 3, mostly at 4 years old	mostly at 3 years old	some at 3, mostly at 4 years old	4 years
"Average" calving interval (days)	660	425	425	NA
that is to say, a calf:	generally 1 every 2 years	mostly 1 each year	mostly 1 each year	
Gestation length (days)	258	270	270	270
Lactation milk yield (kg)	200–700	1690	1300	1046
main Lactation length (days)	180	260	260	305
Live-weights (kg)				
birth	9	NA	NA	13
adult male	325	365	340	NA
adult female	240	235	220	NA
Breeding season (month of year)	9–11	8–10	8–10	8–10
Calving season (month of year)	5–7	4–6	4–6	4–6

There is a staggeringly large breed terminology (listed by Joshi) dealing with no less than 124 different combinations of yak with different local types of cattle, both zebu and *Bos taurus*. Names really begin to multiply among the various backcrosses to different breeds in different districts.

In a recent paper Joshi *et al.* (1994) give some average values for performance characteristics

The live-weights given for both the male and the female yak in the above table are greater than those quoted, also from Nepal, in Table 11.N.1. The weights of the crossbred males are shown as being greater than those of the yak and this may be associated with the fact that because such males are sterile they are likely to be castrated and used for work. The female crossbreds are shown to be slightly less heavy than the corresponding yak, but of the two types of crossbred, those born to yak dams (the Dimjo) are not only the larger but also give more milk. The crossbreds are also larger and more productive than the cattle parent breeds – but as stressed on several occasions in this book, the different types, yak, cattle and crossbreds are not normally kept in the same area on a year-round basis.

The difference in performance between the two reciprocal crosses is reflected in the fact that farmers are said by Joshi (1982) to prefer the Dimjo to the Urang. Although the cattle cows are smaller than the yak females it is unusual for the maternal effects from the dam to last to quite such an extent into the adulthood of their progeny, and an explanation for the reciprocal difference is not altogether clear. Since there are also differences in size and performance among the different types of cattle used for crossing with yak, it may be that females of the smaller types of cattle are mated to yak bulls, and bulls of the larger types of cattle to yak females. This is nowhere stated explicitly, but it is an explanation which, if true, would fit the facts and it may be hoped that the evidence will be collected in the future.

It is of interest that the crosses of yak with Brown Swiss gave less milk than crosses with local breeds of cattle, although bred at a later age for the first time (average 4 years), than even the pure yak. The poorer performance of crosses with fathers of exotic breeds relative to local types of cattle is confirmed in a later personal communication from Joshi who then also refers to disappointing performance of crosses of yak with Holstein Friesian and Jersey. Joshi also mentions that AI is not used for crossbreeding with yak in Nepal.

Some reproductive data are given by Paudyal (1993) based on results from the breeding records of the yak breeding farm situated in Solukhumbu, one of the most important of the yak-producing districts of Nepal. Over a 15 year period (1974–89) 544 matings of yak females were made; this resulted in 307 conceptions (56.4%) and 293 calves (53.9%) of which 15 were stillborn. The average calving interval was 616 days – suggesting that a majority of the animals calved only once every 2 years. However, it is of greater interest that there have been steady changes at this farm over the period from 1974 to 1989. These have led to an improvement in the annual calving rate and a sharp drop in the interval between successive calves. Thus, in successive 5-year periods, the proportion of calves born (per yak mated) increased from 0.44 to 0.58 to 0.70 and the calving interval declined from an initial 851 days, to 704 in the middle period and 514 days in the last 5-year period. Whatever the changes that have been made at the farm – perhaps in management, but unfortunately not specified – they have improved the frequency of calving from less than once in 2 years (some yak calved only every third year) to a frequency where more than 50% of the yak calve annually. Together with the increase in proportion of matings which result in calves, there has therefore been a remarkable improvement in overall reproductive rate. There was also some increase, over that period of years, in the growth rate of the calves in the first 12 weeks – but no change in the birth weights.

Management of yak in Nepal in general follows the transhumance pattern, with high altitude summer pastures, where the animals are not given feed supplements and winter on somewhat lower ground in more sheltered valleys. In many of the valleys there is also crop growing and many of the yak and their crosses spend the winter in sheds where they have to be fed.

Joshi *et al.* give the composition of the "average" yak herd to be: 32 cows (of which half are dry and half lactating), 3 breeding bulls, nearly 12 pack yak, approximately 10 females and 10 males under the age of 5 years, 12 yearlings and just over 15 younger calves – a total of just over 94 animals.

Joshi (1982) provides some results on the economics of keeping yak and crosses of yak with cattle (chauries). Although the absolute figures are likely to change with time, it is the comparison of the pure yak with the chauries (hybrids) which engenders most interest. Thus:

For a yak bull

The capital investment required:	Rs 1782
(Rs 1350 of this for procuring the animal)	
Recurrent costs per year (mostly feed):	Rs 473
Annual returns:	Rs 1109
(mostly from charges @ Rs 15 per service)	
Gross margin:	*Rs 636*

For a lactating yak female

The capital investment required:	Rs 1815
(Rs 1350 of this for procuring the animal)	
Recurrent costs per year (mostly feed):	Rs 621
Annual returns:	Rs 2609
(Rs 1000 from sale of calf, Rs 1600 from sale of milk)	
Gross margin:	*Rs 1988*

For a lactating chaurie (crossbred)

The capital investment required:	Rs 2310
Recurrent costs per year (mostly feed):	Rs 1040
Annual returns:	Rs 2500
(Rs 500 from sale of calf, Rs 2000 from sale of milk)	
Gross margin:	*Rs 1460*

Thus, Joshi's figures suggest that the annual gross margin from the lactating yak was more than a third higher than that from the lactating crossbred female, in spite of the lower absolute milk yield of the yak. The yak female needed a smaller capital investment than the crossbred and the yak calf had a higher value than the calf of the chaurie. If these figures were to apply more widely they might suggest that even under these largely pastoral conditions a relatively high-input-high-output strategy is not necessarily the most profitable. However, the crossbred, or at least the Dimjo kind, has advantages which, over a lifetime should more than compensate for a lower annual return and higher initial investment. Thus, the Dimjo crossbreds calved on average almost a year sooner than the yak and were more likely to have a calf every year. Thus, over the lifetime of a cow of say 12 years, the gross margin from the crossbred should be the greater. However, the gap between the yak and the crossbreds will be narrowed by the ability of these animals to produce milk – perhaps half the 'normal' quantity – also in a year subsequent to a calving, even if they have not calved again in that second season. Since the main end-product is not fresh milk, but butter and cheese, the gap in income between the yak and the chaurie should be further narrowed if, as must be assumed, the fat percentage of the yak milk is higher than that of the crossbred. (The assumption is that the fat percentage of the milk is reflected in the price given for the milk, when sold for the manufacture of butter and cheese).

Nepal enjoys a considerable tourist trade, which in turn provides a ready market both for the cheese and some of the other value-added products from the yak – a point emphasised by Joshi *et al.* (1994) in discussing future developments.

However, there is already change taking place which is affecting the livestock husbandry of the northern areas of Nepal. Joshi *et al.* point out, for example, the increasing use of yak and yak hybrids for transport in mountaineering expeditions and for trekking, thus changing the emphasis given to the different uses of the yak by, for example, peoples like the Sherpas who have a tradition in yak keeping. Other writers have suggested that the overall need for yak is declining in the face of other forms of transport. Bishop (1989), in a detailed study of one village in Nepal, reports that older people there are no longer as willing as in former times to endure the hardship of high altitude life on the lonely summer pastures. They are thus changing from being milk producers to being breeders of hybrids animals. To produce the hybrids they are using cows at the lower altitudes nearer the villages and mating them to yak bulls. The hybrid animals are then sold as replacement stock, making for an easier life for the herdsmen and their families compared with milk production from yak. Cox (1985) has also made a detailed study of one particular area – the relatively isolated Langtang valley area in the north-eastern border region of Nepal. The study looks in detail at the role of the yak in all aspects of the life of the people there, including the cultural and ritualistic side, and notes the changes that are occurring in social and economic attitudes, partly as a result of the opening of a cheese factory in the area. An earlier account of the husbandry and productivity of yak and its hybrids in the same valley was given by Bonnemaire and Teissier (1976). A similarly detailed account is given for another area of Nepal (the Tarap valley in the north-west) by Jest (1976), who also notes what was then the beginning of an impact of industrial cheese-making on the economy of yak production.

Joshi *et al* refer to a deterioration of the yak breeding stock in Nepal and quote, by way of example, the Langtang area which has a tradition of supplying yak breeding stock. The deterioration is said to arise from the enforced reduction of movement of breeding stock across the border with the Tibet region. Thus as also noted for Bhutan (see above) and referred to by Pal (personal communication) in relation to yak in India, there is an increasing problem from inbreeding in the yak population, reflected in reduced performance and poorer reproductive efficiency.

The Government of Nepal has recently initiated an assessment study on the impact of yak cheese factories and also initiated a vocational training programme for working with yak and crossbreds. Trials of crossbreeding yak with exotic breeds of cattle are also continuing, even though the initial results did not compare favourably with the use of local breeds of cattle for this purpose.

Figure 11.2 Milking yak in Nepal [photo courtesy of Dept. of Information, HMG, Nepal]

(The published information of Joshi (1982) and Joshi et al. (1994) was supplemented, for purposes of the above section, by further information directly supplied by Dr D Joshi, Director, National Zoonoses and Food Hygiene Research Centre, P.O. Box 1885, Kathmandu, Nepal.)

PAKISTAN

(Personal source of information: Mr Ashiq Hussein Cheema and Mr Abdul Ghaffar)

Yak in Pakistan live on the high plateau of the Northern areas, in Gilgit and merging, to the south east, into the valley of Ladakh. Yak are to be found up to altitudes of well above 5000 m. The Silk Road, a trade route used by Marco Polo, passes through Gilgit. The districts where most of the yak are kept are those of Hunza, Ashkoman, Yasin, Khaplu and Kharmong.

A mission of scientists was mounted by the Pakistan Agricultural Research Council in 1984 to study the area. They estimated a total yak population, for the whole area, of 25 000 and a further 100 000 hybrids of yak with local cattle (both *Bos taurus* and *Bos indicus*). Milk yield was estimated to be, on average, approximately 600 l (occasional yields up to 1000 l) and an average fat percentage of 6.5. Lactation length was 200 days on average. The yak are only occasionally slaughtered for meat and no weights are given in the report. Between 750 g and 1600 g of coarse hair and from 300 g to 600 g of down fibre is harvested. The down is felted and the long hair made into ropes, saddle blankets, grain storage bags and tents. Most of the adult yak females give birth to a calf only every second year.

The hybrids (zo – male, and zomo – female) are liked for their better growth, higher milk yield, and better work performance. Daily milk yield from a hybrid could be as high as 7.5 l. Hybrids with a yak dam and cattle sire were said to produce more milk and with a higher fat content, than the reciprocal crosses. The hybrid females generally calve every year. (No mention is made whether the hybrids receive better treatment than the yak).

One of the important districts for yak, the former principality of Hunza, was studied in some detail by Kreutzmann (1986) and some further information on yak keeping in the area is derived from his study.

Hunza has permanent settlements of yak holders at altitudes ranging from 2550 m (Pasu) to 3500 (Shimshal). The upper part of the Hunza valley from Gulmit to the border of the Chinese Province of Xinjiang is settled by Wakhi people. Yak are kept pure. Kreutzmann notes that there is no tradition of crossbreeding with other cattle in the Hunza – or in the Wakhan of Afghanistan, and among the Wakhi settlers in the Hunza. It is pointed out that there is no word in the vocabulary of the Brusho or Wakhi peoples for "crossbreeding". Only herders of the Deosai Plateau and the Baltis, in what Kreutzmann also refers to as the "Northern areas", people who speak a Tibetan dialect, also cross-breed their yak – as do their eastern neighbours. In this respect, the absence of crossbreeding, Hunza is not typical of the wider region referred to above

Kreutzmann states that in the Hunza area (but not in some other neighbouring areas) yak form part of the livestock of the owners. Other stock include sheep, goats and other cattle. The cultivated area of the farms is, on average, 1–2 ha, but the number of livestock kept is also relatively small. In total, Kreutzmann recorded 8 villages with yak in the area, and a total of 716 yak. This amounts to only about one yak per household in these villages (in addition to an average of 3.4 cattle and 33 sheep and goats, in the same households).

During the summer (May-September or October), the adult male yak are kept with the sheep and goats on high pastures (4500–5000 m), higher than the temporary summer settlements of the shepherds at 3500 m. The yak are tended only during the winter months when they return closer to the permanent settlements. Women are not allowed to stay on the high pastures, but are responsible for looking after the animals, including the yak, which are milked nearer the settlements. The women also make butter and other milk products. Kreutzmann states that yak are only rarely used as pack animals except to carry milk products and the requisite utensils down from the pastures.

By October/November, according to Kreutzmann's study, the majority of yak are back in the permanent settlements and any animals for sale are disposed of by the herders at that time, often to a tradesman who comes to the villages. Yak meat fetches a lower price than meat of goat or sheep, but a higher price than the meat of other cattle. The hair and down of the yak is also used and woven into mats and plaited into ropes. The tails are apparently used as "dusters".

Kreutzmann notes that much of the farming in the area is already only a part-time occupation for the people and he believes that further economic development in the region is likely to lead to a continuing reduction in the number of yak and consequently to the detriment of ecologically sound exploitation of the resources of the high pastures. In the light of these views it would be of interest to know whether the yak population of the whole area, of which Hunza is only a part, comprises now anywhere near the total numbers estimated in 1984.

(Mr Ashiq Hussein Cheema and Mr Abdul Ghaffar, who kindly provided some of the information given above, are members of the Animal Sciences Institute, Islamabad. The former is also national co-ordinator for FAO in Pakistan.)

Countries of the RUSSIAN FEDERATION

The republics and regions referred to are those of Kirgizia, Tajikistan, Tuva, Altai, and Buryatia where yak have been indigenous for a very long time and the northern Caucasus and Yakutia to which yak have been introduced since the 1970's.

Sarbagishev *et al.* (1989) writing about yak as one of the animal genetic resources of the (then) USSR, refers to a total yak population in 1984 of 136 thousand. The largest numbers were in Kirgizia (nearly 60 thousand), Tajikistan with nearly 17 thousand, Tuva (32 thousand), Altai (16 thousand), Buryatia (nearly 7000) and northern Caucasus (3700). With the extension of yak into new areas, the total yak population had increased by more than 50% between 1970 and 1984, although in Kirgizia a large increase in numbers between 1970 and 1975 was followed, thereafter, by a fall of nearly 9000.

In very general terms the yak in these northern regions are at somewhat lower altitudes than the yak on the summer pastures of Tibet and Qinghai. Altitudes at which yak are kept vary between the regions of the Russian Federation. The most commonly quoted elevations are between 2500 and 3500 metres, but both lower and higher altitudes are also involved. As in other yak territories, different pastures are used in summer and in winter in many of the areas of the Russian Federation, but the use of the same areas all-the-year round is also reported. The ability of yak to survive even in deep snow, avoiding the need to move them to more sheltered areas is referred to as a particular advantage of yak keeping, right from the time when yak first attracted considerable scientific attention (e.g. Denisov, 1935). More recently, Mochalovskii and Abdusalamov (1973) refer to this point again in relation to the introduction of yak from Pamir to the northern Caucasus (altitude 2500–3700 m). They report that even in two exceptionally hard winters following the importation, the yak did not have to be brought to the lower slopes in the winter as they had no difficulty in pawing through the snow to find feed – and in doing so created a way through for sheep.

Yak in the different countries of the Federation differ to some extent in size and performance. Sarbagishev *et al.* (1989) state that the yak of Kirgizia are substantially larger than those of Tajikistan, but this is on account of the fact that those of Kirgizia are not milked and are bred only for meat. Average dimensions (cm.) are given as follows for adult males and females respectively: height at withers 123 and 109; body length 137 and 125; and heart girth 178 and 165. Denisov (1935) stated that the yak of Kirgizia were identical to those of China, but since there is also much variability among the yak in China itself, this statement is not as informative as at first sight appears. Denisov also refers to the yak of the Altai region as being inferior, at that time, and similar to those then prevalent in Mongolia. Koslovskii (1960) offered the view that yak in the Gorno-Altai region were becoming closely inbred, which could explain Denisov's opinion of its yak population (see chapter 3 – *inbreeding*). Koslovskii advocated the introduction of unrelated males or crossbreeding with other cattle.

Sarbagishev *et al.* (1989) refer only to the use of yak for meat and milk. There is little doubt that on the state and co-operative farms, then predominant, this was the prime purpose. However, it is apparent from other sources that in some of the more remote areas of the Russian Federation the traditional uses of the yak as a pack animal and for riding also occurs.

In their article on yak in the USSR, Sarbagishev *et al.* give the mating season for yak in Kirgiz as varying with altitude. In the Tyan Shan, at elevations of 2400–2500 m mating starts in late June (sometimes earlier) and continues to late October (but occasionally into January). In the Altai valley with severer conditions, and an altitude of 3000–4000 m, mating does not begin until mid-July and ends in mid-October. The yak are said to be poly-oestrous and oestrous periods are reported to last for 1–2 days (with a range of 10–118 hours). Cows that calve later than August do not generally breed again in that year. Conception rates are reported to improve at higher altitudes – from 83% in Tyan Shan (2600–3400 m) to 98% in the Pamir mountains (3900–4200 m). As also noted in chapter 4, Sarbagishev *et al.* quote other investigators of yak in the, then, USSR to show that the rearing of the yak calf and its subsequent condition are a major factor in determining the age at which the females reach puberty and are mated for the first time. In areas where the yak cows are not milked this age is usually 16–18 months. In general, the heifers calve for the first time at the age of 3 years, which is a year earlier than typical for many of the yak-producing areas in China (see chapter 5) or in other countries to the south, adjacent to the Himalayas.

With the extension of yak to other areas within the Russian Federation, attention is being given to work on the adaptation of young yak males to lowland environments and to the problems associated with synchronisation of oestrus in the females so that AI can be the more successfully used. This has been applied in particular in the move of yak to parts of the Caucasus and Yakutia. It seems that the yak is found to be a more economical producer of meat than other species. This point is made by Smirnov *et al.* (1990) in relation to yak from the Tuva region introduced to a part of the Northern Caucasus. From the figures given by the authors, the cost of keeping a yak was marginally less than that of keeping a sheep and a unit gain in liveweight from a yak cost only one sixth of a similar gain in beef cattle on the same farm. (Data on meat production from the yak given by these authors are referred to in chapter 7.)

There is a wealth of publications on experiments and investigations on yak and yak hybrids, emanating from the former Soviet Union and now continuing in several of the countries of the Russian Federation. The book by Denisov (1958) on Domestic yak and their hybrids is an important source of reference and widely quoted. Another important source of information, on yak in the former Soviet Union, is the book, written in German, by Schley (1963). A significant proportion of the early literature on yak from the Soviet Union is concerned with a detailed characterisation of the yak, including some of its physiological and biochemical attributes. The production-orientated studies are, however, dominated by the role of crossbreeding of the yak, or hybridisation as it is more commonly called in these investigations, with *Bos taurus* cattle – both local breeds and breeds which had originated elsewhere, but some of which had been in parts of the Soviet Union for a long time.

The concern with hybridisation continues to the present. A paper by Katzina *et al.* (1994) deals with a scheme, designed specifically for meat production from of hybrids with the yak. This is under investigation in two parts of Buryatia at elevations of 1200 and 2500 m respectively. Their paper was, unfortunately, the only contribution to the first international congress on yak in China in 1994 from a country of the Russian Federation. The essence of their scheme was to exploit the fact that successful meat production from relatively young animals is a two-stage process, to combine good maternal qualities with good intrinsic growth and meat qualities of the calf itself. To produce the maternal line, crosses of yak were made with a dual-purpose (milk-meat) type of the Schwyz breed (referred to in earlier years as Brown Swiss) and a milk-type Jersey from Denmark. The former of these breeds recurs frequently in the earlier literature on hybridisation with the yak, whilst the Jersey was a chosen to utilise, it was said, its relatively small size (hence small feed requirements), high milk yield and fat percentage, ease of calving and early maturity. F1 females from crosses of these with yak were, in turn, mated to bulls of "local" breeds of cattle – the Kalmyk and the Kazakh Whitehead, both regarded predominantly as meat breeds – or by AI, with frozen semen, to the Galloway, a British beef breed, also accustomed, in Scotland, to harsh winter conditions. Katzina *et al.* (1994) point out that though the level of heterosis expected in the F2 is lower than that in the F1 (half or less), the F2 calves benefit from having F1 mothers. These F1 dams combine the characteristics of the breeds chosen, but also express heterosis in their maternal qualities. The early results of these trials showed that the success rate of obtaining hybrid calves from the yak was only of the order of 25% (cf. chapter 5). However, weaning weights were achieved of 120 kg for hybrids with the Galloway and 111 kg for those with the local cattle as against 92 kg for yak. The Galloway hybrids also overwintered better, having the better coat insulation.

As already referred to, the interest in hybridisation with yak goes back many years in what was then the Soviet Union. Denisov (1935) refers to the use of the Swiss Brown (later named Schwyz) as well as local Kirghiz (Kazakh) cattle in crosses with yak on a number of state farms, and gives some early results on body weights and body dimensions. He notes that in some respects the crosses are closer to the yak and in other respects closer to the cattle breed. Later, Denisov (1938) provides data from Kazakstan on lactation milk yield as follows: yak 608 kg milk (6.8% fat), hybrids with the Kirghiz cattle 1124 kg (5.7 %), the Kirghiz cattle themselves 1155 kg (4.4%) and crosses of yak with Schwyz 2022 kg (5.3 %). Denisov states specifically that the local cattle, the yak and the hybrids were all herded together. These results, therefore, meet most of the criteria for estimating heterosis (only the reciprocal crosses appear to be missing) unlike many of the other results referred to in this book, where this matter is in question. Denisov's results suggest strongly the importance of heterosis in the milk yield of the hybrids.

An even earlier report of hybridisation occurs in Vlasov *et al.* (1932) from observations in the Oirat district (Altai) where much of the subsequent work continued. At that time the authors reported a yak stock of 6800 and 570 crossbreds, again with the cattle, the yak and the crosses grazing together. Ivanova and Ljubimov (1951) record work at the Gorno-Altai agricultural experimental station, giving milk yields of local Siberian cattle as 700–800 kg (4.3% fat), yak as 300–350 kg (5.5–6.7%), and hybrids of these two as 900–1100 kg (4.9–5.1%). They also report on the use of the Simmental in such crossbreeding, and significantly note that cows of this breed, as well as Siberian cows, have also been mated to yak bulls since 1929. Backcrossing of the hybrids to Simmental produced, in the 2nd and 3rd generation cows giving 2362 kg milk (4.9% fat) in a lactation. By 1950, there were 300 progeny of *inter-se* matings because an aim of the crossbreeding work was to produce a more productive (synthetic) breed suited to the conditions. (More recent publications do not refer to this "synthetic" breed, suggesting that it might not have been successful in the long run). Later work in Gorno-Altai also involved the use of the Shorthorn (Gaidyseva, 1963).

Other areas of the Russian federation from which investigations on yak and yak hybrids are reported include the Tuva region where Katzina and Maturova (1989) reported on reproductive function in the yak, living there at an altitude of 1500–2500 m but, because of the northerly latitude, in fact very cold with less than 7 frost-free days per year. The yak were outdoors throughout the year but received some supplementary feeding when the ground was frozen. None-the-less the yak were breeding, on average, a year sooner than typical for most parts of China. Some results on the reproduction of these yak are given in chapter 5.

Trials involving meat production from yak and local breeds of cattle are also reported from Tajikistan (Norov and Dorotyuk, 1988) and other parts of the Pamir mountain range, bordering on Afghanistan.

Only a small proportion of the many possible references to work with yak and their hybrids have been included here, selected in part to provide a historical perspective on the status and development of yak production in these countries. The impression that comes across is that the general approach to yak keeping has been to encourage the use of the yak, for meat production especially, as a genotype with particular merits in particular situations. Thus the yak is acknowledged for its ability to exploit pastures and environments where cattle or sheep are also kept, but where the use of yak helps to extend the use of the natural resources. This occurs by virtue of the yak's great resistance to cold and to hardship and its adaptability to a low quality diet. Yak are therefore useful both in their own right and as a component of the genotype in hybrids with *Bos taurus*. This is an unsentimental and businesslike approach to the role of the yak in animal production, in countries where state farms and co-operatives were the norm for many years. This approach to the utilisation of the yak also provided the incentive for the relatively recent introduction of the yak to some countries within the Russian Federation which had not had native populations of yak. This makes use of the animals for their special qualities in harsh environments. Yak thus find themselves in these areas on their own merits, uninhibited by the traditions which surround yak in their native territories.

Buryatia

(account based on information provided by Dr E V Katzina)

The Republic of Buryatia lies in the southern part of eastern Siberia between Mongolia and Lake Baikal. (Lake Baikal is the world's largest fresh-water lake – 636 km long and between 25 and 79 km wide). Yak in Buryatia are kept, nowadays, on farms on the Okinsky plateau of the East Sayan mountains at altitudes of 1400–2500 m and at 1200–1800 m in the Zakamensky district of the Lake Baikal watershed (50–54 °N and 100–104 °E). The yak in these two districts were isolated from each other for a long time and are regarded as sub-populations of the Buryat type. The Okinskaya population number 6500 yak and the Zakamenskaya 1200 yak. Breeding females constitute 40–45% of the total number of yak.

The climate of Buryatia is one of extremes, with large variations in temperature across the seasons. Temperature in winter can fall to –50°C. In summer, temperatures can occasionally reach +60°C (at ground level), but even in July it is not uncommon for the temperature at night to drop to –2°C from the heat of the day. Day length is 7–8 hours in winter and 17–18 hours in summer. Frost-free days number between 41 and 79 per year. Precipitation varies between 275 and 410 mm per year, with two-thirds of the annual precipitation in the three months June-August – with July generally being the peak month. Snow can fall in August and snow cover in winter is to a depth of 6–15 cm. In general, the winter in Buryatia is severe, windy and very cold and the summer short and, on average, cold. The average annual temperature is 5–6°C.

Dr Katzina writes that, historically, the Buryat population of yak might be regarded as being the same as those of the adjacent territories of Mongolia and Tuva. However, at present, the Buryat yak are isolated from the others and there appears to be no intermixing. Analyses of antigenic factors in blood also suggest a relatively low degree of relationship between Buryat and Mongolian yak (see also chapter 2).

Performance. The following results are given by Katzina in relation to reproduction:

Age at first mating	–	14–28 months (depending on development of the calf before the onset of winter in the year of birth)
Calving interval	–	1 year for between 40% and 87% of the females (2 years for the remainder)
Gestation length	–	mean 258.8 days (SD 30.9 days)
No. of calves (annually) per 100 females	–	variable from 40 to 87
Breeding season	–	late July to mid September
Calving season	–	April to May (rarely March to early July)
Survival of adult yak	–	100% in a favourable winter 60–70% in a winter with deep snow cover
Calf survival	–	80–100%

Milk production is said to be between 350 and 400 kg in a lactation of 180–210 days (It is not stated whether this is an estimated yield based on calf growth, or whether it is the amount milked, or a mixture of both. In view of a later statement that cows are not milked, the first alternative seems the most likely). The following are results on daily yields and milk composition:

Table 11.RB.1 Daily milk yield, protein content and fat content of Buryat yak cows calving in March to May – according to month of lactation [source: Maturova and Katzina, 1990]

Month after calving	Calving in March-May						Calving June-August					
	Milk [kg]		Protein%		Fat %		Milk [kg]		Protein %		Fat %	
	mean	SE	mean	SE	mean	SE	mean	SE	mean	SE	mean	SE
first	1.5	1.8	5.0	0.84	7.0	0.59	2.5	3.0	5.6	0.87	6.8	0.48
second	3.4	4.3	7.1	0.44	7.6	0.51	1.5	1.0	6.2	0.72	7.2	0.50
third	4.5	3.8	6.8	1.05	8.0	0.56	1.3	0.8	6.3	0.65	7.3	0.67

The results on daily milk yield reinforce the findings of several other studies in different countries, that peak yield coincides with the month of maximum herbage production – in or around July – when herbage quality is also still high.

From another report sent by Dr V N Davydov and Dr E V Katzina it appears that the milk yield and fat percentage of the two sub-populations is not dissimilar. F1 crosses of yak with other cattle are shown, in that report, to have yielded about 100 kg more milk than the yak in the 1940's, but that recent yield from hybrids were much higher. It has to be assumed that this may be due to the use of different breeds of cattle to make the cross. This report makes the further point that the cost of producing milk and meat from yak and yak hybrids is less than the cost of production from cattle. The reason given is that the yak (and hybrids) use mountain pasture almost exclusively, and that they consume only very little hay and make virtually no use of forage from arable land.

The following Table gives some data on body weight of yak in Buryatia.

Table 11.RB.2 Body weight (kg) of male and female yak at different ages in Buryatia – calves born in March-May [source: Maturova and Katzina, 1990]

Age	Male			Female		
(month)	no.	mean	SE	no.	mean	SE
birth	50	13.1	0.4	50	14.1	0.3
1	50	23.2	0.7	50	20.6	0.5
2	50	37.5	1.2	50	34.8	0.9
3	46	54.6	1.7	48	51.0	1.4
4	46	73.4	1.2	47	68.0	1.8
5	43	87.6	1.6	45	79.6	1.7
6	40	96.7	1.6	43	89.7	2.7
7	35	107.3	2.9	40	101.3	3.3
8	35	110.2	3.3	39	104.8	2.4
9	34	112.0	2.7	37	107.3	4.0
10	34	112.8	2.2	37	103.5	2.6
11	34	115.0	2.9	37	105.6	1.7
12	34	129.4	3.0	37	115.1	1.7
18	32	192.3	5.9	34	175.9	4.2
20	32	205.8	6.7	34	185.2	4.7
adult	11	386.4	10.8	32	261.1	3.7

The results in Table 11RB.2. show that management of the animals (see later) is such that there were no weight losses over winter, although there was a slowing in the rate of gain. This is contrast to a number of studies reported in chapter 6 which show large weight losses, even in calves, over the winter period. Results on growth reported by Maturova and Katzina (1990) show that weights at birth and up to 2 months of age were greater for calves born in July and August of the year than those born early (see Table). However, by 6 months old, the early-born calves were almost 40 kg heavier than those born late in the season. This reflects clearly the effect of milk and feed availability on calf growth over the season. It also shows that being born late in the year is a disadvantage for a calf, because its condition is poorer at the onset of the first winter of its life and this, in turn, retards its subsequent development to puberty.

Yak in Buryatia are raised only for meat. Table 11.RB3 provides some slaughter data.

Hair and down fibre are not collected from yak in Buryatia.

Crossbreeding. According to Katzina, hybridisation is undertaken by mating yak to local Buryat cattle and also to "improved" cattle which are themselves crosses of Simmental and local Buryat cattle. Only natural service is used. There are approximately 1500 yak-cattle hybrids.

Table 11.RB.3 Carcass data for 3 yak slaughtered at each of two different ages [source: Maturova and Katzina, 1990]

	18–19 months mean	SD	30–31 months mean	SD
Live-weight (kg)	201	6.2	241	10.5
Carcass weight (kg)	98	4.3	120	6.5
Dressing %	48.7	1.1	49.6	0.9
Weight (kg) of:				
meat	73	22	86.5	18.6
bone	19.6	0.2	22.9	2.9
subcutaneous fat	2	0.7	4.1	0.9

Some F1 (yak-cattle) females are left to mate "accidentally" with bulls of the Buryat breed of cattle because the hybrids are kept together in the herd with the cattle. Female offspring of this backcross generation are milked. The backcross males are castrated and reared for meat like the F1 males. Systematic crossbreeding does not take place in Buryatia, although the meat/milk scheme proposed by Katzina *et al.* (1994), and described earlier in the section on the Russian Federation, is being developed.

Management. Dr Katzina writes that the yak are managed extensively and to simulate as closely as possible the natural conditions dictated by the availability of suitable pastures. During the summer the yak graze freely on alpine and sub-alpine pastures. From October to May they are kept on winter pastures on lower slopes, where most of the calving takes place. New-born calves suckle their dams, which are not milked.

The summer pastures contain 45–50% *Carex* sp., 32–37% grasses, 10–13% legumes and 5–8% cereals. The herbage grows densely to a height of about 18–25 cm. Leaves and branches of trees and shrubs are quite insignificant in the diet of Sayan yak.

No supplementary feeding is given except in extremely harsh winters when some hay may be provided. Young animals, however, are given daily supplements during the winter at a rate equivalent to between 0.77 and 1.29 Scandinavian feed units. Primitive sheds are constructed for yak in the winter. The yak go into these sheds voluntarily to shelter from strong winds or very low temperatures, but not, usually, at other times.

Although yak are not given veterinary treatments, they appear to have fewer illnesses than other types of cattle.

There are no separate economic returns for yak and other cattle in Buryatia. However, it has been calculated, as alluded to earlier, that the cost of producing one unit of liveweight from yak is one-third of the cost of producing the equivalent unit from *Bos taurus* cattle – as also noted in some other countries.

Investigational work. Research with yak has been active in Buryatia and neighbouring regions since the 1930's (several of the studies are referred to in this book). Earlier studies were largely descriptive of the economics and productivity of the yak and of its characteristics – particularly in relation to meat production. Dr Katzina states that the scale of research has recently declined and become more fragmentary. Emphasis has been given in the Buryat Institute of Biology of the Siberian Department of the Russian Academy of Sciences to research on conservation and the rational use of yak – including the hybridisation scheme already referred to. The introduction of yak to parts of North Caucasus and central Yakutia is part of that rationalisation. Attention is also being given to grazing technology and management. As part of the conservation strategy, consideration is being given to re-introducing yak into the wild. Many studies have also been undertaken into more fundamental aspects of the biology of the yak and its crosses. Dr Katzina has provided a list of the 50 most important studies published over recent years. Copies of this list have been lodged with the FAO Regional Office in Bangkok (publishers of this book) and with the International Yak Information Centre (see Appendix 2) from which copies may be obtained.

(Dr E V Katzina, who kindly sent the information for the above account, works at the Buryat Institute of Biology, Siberian Department of the Russian Academy of Sciences, Ulan Ude, Buryatia, Russia.)

of the yak and of its characteristics – particularly in relation to meat production. Dr Katzina states that the scale of research has recently declined and become more fragmentary. Emphasis has been given in the Buryat Institute of Biology of the Siberian Department of the Russian Academy of Sciences to research on conservation and the rational use of yak – including the hybridisation scheme already referred to. The introduction of yak to parts of North Caucasus and central Yakutia is part of that rationalisation. Attention is also being given to grazing technology and management. As part of the conservation strategy, consideration is being given to re-introducing yak into the wild. Many studies have also been undertaken into more fundamental aspects of the biology of the yak and its crosses. Dr Katzina has provided a list of the 50 most important studies published over recent years. Copies of this list have been lodged with the FAO Regional Office in Bangkok (publishers of this book) and with the International Yak Information Centre (see Appendix 2) from which copies may be obtained.

(Dr E.V. Katzina who kindly provided the information for the above account, works at the Buryat Institute of Biology, Siberian Department of the Russian Academy of Sciences, Ulan Ude, Buryatia, Russia.)

12 CONCLUDING CONSIDERATIONS

OVERVIEW

In the context of an expanding yak population in some areas and a contraction in others, an attempt is made to look at the factors involved.

The role of research in assisting the development of yak production is then considered and some limitations on the effectiveness of the current research discussed. Particular attention is given to the design of experiments with yak and appropriate analysis and publication of results. It is noted that more recent research is of an increasingly fundamental nature.

An attempt is then made to identify some areas of research which might be profitable in the future and, in particular, to identify gaps in knowledge. Since most aspects of the performance of the yak are inter-related and also interact with the environment, it is suggested that a systems approach to the study of the problems might be of benefit.

The concluding considerations end with a question about the future and a flight of fancy about a direction that change might take.

Introduction

In the light of the results and considerations of the earlier chapter, the intention, in conclusion, is to do three things:

1. To restate what appear to be the present position and current aims of yak production and the factors influencing the size and distribution of the yak population;
2. To consider briefly the impact of past research on knowledge of yak production, to comment on some limitations in the conduct of research, as it appears from the literature cited, to draw attention to a few fundamental areas of research not referred to in the main body of the book, and to suggest some possible gaps in knowledge;
3. To provide possible pointers to the future.

The perspectives brought to these considerations are more those of an informed "outsider" (GW) than those of an expert "insider" (Cai Li), My distinguished co-author, Professor Cai Li, may be more deeply aware, than I, of the problems of obtaining objective scientific information on yak and of the difficulties in promoting improvements in yak production. Being more on the "outside" allows me, however, to take a less inhibited and constrained approach in making the suggestions which follow.

The present position

The present position is considered in terms of yak population size, the inter-relation of economic and social factors, questions of what constitutes improvement, the interaction of different factors and thoughts on the role of the scientist.

Most of the world's yak population is in China, but there are important populations of yak elsewhere: in Mongolia, several of the countries of the Russian Federation, and of course in the countries and States bordering on the Himalayas and the Tibet-Qinghai plateau. In terms of the world's livestock population, yak numbers are not very significant, as was noted in the Foreword to this book. A global planner might even ignore the animal. But for the utilisation of the vast grazing resources at high altitudes in central Asia, the presence of the yak makes the difference between exploiting these resources or letting them go to waste, and between having an indigenous human population, or a virtually uninhabited wilderness.

The attributes of the yak which allow it to survive, reproduce and provide sustenance for people has been sufficiently covered in the earlier chapters. What is less clear is the extent to which the pastoral peoples of these regions will continue to be content to pursue a subsistence way of life based primarily on yak production, or will develop and justify that production increasingly as an economic activity. Awareness of these socio-economic factors and of the potential and possibilities for change is needed for an analysis of those changes which should be preferred and encouraged. The conclusions will vary between countries, regions and even specific areas.

It has been pointed out by many observers that young people are less willing to embrace the hardships associated with year-round yak herding. However, older people are also seeking alternative forms of production which they find socially and economically more attractive. An example of this, described by Bishop (1989), is the change, in a community in Nepal, from producing milk as the main product from the yak, to using the yak cows only to breed and rear hybrids (yak x cattle) for sale to other herders (with calf rearing replacing the more labour-intensive milking). Social observers point to the fact that, everywhere, a nomadic lifestyle is in decline (e.g. Scholz, 1994) and that this has wide ranging implications for the utilisation of the grazing resources in marginal areas. In some countries, including China, active encouragement of more settled communities is further hastening the decline of nomadism, though the transhumant system remains integral to most of yak production. One of the suggestions that has been made (e.g. by Scholz, 1994) is that with the advent of roads, use might be made of summer grazings at high altitudes by trucking the animals ("mobile cattle raising"). Clearly this might also set limits on the type of production that is possible. Meat could readily be produced in that way (with only a minimal input of herding), although the use of transport would bring increased costs. To produce milk and the traditional milk products under such circumstances would still require the herdsmen and their families to camp on the summer grazings and accept the remoteness and hard work, the lifestyle which is increasingly being questioned. Roads, if available, might alter perceptions of remoteness and give quicker access to markets for the products, but would not affect work associated with milking and making the milk products. Roads may even bring tourists. Thus a whole pattern of life can be affected – but the sociologists' thesis is that it is changing anyway. The aim should be to continue to utilise the natural resources of the mountain pastures, if necessary through appropriate modification of existing systems, or new approaches. It would be a matter of real concern if these resources were neglected, or if the biodiversity associated with the yak were lost.

One of the main factors affecting change, both in social and in production terms, is proximity to alternative opportunities for the yak herders and their families. Thus in areas close to tourism or alternative employment, traditional yak production may be very vulnerable. In remote areas of the vast Qinghai-Tibet plateau the incentives for continuing yak production with traditional products from it, and perhaps a traditional pattern of herding, seems more assured of a longer-term future.

At present, yak numbers in China still appear to be increasing. A decline in numbers in Mongolia and some of the countries of the Russian Federation appears to have halted and in a few cases is in the process of being reversed. Then there are new territories in which yak have been successfully established, such as the Northern Caucasus and Central Yakutia. In other countries such as Nepal, India and probably Bhutan and Pakistan, numbers have declined markedly – perhaps as a result of alternative opportunities and the changing expectations of a younger generation of people.

The difficulties and problems in the path of improvement of yak production are therefore formidable as there is no clear agreement of what constitutes improvement and for whom. It may be useful to illustrate this point with an example. Thus, the establishment of industrial-scale cheese factories in Nepal to utilise yak milk is a measure clearly designed to improve the living standards of the local people and also to provide extra revenue for the nation, through the sale of the yak products to tourists. However, the introduction of the factories has brought about other subtle changes, some of which are documented by Cox (1985) who studied the situation in one area of the Langtang (Nepal) in some detail. The first and most obvious consequence of this major outlet for yak milk has been an increase in the stock numbers in the vicinity of the factories, causing overgrazing. Herders find that the heavier stocking allows them to stay on a summer campsite for perhaps only 3 weeks at a time before having to move on, when formerly they might have stayed 2 months. This problem might get worse if additional milk-producing enterprises are attracted to the lower elevations, because it is argued that the purely seasonal production of these factories is less economic than year-round production would be. Perhaps of even greater moment are social changes for the local herdspeople, as also described by Cox (1985). He notes that the local people now go on trading expeditions with their butter and cheese only very rarely and no longer obtain their other necessities in that way. This is because nearly all the milk produced goes direct to the cheese factory. Since the quantities of milk required by the factory for delivery are greater than normally produced by a single family, co-operative arrangements and agreements with neighbouring families have to be entered into. Because cash has entered into the system for exchanging goods, in place of barter or other forms of transfer, new skills are needed in settling accounts and greater store is set on education and learning the Nepali language. Cox states that the cheese factories have been partially responsible for bringing the Langtang people more into the cultural, political and economic mainstream of Nepal.

This example illustrates the problem of discussing yak only in terms of what the yak produces and what changes might be achieved in levels of production. To restrict consideration to aspects of production would ignore the great cultural and social traditions which accompany yak herding and animal ownership and the social changes which can accompany changes in production and marketing.

One of these important traditions, still widely prevalent, is that ownership of animals confers status on the owner and is counted as a measure of wealth – with the advantage that this form of wealth is less prone to erosion from inflation than is common with wealth stored as money. So long as the ownership of the largest possible number of animals is an over-riding consideration for many, or most herders, much of the science of yak production is an indulgence for those pursuing it – until the herders themselves experience unequivocally the limits to expansion. However, when there is a market for the products – yak milk, yak meat, and hair products – then attempts will be made to increase production to meet that demand. The cheese factories in Nepal, referred to above, are an obvious example which have led to increased milk production. The importance attached to the yak for meat production in Mongolia, and the plans for industrialised production of meat by rotational crossing of yak and cattle in parts of Russia are other examples where the demand is creating the supply. The economics suggest both from Mongolia and elsewhere that yak meat, and yak milk products, can be produced more cheaply than the equivalent products from other livestock in these countries – although the reason for this seems to rest on the ability of the yak to exploit cheaply available natural resources, rather than a possible superiority over other livestock in energetic efficiency of converting feed into livestock product. However, since other cattle in particular do not utilise the same pastures as yak at the higher altitudes, it is the economic efficiency of the yak which is of clearest importance. A similar argument also applies in relation to sheep, as some reports show a yak to cost no more to maintain annually than a sheep – however, in this case, there is considerable overlap, in many areas, in the use of pastures by both yak and sheep.

However, a market for the yak products is not the only incentive needed to expand output. It seems to be a pre-requisite of a market economy that the further incentive required is the availability of other goods which the primary producer can purchase in return for the milk, meat and fibre sold. Since both criteria – a market for the yak product and the availability of other goods for the herder and his family to buy – are increasingly being met in the major yak-producing areas, it seems that an increase in production from the grazing resources and from the yak must be a realistic aim. The investigation of ways to improve yak production and yak producing systems is thus of some importance. The scientists concerned with yak can feel useful after all. To this end the role of research will now be reviewed briefly.

Research

• Past and present

Research, or investigation, is the basis of all scientific knowledge. In the case of yak production, much of the basic knowledge of husbandry and many of the traditions and practices surrounding it are based on centuries of accumulated experience. A matter of trial and error perhaps, with experience passed on and refined over the generations.

Scientifically-based investigation of yak and yak problems, the material of publications and conferences, is mostly a product of this century, dating not much further back than the 1930s. Initially many of the investigations were primarily descriptive of the animal and of the factors affecting its production. Much of this type of investigation continues to this day and has provided, not infrequently, a scientific justification for an existing practice. Yak production is not unique in this respect. Good farming practice in most parts of the world has often been found to be justified in the light of later scientific evidence. Much production-orientated research on yak is quoted in this book, including the significant part of it generated, over the years, by the work of my co-author (Cai Li) and his colleagues. However, what has been quoted is not exhaustive. The selection of references in the preceding chapters do, however, indicate the range of investigations carried out on yak. They are also chosen to give as accurate a picture as possible of the characteristics of the yak and its production, without undue repetition. The investigations show some of the factors which influence variation in performance and also provide a quantitative basis from which to start to suggest what aspects of performance might be changed and to what extent. However, change in one trait often brings with it correlated changes in other characteristics, and may have a bearing on the whole production system. Only little of this type of information forms part of the current literature on yak and some of the necessary considerations for an integrative approach will be referred to later.

The most recent research and that currently in progress involves an increasing proportion of investigations concerned with manipulation. In the sense used here, manipulation implies the study of potential methods of intervening in the production process in order to change particular aspects of yak performance, or the economics of yak production. This includes research on how to influence the reproductive cycle, and how to improve the utilisation of feed, based on an understanding of ruminant physiology and the study of growth promoters. Investigations on optimising herd structure, strategies for sustainable crossbreeding systems, and strategies to minimise inbreeding are also in this class, to the extent that they can lead to direct intervention in the traditional husbandry methods.

Limitations
Two recurring problems have been noted in production-orientated investigations. One is a lack of sufficient numbers for biologically and statistically meaningful results (except in the case of purely descriptive exercises where large numbers are sometimes used). The other is poor experimental design leading to confounding of factors.

Confounding
Examples of confounding or inadequate experimental design have been referred to several times in earlier chapters. Such examples include: comparisons made of the effects of different treatments, where the treatments were not concurrent; comparisons of "breeds" and of pure yak with hybrids and with cattle, when the breeds (and the crosses) being compared are not in the same place, or treated identically. Problems arising from the last example lead to a need to re-examine conclusions about hybrid vigour, since these have often been based on information lacking the basic design for estimating heterosis. Such problems are not restricted to any one centre of investigation or country. They are likely to have arisen not through lack of understanding of the problems involved by the investigators concerned, but to an overriding wish to add to the pool of knowledge on yak – while that pool is still quite small.

Remoteness and practicality
There is a further consideration in relation to the nature and effectiveness of research on yak in general. Restricted resources for research and the logistical problems of making these available in the remote areas where yak are kept must exacerbate any difficulties. Limitations arising from restricted finance, and from often inadequate facilities, are not unique to yak. For yak, however, there can be additional problems arising from the conditions under which yak live. Thus, by way of example, research intended to examine the effects of supplementary winter feeding of yak on their subsequent production would be faced with the problem of finding a source of feed. If, still by way of illustration, the results of such a study were to suggest a worthwhile benefit from supplementary feeding, the problem of conserving feed for winter use on a larger scale would need to be solved, or non-bulky feed supplements found which are cheap to supply. However, the difficulties of translating research findings into practical solutions have rarely detracted from the wish or need to gain the basic knowledge in the first instance. Problems are usually solved one step at a time.

Effectiveness
Thus, what is written here about some lack of effectiveness of some of the research on yak is not said in a spirit of criticism, or due to lack of understanding of the difficulties. The purpose of drawing attention to the problems facing yak research is that these problems can lead to partially wasted effort and to difficulty in drawing valid conclusions. However, even within the available resources, more investment of effort in the planning and executing of experiments, especially those in the field,

may lead to greater rewards in terms of improved production methods. In spite of the traditional nature of much of yak production, extension services are now in place in several of the countries with important yak populations. These services provide advice and assist in the development of yak production systems – but they, in turn, need validly tested information on which to base their recommendations.

Design of field experiments

One of the problems, already referred to, which is often encountered in the field research on yak, as reviewed here, is an insufficient number of animals to allow a true understanding of the effects studied. A related problem of experimental design is a lack of balance in the allocation of animals to different treatment groups (for example, in feeding, management, or stocking rate trials). Balance, if achieved, ensures that the effect of the treatment is the only difference, or at least the largest identifiable difference, between the groups. In the absence of prior records on the animals such balancing is difficult or impossible to achieve, except when treatments are restricted to very specific and limited classes of animal (e.g. female calves born in June). For most older animals, such as milking females, insufficient is known about their previous history with real accuracy – for example precise age, previous calving history, previous treatments, previous individual performance characteristics, parentage, and so on. For these purposes the memory of the herdsman is not really adequate. If these various factors are known from records, statistical adjustment can often be made for some of main factors which differ among the individuals in a group, and the records can also be used to make different groups equivalent to each other. However, in the absence of such records some form of random allocation to treatment groups is needed; but unless the numbers in each group are very large indeed, differences may still arise.

As a contribution to overcoming some of the problems of creating equivalent groups of animals, to which different treatments could later be applied, a simple identification system was devised for investigations on yak undertaken, by the Southwest Nationalities College, in Hongyuan county of Sichuan (on Longri farm referred to in earlier chapters). (The investigations were part of a project supported by UNDP/FAO. The animal component of this project was under the supervision of Professor Cai Li.). The system was also intended to make it simple for herdsmen to recognise which animals belonged to which treatment. Since the procedure could have wider application, it is described briefly in Appendix 1, as an example of successful improvisation. The procedure, and its statistical consequences, are shown in more detail by Chen Zhihua *et al.* (1995).

Another point to be considered is the size of the change ("improvement") which would be thought of as a worthwhile achievement, or which it would be sensible to measure in biological or economic terms – the change considered being that brought about by manipulating some component of the production system. The answer to this question has a direct bearing on the number of animals needed for an experiment and on the experimental design. Herders might, for example, be prepared to alter an aspect of their yak management for an extra ten percent of output, but not for an extra one percent. From the point of view of experimental numbers, a difference of ten percent, in response to a treatment, requires fewer animals to detect and show as statistically significant than an attempt to detect and verify a difference of only one percent.

Statistical rectitude

Another problem encountered in the literature on yak (as in some of the literature of other livestock investigations) is that, in some cases, presentation of the results makes it difficult to know whether appropriate statistical methods and rigour have been applied to the analyses. Sometimes only a mean and standard deviation is given, and occasionally only the former. This is not enough to judge the relative importance and significance of different factors responsible for variation in animal performance. The number of animals used is usually shown, but not always. Again, these are matters which detract from the wider usefulness of the results and could be easily remedied. Several factors lead to the hope and expectation that the statistical problems of data analysis may be problems of the past. There is now increased training in statistical methodology and a greater understanding of the underlying problems in the interpretation of experiments. There is also now a wide availability of computers and of appropriate software (database and statistical), together with the increased power of personal computers to do the work. The change of approach to data analysis is already evident from the more recent crops of publications. However, the introduction of more sophisticated and appropriate statistical analyses of yak data must not be allowed to detract from the need to use sufficiently large numbers of animals in the yak investigations; nor should the use of better statistical methods for final analysis of the data be at the expense of good experimental planning and design. All research workers are likely to be familiar with the temptation to make too much of statistically significant findings which are counter-intuitive, do not make biological sense and are most likely to be due to chance and may even have no significant economic relevance.

Publication of results

Finally, in terms of published results, there is world-wide recognition among editors of scientific journals of a dearth of "negative" results. This suggests that authors may believe, perhaps correctly, that only "positive" results will be found to be of interest and attract further funding for research. Whatever the motivation, the shortage of results which say "this did not work" or "this treatment gave only a very small, or even a negative response" is a further cause of wasted effort, since others may try the same unsuccessful approach in ignorance of the earlier failure. Yak research is unlikely to be immune from this problem. However, because of the greater effort required to conduct research on yak, than on many other species of domestic livestock, it is particularly important for the overall effectiveness of research on yak that the results presented are not selective.

• **Present and future**

Fundamental research

An important component of knowledge for future change in yak production, it can be argued, must be an understanding of the basic physiology and biochemistry of the yak. Increasingly, work in this sphere is being undertaken. Thus, rather than studies of "feeding" practice, there are now studies also of nutritional physiology. Results from such investigations were included among those presented at the first international congress on yak at Gansu agricultural University in 1994 – itself a landmark for the assembly of knowledge and expertise on yak. The setting up of an International Yak Information Centre as a consequence of the congress is another such landmark (see Appendix 2). Titles in the proceedings of the congress included studies on the energy-nitrogen balance of yak (Feng Yanglian and Mo Fang, 1994), energy metabolism (Hu Linghao, 1994 – referred to in chapter 4), digestibility studies (Chen [Y.K] *et al.* 1994), investigations on and related to protein metabolism (Chen [J.] *et al.* 1994; Xue *et al.* 1994; Han, Xie and Hu, 1994) and the effect of hormone implants (Zhao Binyao *et al.* 1994). Studies have been conducted for a long time on the haematological characteristics of yak blood, and protein polymorphisms in milk and saliva. Genetic data from such studies have been used, as in the work of Mashurov and Davydov (see chapter 2), to estimate genetic distances between different species and breeds of cattle, including yak. Results on genetic distance are, in turn, being considered in the context of devising breeding strategies to generate heterosis – even though knowledge of genetic distance is unlikely to supplant the need to test, in practice, the heterosis generated in respect of production traits in specific crosses. Studies are now in progress on aspects of yak immunology, physiological responses to environmental stress and a start is also being made on DNA characterisation of yak (e.g. Li Jiyou *et al.*, 1994; Liu, Xu and Hu, 1994; Qioumei Ji, 1994; Zhao, Zhong and Cai, 1994). Modern technology is also allowing new approaches to the study of male infertility of hybrids.

What is less apparent, as yet, is whether these separate studies, from several different centres, are part of an improvement strategy for yak, or merely a praiseworthy search for knowledge for its own sake. Some authors clearly recognise the potential of their work in a wider context, as in the work on energy metabolism and of genetic distancing, but this is not always made explicit.

As yet, much of this work is based on small numbers of animals and, as most research workers would say, hampered by inadequate support. There is also a distinct danger, to which yak investigations are not immune, that inadequate provision of money and resources for research tempts research workers to choose topics for investigation which are productive of papers in scientific journals, but often not very useful in helping to improve animal production (this is separate from, and in addition to, the problem concerning selection of "positive" results for publication, referred to earlier).

Gaps in knowledge

An opinion on what are the most important gaps in scientific knowledge of yak production is tempting fate, as whatever the answer, it will invite criticism. It all depends on starting assumptions, viewpoint, and personal interest. A herdsman, an extension worker and an academic may each start from a different viewpoint and have a different personal interest. However, in the context of the information in this book and of its publication by the Food and Agriculture Organisation of the United Nations let the viewpoint be that of seeking knowledge to optimise the use of the natural resources, which yak already exploit with some measure of success.

In attempting to identify the gaps in knowledge, it is important to recognise that yak production is part of a system of using natural resources and that different components of the system are inter-related. This is true in terms of the relationships of the animal to its environment and also true in terms of the inter-relationships of different aspects of the yak's performance to each other. Similarly, the several components of the grazing ecology are inter-related.

A systems approach

Among those involved with yak research, there is no lack of recognition of the complexity of yak production and of the many factors involved. The gaps appears to be in 1) using a systems approach to integrate the separate pieces of information, 2) identifying what variables in the system are not sufficiently understood, 3) identifying limiting factors to production and 4) filling identified gaps in knowledge. Some of the answers will arise from systematic examination of what is known and understood, some require new investigations.

Since different components of the system are inter-related, changes in some aspects of the yak's performance, or of the environment, will have greater effects on output than others. But it is also necessary to determine the relative ease or difficulty of making a change in the performance of a trait, and the costs of doing so.

Example. A brief illustration must suffice: where meat output from yak is concerned it is necessary first to determine the relative importance of reproductive rate (calf numbers), individual animal growth, and carcass attributes, to the overall output and economics of production. Reproductive rate itself is a function of age at puberty, frequency of calving, and calf survival – and each of these can be further split into components. If, for example, frequency of calving and calf survival were found to be equally limiting to reproductive rate, it might then be determined which of the two is the easier and less costly to improve. In relation to growth, one of the obvious inefficiencies, in terms of converting feed to animal product, is the significant loss over winter of the weight gained in the previous summer and autumn. This may be an inevitable consequence of using the cheaply available pastures and any intervention may be too costly. But part of the exercise is to consider whether limited inputs at critical times of the year might lessen the weight losses and improve overall economic efficiency. This might happen if, for example, such a limited input allowed castrates to be slaughtered at a younger age and, in consequence, more grazing to be made available for lactating females, or for bigger calf crops – or for fodder conservation.

The illustration above is artificial in the sense that meat output is only one component of yak production and in most countries not the most important. The role of milk production and of fibre, relative to that of meat and draught is part of the equation. A systems approach would include them from the start. The factors which determine total milk output from a herd, or an area of land, or a unit of labour can quite readily be listed. The difficulty lies in understanding their precise inter-relationships in the economics of the system and what effect changes in any one will have on the whole. Many aspects of performance are likely to be most limited by nutrition or management procedures; some may benefit from genetic change; pharmacological or physiological intervention may be indicated in a few situations. The whole matter of the grazing ecology is superimposed on the animal component – or, some would say, the other way round.

No single trial could be set up to investigate the effects of all components simultaneously. The situation is too complex. But the principle, as developed in other situations (e.g. Hill Farming Research Organisation, 1979) could be applied to yak production, especially if different centres for yak research and development were to co-operate in a co-ordinated approach to their studies.

Underlying information

From what appears to be known at present, it is possible to make tentative suggestions of some likely gaps in the underlying information needed to construct an econometric model of yak production.

Breeds. Different types, breeds, strains and local varieties of yak exist but, for the most part, they exist in different localities often with different climate, nutrition and management – though with broad similarities in these respects. It would be useful to find out whether, for a given set of conditions in an area or region, one yak breed or strain would make better use of these environmental conditions than another breed or strain and hence produce more, especially milk and meat, from the same area of pasture land. One breed may make better use of poor conditions than another breed. In other circumstances a breed from elsewhere may respond better than the local breed to improvements in management and nutrition which are being introduced. Such breed or strain comparisons would be helpful in defining breeding strategies. They would also help to show, with appropriate investigations, whether nutrition, for example, is always the over-riding limitation on production and whether to the same extent for all breeds of yak.

Since there are several breeds or strains to chose from for such comparisons it would be useful to eliminate some of the contenders beforehand. In the particular case of testing breeds (or strains) for improved conditions, it would help to know in advance whether a breed is capable of responding to improved nutrition and management practices in its own locality, before including it in a breed comparison elsewhere. If it has been shown to be incapable of responding adequately to better feeding and management it could be eliminated as a contender – at least in the first instance. To pre-screen for resilience to poor conditions prior to starting a breed comparison is less easy.

If, as a result of such breed (or strain) comparisons, a breed which is not native to a locality were found to have advantages over the local yak, consideration has then to be given to the alternative ways of introducing it – but it might also point to the scope for selection within a breed or strain that is already indigenous to the area.

Crossing and inbreeding. As already referred to, comparisons involving cattle-yak hybrids only exceptionally provide true estimates of heterosis, yet such estimates are needed if there is a role for commercial yak farming with breeding strategies intended to maximise heterosis (as reported from some countries of the Russian Federation). Hence, trials designed to determine heterosis would be useful – especially in view of the many of cattle breeds being considered in producing the hybrids. Further, as the crossbreeding of domestic with wild yak suggests, there may be heterosis generated by crossing breeds or types of yak which have become genetically separated by time and distance. The literature on yak shows very little such work in the past. Some of the potential advantages from crossing among yak breeds (or wild yak with domestic) may also reflect a counteracting of the effects of inbreeding. Inbreeding itself seems to be an emotive topic, so that some people do not wish to recognise the occurrence of inbreeding, while others blame it for all poor performance in yak. Neither view is likely to be helpful nor necessarily correct, but again this problem points to some need to investigate the actual extent of inbreeding and its relationship to performance, to provide the basis for recommending appropriate action.

Reproduction and herd output. A further production-related problem, as yet insufficiently understood, is the relation of reproductive rate of yak cows to herd output, in the long term. It is easy to say that an increase in the frequency of calving would lead to increased productivity of the herd. However, increased calf numbers can readily lead to overstocking of pastures – already a problem in some areas, especially in winter. Other, concomitant, husbandry methods would need to change. For example, the less productive animals would have to be disposed of sooner and castrates, intended for meat, slaughtered at younger ages (as alluded to earlier). This situation highlights the importance, stressed above, of studying the whole system and not only selected components of it.

The gap in knowing whether inputs of extra feed, or management aids, at critical times, would lead to better sustained reproduction, milk production and better calves – and whether this would be cost-effective – has already been referred to. A systematic approach to finding out precisely why yak in some countries routinely calve more often than in others, or reach puberty and slaughter weights much earlier could be a useful start. Is it only a question of nutrition?

Again in relation to reproduction, the attractions and relative success of increasing calving rate by hormonal intervention need to be viewed in the context of the long-term effects on the cow – as she may not be able to cope in subsequent years, without other concomitant changes in feeding and management. In the context of providing the animals with minimal inputs for maximum return it would also be useful to find out whether the reproductive response of the yak to stimulus from nutrition, or the other aspects of environment, is a threshold character.

Specific nutrients. Alongside such considerations, more detailed study of ruminant physiology and the way in which yak handle different nutrients would clearly be helpful. Some of this work is in hand, but as yet not nearly enough to determine whether specific nutrients may be limiting factors and whether specific nutrient supplements at critical times would elicit a cost-effective response from the animal.

In the context of specific nutrients, there appears to be almost no information in the literature on whether natural yak diets are limited for the yak by particular deficiencies, excesses or imbalances – of, for example, trace metals. Some blood values for minerals found in the literature on yak are not enough for this purpose, as they only indicate a current level without showing whether it is too high, or too low, or optimum in relation to other constituents – unless additional information is also available by which to judge. Much of the relatively low productivity of yak can be directly attributed to malnutrition in winter and early spring. But it would be a pity if the role of specific minerals, and trace elements in particular, were not investigated as possible factors limiting health and production in yak. This is particularly important in the light of evidence from elsewhere which suggests that different types of animal and even different breeds within a species may respond differently to the same amounts of trace elements, because of genetic differences in the efficiency of their absorption by the animal. (Possible evidence from Whipsnade wild animal park, that yak may require different amounts of copper in their diet from other cattle, and a review of the subject, is referred to in chapter 9). Large pasture tracts of Australia became productive for animals only when it was found that copper, cobalt or selenium were deficient (or unavailable to the animal due to excess of other constituents) in various parts of the country. It is not immediately obvious from the literature that such investigations are currently in progress in yak. In terms of a systems approach, evidence in this area of nutrition would allow these factors to be eliminated or included as limits on yak performance.

Adaptability. Though not directly related to current yak production systems, the idea that yak cannot tolerate lower altitudes, except if very cold, may need re-assessment in the light of yak successfully kept for many decades in animal parks (e.g. Whipsnade in England, see also chapter 4). Closer physiological study of the process of adaptation might answer the question whether it is a mainly a matter of giving sufficient time for adaptation, or whether other factors are involved, and hence whether yak could play a useful role in other parts of the world. Such studies might also provide clues on why yak hybrids, and perhaps other types of cattle and perhaps sheep, have not adapted to the extremes of altitude and cold of the yak and what might be done to change this.

From an even more futuristic point of view it would be of interest to know whether the factors involved in the physiological adaptation of the yak to cold, high altitude and long periods of food deprivation are similar to, or different from, the corresponding factors in other animals which live under somewhat comparable conditions – such as llama or alpaca, or even the Scottish Blackface sheep when it comes to food deprivation. Such information if linkable in the future to molecular genetics, might then provide the means of introducing such factors across species – to make the yak "better", or to introduce yak characteristics to other species which may be better at milk or meat production at present, but incapable of surviving in the environment of the yak.

Grazing ecology and range management. As on the animal side, there has been much characterisation of plant species and plant communities of the yak pastures. However, it is less obvious how much is as yet known about the impact of range management techniques on pasture output in the high mountainous regions of central Asia – or whether experience from elsewhere is directly relevant. It can be argued, of course, that much of traditional nomadic or transhumant style of yak herding is also a form of pasture management – both in the interests of exploiting plant growth and of reducing animal disease, parasite infection in particular. Moreover, so long as much of yak keeping remains traditional, the scope for change is small except perhaps in enforcing a control on stocking rate. However, as an insurance against an uncertain future and to safeguard the utilisation of the vast pasture resources at high altitude, more studies on grazing ecology and range management might well repay the effort. In particular it would be useful to know what levels of herbage utilisation can be tolerated by different plant communities before ecological damage arises. Such information might help more specifically to avoid over-grazing before it occurs.

The future ?

As noted at the start of this chapter, it remains to be seen whether the herding of yak will centre in the future mainly on yak keeping as "a way of life", or whether it will be conducted mainly, or only, as an economic activity for the production of meat and milk from otherwise unused, or under-used natural grazing resources. It seems rather more likely than not, that herders and their families will increasingly demand greater rewards for their labour, even though the move to meeting this aspiration may take longer in some areas than others. It also seems likely that for a long time to come the need or desire for more food, including animal products, will continue, or even increase, in many parts of the world, including central Asia and adjacent territories. The introduction of yak and yak crosses might have failed, or at least been "suspended", in Northern Canada and parts of Alaska, adjacent to areas of over-production of meat. It is more likely that in poorer parts of the world a similar move to extend the use of yak to suitable, but under-utilised, areas would be welcomed – if such an introduction of the yak were found to be feasible. It ought to be inconceivable, from a rational point of view, that the mountain pastures of Central Asia, where yak still abound, would be left unused because of a change in the social demands of the people.

The argument thus veers in the direction of saying that the future for the yak seems assured, at least in the medium term, although the pattern of production which may be adopted is much less certain.

In a less money-driven world the yak might also still find a role in other cold, inhospitable parts of the world, such as Alaska, perhaps Greenland or the Andes, where its resilience to hardship and periods of near-starvation could be of benefit. The limitation on a wider distribution for the yak is not so much a function of its adaptability, which is open to test, but a function of the economics of marketing.

In the much longer term, and in the context of a still expanding world population, it will be of interest to find out whether the special merits of the yak are inherited in a way which make them transmissible to other species of animal in the brave new future of genetic engineering. If so, a future generation might yet see big-sized sheep or goats with the yak's tolerance of higher elevations, pigs with yak genes outdoors in Alaska, Hereford- or Charolais-type cattle with the adaptability of yak on the high plateaux of central Asia, and herders in helicopters with remote control.

Even a few years ago such a flight of fancy would have appeared foolish. With the enormous advances that are taking place in the knowledge of genetic structures and their function and in the technology of genetic engineering, what appeared only fanciful then seems within the realms of possibility now – even if still a very remote possibility where yak are concerned. So, future investigators might be well advised to identify which precise characteristics are unique to the yak and which might also be useful in other species, or for the yak in other territories. The investigators might also attempt to be very specific about which of the physiological responses of the yak to its environment might be altered, so as to make the animal an even better user of the natural mountain pastures of central Asia.

The argument thus veers in the direction of saying that the future for the yak seems assured, at least in the medium term, although the pattern of production which may be adopted is much less certain.

In a less money-driven world the yak might also still find a role in other cold, inhospitable parts of the world, such as Alaska, perhaps Greenland or the Andes, where its resilience to hardship and periodic near-starvation could be of benefit. The limitation to a wider distribution for the yak is not so much a function of its adaptability, which is open to test, but a function of the economics of marketing.

In the much longer term, and in the context of a still expanding world population, it will be of interest to find out whether the special merits of the yak are inherited in a way which make them transmissible to other species of animal in the brave new world of genetic engineering. If so, a future generation might yet see big-sized sheep or goats with the yak's tolerance of higher elevations; pigs with yak genes outdoors in Alaska; Hereford or Charolais-type cattle with the adaptability of yak on the high plateaux of central Asia; and herders in helicopters with remote control.

Even a few years ago such a flight of fancy would have appeared foolish. With the enormous advances that are taking place in the knowledge of genetic structures and their function and in the technology of genetic engineering, what appeared only fanciful then seems within the realms of possibility now – even if still a very remote possibility where yak are concerned. So, future investigators might be well advised to identify which precise characteristics are unique to the yak and which might also be useful in other species, or for the yak in other territories. The investigations might also attempt to be very specific about which are the physiological responses of the yak to its environment that must be altered, so as to make the animal an even better user of the natural mountain pastures of central Asia.

REFERENCES

[References which also provide Abstract source were seen only in abstract.]

Agricultural Exploitation Academy of XianJiang (1984). Report on the result of yak's interspecific hybridization. *Journal of China Yak*, 1984 (1), 71–75.

Agricultural Research Institute of Ganzi Tibetan Autonomous Prefecture (1977). *Agricultural and Animal Husbandry Information of Ganzi Prefecture*, 1977 (2).

Agriculture and Animal Department on the Qiangtang Grassland, Study Group of (1978). The observation on wild animals on the Qiangtang Grassland. *Scientific Research Material Collection*, pp. 60–66.

Agriculture and Livestock Bureau of Ganzhi Tibetan Autonomous Prefecture in Sichuan Province (1984). The resources of livestock breeds in Ganzhi Tibetan Autonomous Prefecture of Sichuan Province.

Anand, I., Heath, D., Williams, D., Deen, M., Ferrari, R., Bergel, D. & Harris, P. (1988). The pulmonary circulation of some domestic animals at high altitude. *International Journal of Biometeorology*, **32**, 56–64.

Anand, I.S., Harris, E., Ferrari, R., Pearce, P. & Harris, P. (1986). Pulmonary haemodynamics of the yak, cattle, and cross breeds at high altitude. *Thorax*, **41**, 696–700.

Animal and Veterinary Institute of Tibet (1978). The observation on the oestrus of yak. *Scientific Research Material Collection*, pp. 50–52.

Belkin, V.Sh., Astakhov, O.B. & Gutorov, S.L. (1985). [Capillarization of myocardium in the yak.] *Arkh. Anat. Gristol. Embriol.*, **88**, 53–57.

Belyyar, D.K. (1980). *Domestication of Yakutsk*. Siberian Publication House.

Bishop, N.H. (1989). From zomo to yak: change in a Sherpa village. *Human Ecology*, **17**, 177–204.

Biswas, D., Barari, S.K. & Pal, R.N. (1994). Ticks and lice infestations in yak. Proceedings of First International Congress on Yak. *Journal of Gansu agricultural University* (Special issue, June 1994). pp. 322–324.

Blaxter, K.L., Graham, N.McC. & Wainman, F.W. (1959). The environmental temperature, energy metabolism and heat regulation in sheep. III. The metabolism and thermal exchanges of sheep with fleeces. *Journal of agricultural Science (Cambridge)*, **52**, 41–49.

Bonnemaire, J. & Teissier, J.H. (1976). [Some aspects of breeding at high altitudes in the central Himalayas: yaks, cattle, hybrids and crossbreds in the Langtang Valley (Nepal).] In: Le Yak. Son rôle dans la vie materielle et culturelle des éleveurs d'Asie centrale. *Ethnozootechnie* No. 15, France, 91–118.

Boulnois, L. (1976). [The yak and the travels of western naturalists.] In: Le Yak. Son rôle dans la vie materielle et culturelle des éleveurs d'Asie centrale. *Ethnozootechnie* No. 15, France, 7–22.

Cai Li (1989). *Sichuan Yak*. Sichuan Publication House, Chengdu.

Cai Li (1992). *China Yak*. Agricultural Publishing Company, Beijing.

Cai Li, Hu Angang & Du Shaodeng (1960). The experiment of improving feeding and management to increase milk yield of yak and Pien Niu.

Cai Li *et al.* (1975). Determination of physiological and biochemical indexes in yak. *Journal of Chinese Animal Science*, 1975 (6), 29–31.

Cai Li *et al.* (1980a). [Agriculture and Livestock Bureau of Ganzhi Tibetan autonomous Prefecture of Sichuan Province and SW College of Minority Nationalities]. The good meat-purpose yak – the investigation and study of Jiulong Yak. *Journal of China Yak*, 1980 (1), 14–40.

Cai Li *et al.* (1980b). [Agriculture and Livestock Bureau of Ganzhi Tibetan autonomous Prefecture of Sichuan Province and SW College of Minority Nationalities. The general survey and identification for Jiulong yak. *Journal of China Yak*, 1980 (3), 17–24.

Cai Li *et al.* (1984a). [Yak Research Office of SW College of Minority Nationalities and Xiangdong livestock farm in Ruoergai County] Analyses on effect of yaks' improvement by using AI with the frozen semen of common bulls. *Journal of Sichuan Grassland*, 1984 (1), 39–48.

Cai Li *et al.* (1984b). [Yak Research Office of SW College of Minority Nationalities and Grassland Institute of Sichuan Province] The research on the interspecific cross combination between female yak and common bull. The research on the utilization and exploitation of grassland in the northwestern part of Sichuan Province, National Publishing House of Sichuan Province. pp. 107–113.

Cai Li *et al.* (1986). Optimization of the age-sex distribution of yak's population and the correlated slaughter program in Ruoergai County. *Journal of South-west Nationalities College, Animal Husbandry & Veterinary Edition*, 1986 (4), 22–30.

Cai Li *et al.* (eds) (1987). [Editorial Committee of Fauna of Livestock and Poultry Breeds in Sichuan.] *Fauna of Livestock and Poultry Breeds in Sichuan.* Sichuan Science and Technology Publishing House.

Cai Zhaoguang, Huang Baoning, Lang Baining & Lei Gengxin (1986). *An Atlas of Rangeland and Its Main Plant Resources on the Qinghai-Tibet Plateau.* Volume Qinghai. Agricultural Publishing House: Beijing.

Cayla, L. (1976). [Some mythological aspects of yak in Tibet.] In: Le Yak. Son rôle dans la vie materielle et culturelle des éleveurs d'Asie centrale. *Ethnozootechnie* No. 15, France, 23–34.

Chen Xiafei, Lei Degian & Liu Shijie (1981). Investigation on Maiwa yak. Investigative reports on the resources of livestock and poultry breeds in Aba Tibetan Autonomous Prefecture, 1981.

Chen Zhihua, Wen Yongli & Cai Li (1994). The systematic analysis of influence factors on the newborn weight of yak. *Journal of South-west Nationalities College* (Natural Science Edition), 1994 (4), 325–331.

Chen Zhihua, Wen Yongli & Cai Li (1995). [A new method of stochastic experiment divided into groups for scientific research in yak.] *Journal of South-west Nationalities College* (Natural Science Edition), 21 (2), 143–147.

Chen, J., Han, X.T. & Han, Z.K. (1994). Effects of dietary crude protein levels on serum cortisol, insulin and thyroid hormones of yak. Proceedings of First International Congress on Yak. *Journal of Gansu agricultural University* (Special issue, June 1994), pp. 196–197.

Chen, Y.K., Yuan, Y.Q., Liu, B. & Huang, H.Z. (1994). Study on methods to determine intake and digestibility of herbage for yak in the cold season. Proceedings of First International Congress on Yak. *Journal of Gansu agricultural University* (Special issue, June 1994), pp. 222–224.

Chen, Z.X. (1983). The distribution and characteristic of Brucellosis in Qinghai Province. Journal of Animal Science and Veterinary Medicine of Qinghai Province, 1983 (6), 4–6.

Cheng Peilieu (1984). Livestock breeds of China. FAO Animal Production and Health Paper No. 46, Rome. pp. 96–108.

Cheng, Z.D. et al. (1985). [Leptospirosis in yak in some areas of Sichuan Province: a retrospective study.] Chinese Journal of Veterinary Science and Technology No. 1, 17–19. [Abstract in Veterinary Bulletin, 1986, 56(2780).]

Cincotta, R.P., Soest, P.J., Robertson, J.B., Beal, C.M., Goldstein, M.C. & Van-Soest, P.J. (1991). Foraging ecology of livestock on the Tibetan Changtang; a comparison of three adjacent grazing areas. Arctic and Alpine Research, 23, 149–161. [Herbage Abstracts, 62, 116.]

Cox, T. (1985). Herding and socio-economic change among Langtang Tibetans. Contributions to Nepalese Studies, 12, 63–74.

Deakin, A., Muir, G.W. & Smith, A.G. (1935). Hybridization of domestic cattle, bison and yak. Report of Wainwright experiment. Publication 479, Technical Bulletin 2, Dominion of Canada, Department of Agriculture, Ottawa.

Deng, C.H. (1983). Salmonellosis in yak. Veterinary Medicine of China, Supplementary, 28–29.

Denisov, V.F. (1935). [Some data on the yak and its hybrids in Kirghizstan.] Trud. Kirgiz. Kompl. Eksp., 4, 115–171. [CAB Animal Breeding Abstracts, 4, 298–300.]

Denisov, V.F. (1938). [Hybridisation of the yak with Kirghiz cattle and the Schwyz.] Izv. Acad. Nauk. SSSR (Otd. mat. est., Ser. biol.), 863–878. [CAB Animal Breeding Abstracts, 7, 116–117.]

Denisov, V.F. (1958). Domestic Yak and Their Hybrids. Selkhozgiz: Moscow. 116 pp.

Ding, X.T. & Chen, D.M. (1994). Preliminary study on the reproductive performances of Yak, Chauri and Ago cattle. Proceedings of First International Congress on Yak. *Journal of Gansu agricultural University* (Special issue, June 1994). pp. 307–309.

Dong Baosen (1985). A preliminary study on the yaks died from falling off slope. Journal of China Yak, 1985 (3), 51–53.

Dor, R. (1976). Note sur le yak au Pamir. In: Le Yak. Son rôle dans la vie materielle et culturelle des éleveurs d'Asie centrale. Ethnozootechnie No. 15, France. 126–132.

Dou Yaozong, Yang Zai & Xue Zengya (1985). Studies on the geographic ecology and population ecology of the yak in Tibet. Journal of South-west Nationalities College, Animal Husbandry & Veterinary Edition, 1985 (2), 29–33.

Doxey, D.L. (1977). Haematology of the ox. In: Comparative Clinical Haematology (eds. R.K. Archer & L.B. Jeffcott). Blackwell Scientific Publications: Oxford.

Du Fusheng (1987a). The research and production on frozen semen of male yak. A research on the utilization and exploitation of grassland in the north-western part of Sichuan Province, National Publishing House, 1984, pp. 151–156.

Du Fusheng (1987b). Production of frozen semen of Jiulong yak. Journal of China Yak, 1987 (1), 15–17.

Dubrovin, A.T. (1992). Yak breeding in the northern Caucasus. Zootekhniya, No. 3–4, 18–20.

Dyblor, E. (1957). The first time to discovery of yak fossils in Yakutsk. Vertebrate Palasiatica, 1(4), 293–300.

Epstein, H. (1969). Domestic Animals of China. Commonwealth Agricultural Bureaux, Farnham Royal, England. pp. 20–25.

Epstein, H. (1977). Domestic Animals of Nepal. Holmes & Meier, New York. pp. 20–37.

Feng Dagang & Su Lei (1994). Small intestinal strangulation with deferent duct in 40 castrated Pienniu. Proceedings of First International Congress on Yak. *Journal of Gansu agricultural University* (Special issue, June 1994). pp. 327–330.

Feng Yanglian & Mo Fang (1994). Studies on energy-nitrogen balance in the rumen for ruminant feeding. Proceedings of First International Congress on Yak. *Journal of Gansu agricultural University* (Special issue, June 1994), pp. 185–188.

Flerow, C.C. (1980). On the geographic distribution of the genus *Poephagus* during the Pleistocene and Holocene. Quaternary Paleontol. (East) Berlin, 4, 123–126.

Gaidyseva, V.D. (1963). [Preliminary results of crossing the yak with beef cattle in Gorno Altai.] Zivotnovadstvo, 25(5), 56–58. [CAB Animal Breeding Abstracts, 31, 472.]

Grassland Institute of Sichuan Province and Longri Breeding Stock Farm of Sichuan Province (1982). A fattening trial on yak and Pien Niu of Holstein-Friesian bull and female yak on grassland. *Journal of China Yak*, 1982 (1), 29–33.

Grassland Institute of Sichuan Province and Waqie Livestock Farm of Hongyuan County (1985). The research of supplementary feeding to improve lactation performance of female Pien Niu in cold season. *Journal of China Yak*, 1985 (2), 30–39.

Guo Aipo & Huang Wenxiu (1983). A study on the chromosomes of yak, common cattle and their hybrid. First volume of survey for Hengduan Mountain in research of Qinghai-Tibet Plateau, Yunnan People's Publishing House, pp. 365–372.

Han Zhengkang & Lu Tianshui (1980a). Study on physiological lactation features in yak. *Journal of Nanjing Agricultural College*, 1980 (1), 137–146.

Han Zhengkang & Lu Tianshui (1980b). Features of lactation physiology of F_1 hybrid of interspecific cross between female yak and common bull. *Journal of China Yak*, 1980 (2), 5–15.

Han, X.T., Xie, A.Y. & Hu, L.H. (1994). Microbial protein synthesis in the rumen of yaks receiving diets containing straw and concentrate in various proportions. Proceedings of First International Congress on Yak. *Journal of Gansu agricultural University* (Special issue, June 1994), pp. 218–221.

Hawkey, C.M., Ashton, D.G., Hart, M.G., Cindery, R.N. & Jones, D.M. (1983). Normal and clinical haematology in the yak (*Bos grunniens*). *Research in Veterinary Science*, **34**, 31–36.

Hill Farming Research Organisation (1979). *Science and Hill Farming.* The Hill Farming Research Organisation, Edinburgh. V + 184 pp. (Copies from Macaulay Land Use Research Institute, Aberdeen, Scotland.)

Hu Angang, Cai Li & Du Shaodeng (1960). An investigation on yak in Ganzi County. *Journal of South-west Nationalities College, Animal Husbandry & Veterinary Edition*, 1960 (4), 46–50.

Hu Linghao (1994). Study of energy metabolism and ruminal metabolism in growing yaks. Proceedings of the First International Congress on Yak. *Journal of the Gansu agricultural University* (Special issue, June 1994), pp. 188–195.

Huang Wenxiu & Wang Sufang (1980). A research on the character and regulation of ecological distribution of livestock on the Tibet Plateau. *Journal of Natural Resource*, 1980 (2).

Institute of Animal Science [China] (1986). *Bovine Breeds in China.* Shanghai Scientific and Technical Publishers. pp. 117–132.

Ivanova, V.V. & Ljubimov, I.M. (1951). [The introduction of a breed with high butterfat yield into farms in Gorno Altai.] *Sovetsk. Zootch.* 1951, (3), 26–37. [*CAB Animal Breeding Abstracts*, **20**, 456–457.]

Jain, Y.C. (1989). Yak husbandry in Himachal Pradesh. *Indian Dairyman*, **41**, 202–208.

Jain, Y.C. & Yadava, R.S. (1985). Yield and composition of milk of Himachali yak, yak hybrid and hill cow. *Indian Journal of Animal Sciences*, **55**, 223–224.

Jest, C. (1976). L'élevage du yak dans l'Himalaya du Nepal. In: Le Yak. Son rôle dans la vie materielle et culturelle des éleveurs d'Asie centrale. *Ethnozootechnie* No. 15, France, 78–90.

Jia Huaigong (1966). An investigation and study on yak in Tibet. *Collection of Theses of Comprehensive Survey in Tibet*, Scientific Publishing House, China, pp. 1–19.

Jiang Ruisheng & Bai Yinghua (1985). Investigation on the reproductive status of Zhongdian yak. *Journal of China Yak*, 1985 (3), 25–28.

Joshi, D.D. (1982). *Yak and Chauri Husbandry in Nepal.* H.M. Government Press, Singha Durbar, Khatmandu, Nepal, **XVII**, 145 pp.

Joshi, D.D., Lund, P.N., Miller, D.J. & Shrestha, S.K. (1994). Yak production in Nepal. Proceedings of First International Congress on Yak. *Journal of Gansu agricultural University* (Special issue, June 1994). pp. 105–112. [Reprinted in *Asian Livestock (FAO Bangkok)*, 1994, **XIX** (10), 132–136.]

Kalia, H.R. (1974). Appraisal of cow (*Bos indicus*) x yak (*Bos grunniens*) crossbreeding work in cold and elevated regions of Himachal Pradesh (India). Proceedings of First World Congress on Genetics Applied to Livestock Production, 1974, vol. 3, pp. 723–730. Madrid.

Katzina, E.V. (1993). [Lactation and biological properties of yak milk associated with nutritive value.] *Sel'skokhozyaistvennaya – Biologii*, 1993, No. 2, 108–114. [*CAB Animal Breeding Abstracts*, 63, No. 680.]

Katzina, E.V., Davydov, V.N. & Baldanov, N.D. (1994). Elaboration of the scheme of production and usage of industrial hybrids of yak and meat cattle. Proceedings of First International Congress on Yak. *Journal of Gansu agricultural University* (Special issue, June 1994). pp. 44–48. (Reprinted in *Asian Livestock (FAO Bangkok)* 1994, **XIX**(10), 137–139.)

Katzina, E.V. & Maturova, E.T. (1989). [The reproductive function of yak cows.] *Doklady Vsesoyuznoi Ordena Lenina Akademii Sel'skokhozyaistvennykh Naukim V.I. Lenina*, 1989, No. 4, 26–29. [*CAB Animal Breeding Abstracts*, 58, No. 352.]

Kozlovskii, B. (1960). [The greater use of commercial crossing in yak breeding.] *Molochnoe i Myasnoe Skotovodstvo*, **5**(11), 32–36. [*CAB Animal Breeding Abstracts*, **29**, 270.]

Kreutzmann, H. (1986). A note on yak-keeping in Hunza (Northern areas of Pakistan). *Production Pastorale et Société* No. 19, 99–106.

Lalthantluanga, R., Wiesner, H. & Braunitzer, G. (1985). Studies on yak haemoglobin (*Bos grunniens*, Bovidae): Structural basis for high intrinsic oxygen affinity? *Biol. Chem. Hoppe-Seyler*, **366**, 63–68.

Langjie Zeren, Zhong Chuanyou, Wang Yingze & Ren Mugiu (1987). Supplementary feeding trial for fattening hybrid of Holstein-Friesian and yak in warm season. *Journal of China Yak*, 1987 (4), 51–55.

Larrick, J.W. & Burck, K.B. (1986). Tibet's all-purpose beast of burden. *Natural History*, **95**, 56–65.

Lei Huanzhang (1964). Observation on the genital, physiological and reproductive features of yak. *Journal of Chinese Animal Science*, 1964 (7), 1–3.

Lei Huanzhang *et al.* (1983). Report on the investigation of yak in Qinghai. Investigative report on the resource of livestock and poultry breeds in Qinghai Province. pp. 50–101.

Lei Huanzhang *et al.* (1985). Studies on the ecological reaction of criss-cross grazing of yak and its hybrid in the cold and warm seasons. *Journal of China Yak*, 1985 (2), 13–23.

Lei Huanzhang *et al.* (1986). Study on selecting and breeding the superior type of yak. *Journal of China Yak*, 1986 (2), 10–22.

Lei, H.Z., Zhao, Y.B., Zhang, H.W., Tong, Z.B. & Lu, K.L. (1994). Studies on yak selection (1982–1986). Proceedings of First International Congress on Yak. *Journal of Gansu agricultural University* (Special issue, June 1994). pp. 139–143.

Li Jiyou, Han Jianlin, Wu Jianping & Men Zhengming (1994). Advance on the research of chromosomes in yak (*Bos grunniens*). Proceedings of First International Congress on Yak. *Journal of Gansu agricultural University* (Special issue, June 1994), pp. 73–76.

Li Kongliang *et al.* (1986). The experiment of tameness of the male yak containing half blood of wild yak, production of its frozen semen and AI. *Journal of China Yak*, 1986 (1), 42–44.

Li Shihong (1985). Discussion for the adaptability of yak. *Journal of China Yak*, 1985 (3), 22–25.

Li Shihong *et al.* (1981). The preliminary observation on yak's heat resistance. *Journal of China Yak*, 1981 (2), 1–4.

Li Shihong *et al.* (1984). The observation on yak's heat resistance. A research on the utilization and exploitation of grassland in the northwestern part of Sichuan Province, National Publishing House of Sichuan Province, pp. 171–174.

Li Xuewen, Liu Wulin, Luo Zibin & Zhang Zhengxiang (1983). The preliminary test of hybrid's fattening and slaughtering. *Journal of China Yak*, 1983 (1), 35–37.

Liang Daxin (1948). Yaks in Xikong. *Journal of Chinese Agricultural Association*, No. 186.

Liu Qian & Cheng Wending (1994). Studies on fattening yak. Proceedings of the First International Congress on Yak. *Journal of the Gansu agricultural University* (Special issue, June 1994), pp. 224–227.

Liu Wulin & Liu Shengyu (1982). The observations and analyses for female yaks' characters of Qinghai yak. *Journal of China Yak*, 1982 (4), 5–7.

Liu Zhengqui (1981). The reproductive characters of Qinghai yak. *Journal of China Yak*, 1981 (4), 5–7.

Liu Zhiyao &Shuai Weiwen (1985). The study on yak's oestrus synchronization by using three-combined-hormone. *Journal of China Yak*, 1985 (2), 24–27.

Liu, S.G., Xu, H. & Hu, Q.H. (1994). Constructing yak DNA fingerprints by using human mini-satellite probes. Proceedings of First International Congress on Yak. *Journal of Gansu agricultural University* (Special issue, June 1994), pp. 92–95.

Liu, W.D. (1994). Observations on growth-decline rule of roundworm and its larva in yak's stomach and intestine. Proceedings of First International Congress on Yak. *Journal of Gansu agricultural University* (Special issue, June 1994). pp. 339–343.

Local Disease Control Office of Central Government (1983). Brucellosis and its control in China. Government Document. 12 pp.

Lu Guaihui (1980). The regulation of change of yak's body weight and relationship between its slaughtered age and different seasons under the condition of natural grazing. *Abstract Collection of Theses of Animal Husbandry and Veterinary Medicine of China*, **26**.

Lu Hongji, Zhu Xinshu, Li Kongliang & Nang Minqiang(1987). A test on improving yaks' productive performances by introducing wild-yak blood. *Journal of China Yak*, 1987 (2), 8–12.

Lu Zhonglin & Li Kongliang (1994). Distribution, types and utilization of wild yaks in China. Proceedings First International Congress on Yak, p. 23–26. Reprinted in *Asian Livestock (FAO, Bangkok)*, **XIX**(10), 122–123.

Lu Zhongling, Ma Xiwen, Gao Shukuan & Liang Huiru (1982). The hair quality of Luqu yak. *Journal of South-west Nationalities College, Animal Husbandry & Veterinary Edition*, 1982 (1), 17–20.

Lu, G.Z. & Ling, C.W. (1985a). Animal Infectious Diseases in Tibet. (Publisher ?) pp. 75–206.

Lu, G.Z. & Ling, C.W. (1985b). Animal Infectious Diseases in Sichuan Province. (Publisher ?) pp. 84–85, 219–221.

Lu, W.F. (1986). Current research of yak Salmonellosis in China. *Animal Science and Veterinary Medicine of Gansu Province*, 1986 (3), 23–25.

LuoSang Jiangcuo & Chen Yu (1987). A report on the experiment of artificial insemination of yak in Shenzha County. *Journal of China Yak*, 1987 (3), 51–57.

Lydekker, R. (1898). *Wild Oxen, Sheep and Goats of All Lands.* Rowland Ward Ltd: London.

Lydekker, R. (1912). *The Ox and Its Kindred.* Methuen & Co. Ltd: London.

Ma Tianfu (1983). The first report on induction of yak's oestrus with drugs. *Journal of China Yak*, 1983 (2), 16–18.

Ma Zongxiang & Du Yaozong (1982). Study on the pattern of seasonal changes of yak's body weight. *Journal of China Yak*, 1982 (1), 21–28.

Machurov, A.M. & Davydov, V.N. (1995). The revealing of indices of immunogenetic similarity and distance between yaks of Buryatia and other populations of Bovidae. 8–page report from Buryat Institute of Biology (personal communication).

Machurov, A.M. *et al.* (1993). The immunogenetic similarity and distance between the Schwyz cattle and 86 populations of Bovidae. *Genetics (Russia)*, 29 (4), 646–653.

Magasch, A. (1990). Statische Massmalen diagnostischer Zuchthygienemerkmale bei Yakkühen in der Mongolei. *Wiss. Zeitschift der Humboldt-Universität zu Berlin R. Agrarwiss*, **39**, 359–366.

Magasch, A. (1991a). Ergebnisse von Untersuchungen über die Physiologie des Sexualzyklus beim weiblichen Yak. *Monatschefte für Veterinärmedicin*, **46**, 257–258.

Magasch, A. (1991b). Anwendung biotechnischer Verfahren bei der Reproduktion des Yaks. *Monatshefte für Veterinärmedicin*, **46**, 257–258.

Mason, I.L. (1988). *World Dictionary of Livestock Breeds,* 3rd ed, Vol. XX. CAB International, Wallingford, UK. 348 pp.

Maturova, E.T. & Katzina, E.B. (1990) [The yak of Sayan.] The Buryat Scientific Centre of the Siberian Division of the USSR Academy of Sciences, Ulan-Ude, 1990. 168pp (in Russian).

Meyer, F. (1976). Notes on products from the yak and its crosses used in Tibetan medicine. In: Le Yak. Son rôle dans la vie materielle et culturelle des éleveurs d'Asie centrale. *Ethnozootechnie* No. 15, France, 35–45.

Miller, D.J. (1987). Rangelands of the Himalayan Kingdom of Bhutan. *Rangelands*, **9**, 257–259.

Miller, D.J. (1990). Grasslands of the Tibetan plateau. *Rangelands*, **12**, 159–163.

Miller, D.J., Harris, R.B. & Cui-Quan Cai (1994). Wild yak and their conservation in the Tibetan Plateau. Proceedings of First International Congress on Yak. *Journal of Gansu agricultural University* (Special issue, June 1994). pp. 27–35.

Mochalovskii, A. & Abdusalamov, Sh. (1973). [The Pamir yak in the Caucasus.] *Molochnoe i Myasnoe Skotovodstvo*, 1973, No. 8, 21. [*CAB Animal Breeding Abstracts*, **42**, No. 163.]

Norov, A. & Dorotyuk, E. (1988). [Meat production of bulls of different genotypes in Tadzhikistan.] *Molochnoe i Myasnoe Skotovodstvo*, 1988, No. 1, 43–44. [*CAB Animal Breeding Abstracts*, 57, No. 1472.]

Northwestern China Institute of Livestock and Vet. (1965). The observation on the biologic characters of yak and effects of cross-breeding female yak with dairy bull. The collection of materials of studies and investigations on livestock and vet. during 1959 and 1962, vol. 3, *Animal Fascicle*, 347–362.

Olsen, S.J. (1991). Confused yak taxonomy and evidence of domestication. *Illinois State Museum Scientific Papers*, **23**, 387–393.

Ouyang Xi & Wang Qianfei (1984). A preliminary observation on the structure of dermal histology of yak. *Journal of South-west Nationalities College, Animal Husbandry & Veterinary Edition*, 1984 (3), 12–21.

Ouyang Xi *et al.* (1983). Effects of seasonal change of natural ecological conditions on yak's hair-coat. *Journal of South-west Nationalities College, Animal Husbandry & Veterinary Edition*, 1983 (4), 1–5.

Ouyang Xi *et al.* (1984). An observation on adaptation of calf yak. A research on utilization and exploitation of grassland in the north-western part of Sichuan Province, Sichuan National Publishing House, pp. 159–161.

Ouyang Xi *et al.* (1985). Studies on the cold resistance of yak. *Journal of South-west Nationalities College, Animal Husbandry & Veterinary Edition*, 1985 (4), 28–34.

Pal, R.N. (1990). Indian yaks (*Poephagus grunniens* L.). *Asian Livestock (FAO, Bangkok)*, **XV**(9), 97–106.

Pal, R.N. (1993a). Yak (*Poephagus grunniens* L.) of India. *Animal Genetic Resources Information*, **12**, 63–71.

Pal, R.N. (1993b). Halting the decline of the yak population in India. *World Animal Review*, **76**(3), 56–57.

Pal, R.N. (1993c). Domestic yak (*Poephagus grunniens* L.): a research review. *Indian Journal of Animal Sciences*, **63**, 743–753.

Pal, R.N., Barari, S.K. & Basu, A. (1994c). Yak (*Poephagus grunniens* L.), its type – a field study. *Indian Journal of Animal Sciences*, **64**, 853–856.

Pal, R.N., Barari, S.K. & Basu, A. (1994d). Colour pattern in yaks (*Poephagus grunniens* L.). *Indian Journal of Animal Sciences*, **64**, 890–892.

Pal, R.N., Barari, S.K. & Biswas, D. (1994a). Yak (*Poephagus grunniens* L.) husbandry in India. Proceedings of First International Congress on Yak. *Journal of Gansu agricultural University* (Special issue, June 1994). pp. 16–21. [Reprinted in *Asian Livestock (FAO, Bangkok)*, 1994, **XIX**(10), 126–128.]

Paudyal, R.M. (1993). The yak and its importance in Central Asia and particularly Nepal. MSc Thesis, Centre for Tropical Veterinary Medicine, University of Edinburgh. 67 pp.

Peng, X.K. (1987). Brucellosis and its characteristics in Sichuan Province. *Journal of South-west Nationalities College, Animal Husbandry & Veterinary Edition*, 1987 (2), 32–35.

Phillips, R.W., Johnson, R.G. & Moyer, R.T. (1945). *The Livestock of China*. U.S. State Department Publication No. 2249.

Phillips, R.W., Tolstoy, I.A. & Johnson, R.G. (1946). Yaks and yak-cattle hybrids in Asia. *Journal of Heredity*, **37**, 163–170, 207–215.

Phillipson, A.T. (1970). Ruminant digestion. In: *Dukes' Physiology of Domestic Animals*. Cornell University Press. 8th ed. pp. 424–483.

Prasad, S., Sharma, K., Ramokaut, K.L. Ahuja (1978). Isolation of foot-and-mouth disease virus from yak. *Veterinary Record*, **102**, 363–364.

Pu Futang, Zhang Rongchang, Guo Wanlong & Yuan Deron (1987). Determination on the meat composition and meat performance of Tianzhu White yak. *Journal of China Yak*, 1987 (4), 22–25.

Purevzav, Z. & Beshlebnov, A.V. (1967). [Some data on the physiology of reproduction in the yak.] *Zhivotnovodstvo Mask.*, **29**, 92–94. [*ABA*, **36**, 302–303.]

Qi Guangyong (1984). The behaviour of young calf yak. A research on utilization and exploitation of grassland in the north-western part of Sichuan Province. Sichuan National Publishing House, pp. 162–170.

Qian Yanwen (1979). *The Origin of Feeding Animal. Biohistory*. Vol. 5. Scientific Publishing House.

Qioumei, J. (1994). Construction of yak genomic library and dissociated GH gene. Proceedings of First International Congress on Yak. *Journal of Gansu agricultural University* (Special issue, June 1994), pp. 102–103.

Qiu Huai (1957). *Cattle Feeding*, Vol. 1. Publishing House of Animal Husbandry, China

Qiu Zhongquan & Zhu Qiming (1981). The histological study on reproductive organs of female yak. *Journal of China Yak*, 1981 (4), 25–28.

Ren Jizhou & Chu Cheong Ping (eds) (1993). Proceedings: Conference on Grazing Industry in Southern China. Gansu Grassland Ecological Institute, Gansu Science and Technology Press.

Ren Jizhou & Jin Juhe (1956). The observation on grazing habit of yak herd. *Journal of Animal Husbandry and Veterinary Medicine of China*, **2**.

Research Cooperative Group for China Yak (1980–1987). The 30 investigation reports on China yak resource. *Journal of China Yak*, No. 1–26.

Ryder, M.L. & Stephenson, S.K. (1968). *Wool Growth.* Academic Press (London & New York). XVIII + 805 pp.

Sahu, R.N., Katiyar, R.D. & Khera, R.C. (1981). Blood studies in yaks of Sikkim. *Indian Veterinary Journal*, **58**, 614–616.

Sarbagishev, B.S., Rabochev, V.K. & Terebaev, A.I. (1989). 9. Yaks. In: *Animal Genetic Resources of the USSR. FAO Animal Production and Health Paper* No. 65, Rome, pp. 357–364.

Scheller, S. (1993). Leder vom Dach der Welt. *Leder-und Häutemarkt*, **45**, 43–64.

Schley, P. (1967). Der Yak und seine Kreuzung mit dem Rind in der Sowjetunion. *Giessener Abhandlungen zur Agrar und Wirtschaftsforschung des Europäischen Ostins*, **44**. 131 pp. Wiesbaden.

Scholz, F. (1994). Nomadism – mobile livestock keeping: forms, decline and prospects for a traditional way of life and of economic activity. (In German.) *Geographische-Rundschau*, **46** (2), 72–78 *(World Agricultural Economics and Rural Sociology Abstracts*, 1994, **36**, No. 6299).

Setchell, B.P. (1993). Male reproduction. In: *Reproduction in Domesticated Animals* (ed. G.J. King). Elsevier Science Publishers B.V.: Amsterdam.

Shao Binquan & Zhao Yanben (1984). Preliminary study on yak's synchronous oestrus. *Journal of China Yak*, 1984 (1), 81–88.

Shao Binquan *et al.* (1986). Experiment of oestrus synchronization of yak. The second report. *Journal of China Yak*, 1986 (2), 41–43.

Sharma, K.B., Garg, M.C., Arora, S.P. & Negi, G.C. (1989). Utility of yak (*Poephagus grunniens*) at high altitudes. *Indian Dairyman*, **41**, 383–384.

Shuai Yongru *et al.* (1988). [Diagnosis of enzootic abortion in yak.] *Scientia Agricultura Sinica*, **21**, 76–81. [Abstract in *Veterinary Bulletin*, 1990, **60**(129).]

Shuqin Cheng *et al.* (1994). Study on yak Fascioliasis: analysis of excretory/secretory antigens of *Fasciola hepatica* by SDS-PAGE and Western blotting. Proceedings of First International Congress on Yak. *Journal of Gansu agricultural University* (Special issue, June 1994). pp. 324–327.

Smirnov, D.A., Shevkhuzhev, A.F., Gusel'nikova, A.A. & Kokurina, T.M. (1990). Meat yield and meat quality of yaks. *Sel'skokhozyaistvennykh Nauk Im. V.I. Lenina. (Soviet Agricultural Sciences)* No. 1, 46–49.

Société d'Ethnozootechnie (1976). Le Yak. Son rôle dans la vie materielle et culturelle des éleveurs d'Asie centrale. *Ethnozootechnie* No. 15, France.

Survey Group of Chinese Academy (1981). [The synthetical survey group of Academia Sinica on Qinghai-Tibeton Plateau.] *Tibet Livestock.* Science Publishing House, China.

Turner, S. (1800) (1971 reprint of original edition). An account of an embassy to the Court of the Teshou Lama in Tibet. Original edition: G. & W. Nicol, Booksellers, London. Reprint: *Bibliotheca Himalayica*, Series I, vol. 4, Manjusri Publishing House, New Delhi.

Verdiev, Z. & Erin, I. (1981). Yak farming is milk and meat production. *Molochnoe i miasnoe skotovodstvo*, 1981 (2), 16–17.

Vlasov, P., Gershenzon, S. & Poliakov, A. (1932). [Hybrids of yak and cattle.] *Probl. Zhivotn. no. 1*, 48–57. [*CAB Animal Breeding Abstracts*, **1**, 95–96.]

Wang Jie (1984a). Analysis of the amino acid in the yak's hair and down. *Journal of South-west Nationalities College, Animal Husbandry & Veterinary Edition*, 1984 (2), 23–25.

Wang Jie (1984b). Observation on the ultramicroscopic structure of the hair fiber of yak. *Journal of South-west Nationalities College, Animal Husbandry & Veterinary Edition*, 1984 (4), 9–14.

Wang Jie *et al.* (1984). The physical properties of the hair of yak. *Journal of South-west Nationalities College, Animal Husbandry & Veterinary Edition*, 1984 (1), 25–29.

Wang Yanhong (1994). Experiment of prevention from yak hypodermiasis larva in Tianzhu (White yak). Proceedings of First International Congress on Yak. *Journal of Gansu agricultural University* (Special issue, June 1994). pp. 343–345.

Wang Yuchang & Wang Yanhong (1994). Conservation and improvement of the Tianzhu White yak. Proceedings of First International Congress on Yak. *Journal of Gansu agricultural University* (Special issue, June 1994). pp. 80–85.

Wang, J.L. & Yao, R.Q. (1984). Brucellosis infection in hare, mouse and wild birds. *Wild Animal*, **2**, 42–43.

Weggi, S. (1983). Observations on streptococcal mastitis in yaks. *Chinese Journal of Veterinary Medicine*, **9**, 12–14. [*CAB Dairy Science Abstracts 46*, No. 1405.]

Wei Ronglu, Liu Donsong, Bao Shan & Ren Xia (1981). Analyses of effect on meat of F1 hybrid of interspecific cross between female yak and common bull. *Journal of China Yak*, 1981 (2), 5–15.

Wen Yongli & Chen Zhihua (1994). [The linear relation between 184-day milk yield of Maiwa female yaks and its correlative traits.] *Journal of South-west Nationalities College* (Natural Science Edition), 20 (2), 166–170.

Wen Yongli, Chen Zhihua, Chen Yu, Zhao Changlin, Chen You Kang & Wang Jinfeng (1993). [Influences of two simple methods of supplement during the winter on the performances of female yaks.] *Journal of South-west Nationalities College* (Natural Science Edition), 19 (3), 236–241.

Wen Yongli, Wu Kang & Zhang Zhongming (1987). The study on improving milk production of female Pien Niu with supplementary feeding in warm season in the frigid pastoral area. *Journal of South-west Nationalities College, Animal Husbandry & Veterinary Edition*, 1987 (2), 44–47.

Wen Zhenzhong, Xie Zhonglun (1985). The relationship between the distribution and ecological environment of yak, sheep and goat in Qinghai Province. *Journal of South-west Nationalities College, Animal Husbandry & Veterinary Edition*, 1985 (2), 34–46.

Wen, Y.L., Zhong, G.H., Zhi, X.D., Liu, C.L. & An, N.Y. (1994). Study on the milkability of Jioulong yak cows. Proceedings of First International Congress on Yak. *Journal of Gansu agricultural University* (Special issue, June 1994). pp. 161–163.

White, W.T., Phillips, R.W. & Elting, E.C. (1946). Yaks and yak-cattle hybrids in Alaska. *Journal of Heredity*, **37**, 355–358.

Wiener, G. (1987). The genetics of copper metabolism in animals and man. In: *Copper in Animals and Man* (eds. J.McC. Howell & J.M. Gawthorne), Vol. 1. CRC Press Inc.: Bocca Raton, Florida. pp. 45–61.

Winter, H. & Tshewang, U. (1989). The crossbreeding of yaks in Merak-Sakten (Bhutan). *Zuchthygiene*, **24**, 116–122.

Winter, H., Seawright, A.A., Hrdlicka, J., Tshewang, U. & Gurung, B.J. (1992). Pyrrolizidine alkaloid poisoning of yaks (*Bos grunniens*) and confirmation by recovery of pylloric metabolites from formalin-fixed liver tissue. *Research in Veterinary Science*, **52**, 187–194.

Winter, H., Seawright, A.A., Noltie, H.J., Mattocks, A.R., Jukes, R., Kinzang Wangdi & Gurung, B.J. (1994). Pyrrolizidine alkaloid poisoning of yaks: identification of the plants involved. *The Veterinary Record*, **134**, 135–139.

Winter, H., Tshewang, U., Gurung, B.J. & Beattie, A.W. (1989). Haemoglobin and packed cell volume of yaks at high altitude. *Australian Veterinary Journal*, **66**, 299–301.

Wu Derun & Ma Juru (1985). Effects on reproductive and survival rate, growth and development of yak by milking and not milking. *Journal of China Yak*, 1985 (3), 28–29.

Wu Guoying *et al.* (1983). Study on the physical and chemical characters of hair fiber of special animal. The proceedings of the Conference on Physical and Chemical Characters of Hair in China, 1983.

Xiao Zhiqing (1984). Preliminary evaluation of growing and developing laws of the Pien Nius from different sires. *Journal of South-west Nationalities College, Animal Husbandry & Veterinary Edition*, 1984 (2), 17–22.

Xiong Zaiyue (1982). Observation on the introduction of yak into Zhang County. *Journal of China Yak*, 1982 (2), 75–77.

Xu Guiling (1985a). The differentiation of wild yak and domestic yak and economic value of wild yak in breeding. *Journal of China Yak*, 1985 (1), 21–25.

Xu Guiling (1985b). Effects of different methods of milking, suckling and feeding on the gains of calf yak and young yak. *Journal of China Yak*, 1985 (2), 39–43.

Xu Guiling *et al.* (1983). Analysis of factors concerned with the milking performance and milk quality of yak. *Journal of China Yak*, 1983 (1), 21–29.

Xu Kanzhu *et al*. (1964). The study on the histology and anatomy of reproductive organs and the reproductive functions of yak and its hybrid. *Journal of China Yak*, 1964 (3), 18–21.

Xu Rongcan & Wu Zhiqiang (1984). A test report about physiologic indexes of yaks in Dari area.

Xue Jiying & Yu Zhengfeng (1981). The property and utilization of yak's down hair. *Journal of China Yak*, 1981 (1), 1–5.

Xue Liqun (1983). The changes of the progesterone level in milk fat of yak during the oestrous cycle and early pregnancy. *Journal of Veterinary Science and Animal Industry*, 1983 (3), 193–196.

Xue, B. *et al.* (1994). Study on protein requirements of growing yak. Proceedings of First International Congress on Yak. *Journal of Gansu agricultural University* (Special issue, June 1994), pp. 198–202.

Yan Ping, Lu Zhonglin & Lu, H.J. (1994). Study on production and quality of hair for (crosses of) wild yak with domestic yak. Proceedings of First International Congress on Yak. *Journal of Gansu agricultural University* (Special issue, June 1994). pp. 154–156.

Yan, Z.S. & Ran, G.C. (1981). An investigation report on yak calf scours in Yajiang County. *Infectious Diseases in Livestock*, 1981 (2), 30–33.

Yang Tingyou (1984). The preliminary study on synchronization of yak's oestrus. *Journal of South-west Nationalities College, Animal Husbandry & Veterinary Edition*, 1984 (3), 50–53.

Yang, C.Y. (1987). An investigation report of Pasteurellosis in Baiyu County. *Animal Science and Veterinary Medicine of Sichuan*, 1987 (1), 34–35.

Yong Conglie *et al.* (1982). The experiment to improve the reproductive and survival rate in yak's interspecific cross. *Journal of China Yak*, 1982 (1), 38–40.

Yousef, M.K. (1985). Physiological adaptations of less well-known types of livestock in cold regions: yak and reindeer. In: *Stress Physiology in Livestock*. Vol. II. Ungulates (ed. M.K. Yousef). CRC Press Inc: Boca Reton Fa. pp. 142–148.

Yu Daxin & Qian Defang (1983). A survey of Xinjiang yak. *Journal of China Yak*, 1983 (1), 57–64.

Yu, S.J., Huang, Y.M. & Chen, B.X. (1993). Reproductive patterns of the yak. 1. Reproductive phenomena of the female yak. *British Veterinary Journal*, **149**, 579–583.

Yuan, S.Y. (1962). An investigation report on animal husbandry and veterinary medicine techniques of Ganzi Tibetan Autonomous Prefecture. Scientific and Technology Committee of Sichuan Province, Scientific and Technology Association of Sichuan Province.

Yuan, S.Y. (1979). An investigation report on Maiwa Yak Brucellosis. *Journal of South-west Nationalities College* (Animal Science and Veterinary Medicine Edition), 1979 (6), 30–32.

Zagdsuren Yo (1994a). Heterosis in yak hybrids. Proceedings of First International Congress on Yak. *Journal of Gansu agricultural University* (Special issue, June 1994). pp. 59–62.

Zagdzuren Yo (1994b). Some possibilities to increase meat and milk production of yak husbandry. Proceedings of First International Congress on Yak. *Journal of Gansu agricultural University* (Special issue, June 1994). pp. 113–118.

Zeuner, F.E. (1963). *A History of Domesticated Animals*. Hutchinson: London. pp. 352–353.

Zhang Deshou, Zhang Rongchang & Pu Futang(1985). The physiological and biochemical indexes in blood of adult female Tianzhu White yak. *Journal of Animal Husbandry and Veterinary Medicine of Gansu*, 1985 (1), 8–9.

Zhang Hongwu, Zhao Yibin & Lei Huangzhang (1985). Study on ecological reaction of yak and its hybrid during pasturing in cold season. *Journal of China Yak*, 1985 (3), 15–21.

Zhang Jiachuan (1984a). The test of cross combination of yak and common cattle. *Journal of South-west Nationalities College, Animal Husbandry & Veterinary Edition*, 1984 (1), 30–35.

Zhang Rongchang (1975). Evaluation on the performance of yak's hair production in Nannigou Production Group on the Zhuaxixiunong grassland of Tianzhu County. *Journal of Gansu Agriculture University*, 1975 (3).

Zhang Rongchang (1977a). The hair quality of white yak on Zhuxixiunong grassland of Tianzhu County. *Journal of Gansu Agriculture University*, 1977 (2).

Zhang Rongchang (1979). The reproductive characters of yak. *Journal of China Yak*, 1979 (4), 63–71.

Zhang Rongchang (1985). China: the yak. *World Animal Review (FAO)* No. 54, 24–29.

Zhang Rongchang (1987). Production of yak in Mongolia, Soviet Union, Nepal and India. *Journal of China Yak*, 1987 (3), 8–13.

Zhang Rongchang, Kong Linglu & Jin Yong (1983). The milking characters of yak and Pien Niu. *Journal of China Yak* 1983, 14–18.

Zhang Rongchang, Wu Jianping, Han Jianlin, Bob Fajia & Yian Ping (1994). Anatomical physiology of yak adapting to the low oxygen content on the high plateau. Proceedings of First International Congress on Yak. *Journal of Gansu agricultural University* (Special issue, June 1994). pp. 236–240.

Zhang Rongchang *et al.* (1982). Observation on grazing habits of yak and steers of interspecific hybrid. *Journal of China Yak*, 1982 (4), 5–12.

Zhang Rongchang *et al.* (1986). Determination on the main composition in milk of Tianzhu White yak. *Journal of China Yak*, 1986 (2), 23–26.

Zhang Yinsong (1985). Observation and analysis on milk production of yak in Qilian area. *Journal of China Yak*, 1985 (1), 51–56.

Zhang Yun (1994). The relationship between season and age of stud yak bull in Dangxin. Proceedings of First International Congress on Yak. *Journal of Gansu agricultural University* (Special issue, June 1994). pp. 303–307.

Zhao Bingyao & Zhang Jianwen (1994). Present situation, problems and prospects of wild yak utilization in Gansu. Proceedings of First International Congress on Yak. *Journal of Gansu agricultural University* (Special issue, June 1994). pp. 137–139.

Zhao Bingyao (1982). Study on the three physiological indexes of yak. *Journal of China Yak*, 1982 (4), 24–30.

Zhao Bingyao *et al.* (1984). An experiment on the cross combination of interspecific hybridization between female yak and common bull. *Journal of China Yak*, 1984 (1), 47–70.

Zhao Bingyao, Jing Ba, Chen Rutian, Lu Caiqin & Bai Yongfu (1994). Feeding effects of Xudazhuang on yak fattening during cold and warm seasons. Proceedings of First International Congress on Yak. *Journal of Gansu agricultural University* (Special issue, June 1994), pp. 202–204.

Zhao Yibing *et al.* (1986). Study on the comprehensive utilization of yak calf. *Journal of China Yak*, 1986 (2), 61–72.

Zhao Zhengrong (1957). *Animal Husbandry in the Median Part of Gansu Province.* Scientific Publishing House, China.

Zhao, X.B., Zhong, G.H. & Cai Li (1994). Studies on mitochondrial DNA RFLP of yaks and cattle-yak. Proceedings of First International Congress on Yak. *Journal of Gansu agricultural University* (Special issue, June 1994), pp. 96–98.

Zhen Zhongchao (1994). Population structure of yak herd in Naqu Prefecture of Tibetan autonomy. Proceedings of First International Congress on Yak. *Journal of Gansu agricultural University* (Special issue, June 1994). pp. 172–175.

Zhong Guanghui, Ma Li, Hu Ruilin & Sun Ziran (1986). Observation on the adaptability of yak introduced into Lingshan Region of Beijing. *Journal of South-west Nationalities College, Animal Husbandry & Veterinary Edition,* 1986 (1), 9–14.

Zhong Jingcheng (1994). Polygenic inheritance unbalance hypothesis about sterility of the male yak-cattle (hybrid). Proceedings of First International Congress on Yak. *Journal of Gansu agricultural University* (Special issue, June 1994). pp. 284–287.

Zhou Shourong (1984). Study on the forage and feeding habits of yak. A research on the utilization and exploitation of grassland in the north-western part of Sichuan Province. Sichuan National Publishing House, pp. 134–137.

Zhu, H.Q. & Jiang, X.S. (1986). A study on liver fluke host of yak and sheep in Northwest of Sichuan. *Journal of South-west Nationalities College, Animal Husbandry & Veterinary Edition,* 1986 (1), 25–26.

APPENDIX 1

A simple procedure for identifying animals to achieve random allocation to treatments in experimentation

To help overcome some of the problems of creating equivalent groups of animals, to which different treatments could later be applied, a simple identification system was devised for investigations on yak undertaken in Hongyuan county of Sichuan by the Southwest Nationalities College. (The investigations were part of a project supported by UNDP/FAO). The system was also intended to make it simple for herdsmen to recognise which animals belonged to which treatment.

The procedure for allocating animals to treatment (and control) groups required that the animals were first divided by sex and by rough age classes (calves, young stock, and adults). Animals of each sex and age class were then run through a race and successive animals were allocated different colour tags, the number of colours determined by the number of treatment groups envisaged (four in the case of the trials undertaken). Within each colour, a unique numeral was allocated to each animal. Thus the first animal through the race might be given a red tag with the number 1, the next animal would get a yellow tag also with number 1, and so on for as many colours as needed. When number 1 had been allocated for each colour, the colour sequence would be repeated and the next animal with a red tag (in this example) would be number 2, followed by yellow 2, and so on. Thus, in this particular situation, 4 groups of yak were created where any differences between the groups were entirely random. Given sufficient numbers of animals, such differences should be very small.

The use of large, differently coloured ear tags had the further advantage, apart from assisting the random subdivision of a large herd of yak, that specific colour groups could be allocated to different treatments, or to a control group. The colours could be easily identified from a distance. Because animals on a particular treatment (for example, supplementary winter feeding) all had the same colour identification, herdsmen could see at a glance that no unwanted animals were present in any group.

The procedure, and its statistical consequences are described in more detail by Chen Zhihua *et al.* (1995). Analyses of data showed that although there were some random differences among the groups, none of these were statistically significant, for example in relation to body weight or body dimensions. This simple procedure shows that in situations typical of many field studies with yak, effective randomisation can be achieved, as an aid to experimental design, even in the absence of prior animal identification and without the records more usual of intensive animal husbandry experimentation.

APPENDIX 2

International Yak Information Center (IYIC)

This Centre was set up at Gansu Agricultural University at the conclusion of the First International Congress on yak held there in August 1994. The aim of the Centre is to develop a data base on research and other activities related to yak (including a register of those involved). The information collated by the Centre is intended to be made available on a regular basis to countries with yak and to relevant national and international agencies. It was also proposed to produce a Newsletter. The Director of IYIC is Professor Zhang Rongchang.

The full title and address of the Centre is:

International Yak Information Center
Gansu Agricultural University
Yingmentan, Anning District
Lanzhou
Gansu 730070
P.R. China

Telephone and fax numbers for Gansu Agricultural University are:

telephone: (country code +) (0)931 7668011
fax: (country code +) (0)931 7668010

SUBJECT INDEX

(f indicates reference to the topic on the page shown and on several succeeding pages.)